MATHEMATICS
Exploring Your World

AUTHORS

Grades K–2 Team
Herbert P. Ginsburg
Deborah B. Gustafson
Larry P. Leutzinger

Problem Solving Team
Lucille Croom
Gerald A. Goldin
Stephen Krulik
Henry O. Pollak
Jesse A. Rudnick
Dale G. Seymour

Grades 3–8 Team
Ruth I. Champagne
Carole E. Greenes
William D. McKillip
Lucy J. Orfan
Fernand J. Prevost
Bruce R. Vogeli
Marianne V. Weber

SILVER BURDETT & GINN

MORRISTOWN, NJ • NEEDHAM, MA
Atlanta, GA • Cincinnati, OH • Dallas, TX
Deerfield, IL • Menlo Park, CA

Table of Contents

Introducing . . .
MATHEMATICS Exploring Your World   ix–xi

1

THEME Numbers Shape Our World
Working with Whole Numbers and Decimals

Be a Problem Solver	1
Activity Exploring Number Patterns	2–3
Activity Exploring Number Sequences	4–5
Exponents	6–7
The Decimal Number System	8–9
Mental Math: Powers of 10	10–11
Activity Understanding Place Value	12–13
Activity Exploring Number Systems	14–15
Midchapter Review	16
Exploring Problem Solving Is Business All Fun and Games?	17
Problem Solving Strategies Alternate Solutions	18–19
Mental Math: Using Properties and Strategies	20–21

Estimating Sums and Differences	22–23
Using Decimals: Adding and Subtracting	24–25
Estimating Products	26–27
Estimating Quotients	28–29
Using Decimals: Multiplying and Dividing	30–31
Using Problem Solving How Much Postage?	32–33

CHAPTER RESOURCES
CHAPTER REVIEW	34
CHAPTER TEST	35
EXTENSION Magic Squares	36
MAINTAINING SKILLS	37

2

THEME Traveling Back in Time
Number Theory and Fractions

Be a Problem Solver	39
Activity Exploring Primes	40–41
Prime Factorization	42–43
Greatest Common Factor and Least Common Multiple	44–45
Activity Exploring Conjectures	46–47
Relating Fractions and Decimals	48–49
Understanding Repeating Decimals	50–51
Comparing Fractions	52–53
Midchapter Review	54
Exploring Problem Solving What Is Puzzling You?	55
Problem Solving Strategies Too Much or Too Little Information	56–57
Estimating Sums and Differences	58–59
Adding Fractions and Mixed Numbers	60–61

Subtracting Fractions and Mixed Numbers	62–63
Multiplying Fractions	64–65
Multiplying Mixed Numbers	66–67
Estimating Products	68–69
Dividing Fractions and Mixed Numbers	70–71
Using Problem Solving What Is the Secret?	72–73

CHAPTER RESOURCES
CHAPTER REVIEW	74
CHAPTER TEST	75
COMPUTER LINK Euclidean Algorithm	76–77
EXTENSION Continued Fractions	78
MAINTAINING SKILLS	79

3

THEME Businesses That Serve Us

Pre-Algebra: Expressions and Equations

80

Be a Problem Solver 81
Writing Expressions 82–83
Evaluating Expressions 84–85
Evaluating Expressions with Variables .. 86–87
Writing Equations 88–89
Solving Equations 90–91
Midchapter Review 92
Exploring Problem Solving 93
   Which Is More Money?
Problem Solving Strategies 94–95
   Simulation
Inverse Operations 96–97
Solving Addition and Subtraction 98–99
   Equations

Solving Multiplication and 100–101
   Division Equations
Solving Two-Step Equations 102–103
Formulas 104–105
Using Problem Solving 106–107
   Concrete Functions

CHAPTER RESOURCES
CHAPTER REVIEW 108
CHAPTER TEST 109
EXTENSION   An Exasperating 110
   Expression
FAMILY MATH   Find the Missing 111
   Number
CUMULATIVE REVIEW 112–113

4

THEME Geometry Shapes Our World

Geometry

114

Be a Problem Solver 115
Angles and Intersecting Lines 116–117
Parallel Lines and Transversals 118–119
Angles and Polygons 120–121
Triangles 122–123
Congruence 124–125
Midchapter Review 126
Exploring Problem Solving 127
   Is It More Than Half?
Problem Solving Strategies 128–129
   Patterns
Activity   Exploring Quadrilaterals .. 130–131
Angles and Circles 132–133

Activity   Exploring Polyhedra 134–135
Activity   Exploring Cylinders, ... 136–137
   Cones, and Spheres
Activity   Exploring Different 138–139
   Perspectives
Using Problem Solving 140–141
   Venn Diagrams

CHAPTER RESOURCES
CHAPTER REVIEW 142
CHAPTER TEST 143
COMPUTER LINK   Polygons and Stars .. 144–145
EXTENSION   Hole in One 146
MAINTAINING SKILLS 147

5

THEME Oceans

Pre-Algebra: Integers
148

Be a Problem Solver	149	Properties of Integers	164–165
Writing and Comparing Integers	150–151	Integer Expressions	166–167
Activity Exploring Addition and Subtraction of Integers	152–153	Solving Integer Equations	168–169
		Graphing Ordered Pairs	170–171
Adding and Subtracting Integers	154–155	**Using Problem Solving** Interview: Calculators at a Restaurant	172–173
Multiplying Integers	156–157		
Dividing Integers	158–159		
Midchapter Review	160	**CHAPTER RESOURCES**	
Exploring Problem Solving The Top Score	161	CHAPTER REVIEW	174
		CHAPTER TEST	175
Problem Solving Strategies Working Backwards	162–163	EXTENSION Graphing Pictures	176
		MAINTAINING SKILLS	177

6

THEME Exploring Frontiers

Rational Numbers
178

Be a Problem Solver	179	**Activity** Exploring Square Roots	200–201
Understanding Rational Numbers	180–181	**Activity** Understanding and Estimating Square Roots	202–203
Ordering Rational Numbers	182–183		
Adding and Subtracting Rational Numbers	184–185	Pythagorean Rule	204–205
		Missing Sides of Right Triangles	206–207
Multiplying and Dividing Rational Numbers	186–187	**Using Problem Solving** What Is the Quickest Route?	208–209
Solving Equations	188–189		
Powers of 10	190–191		
Scientific Notation	192–193	**CHAPTER RESOURCES**	
Scientific Notation: Numbers Less Than 1	194–195	CHAPTER REVIEW	210
		CHAPTER TEST	211
Midchapter Review	196	EXTENSION Triangles and the Pythagorean Rule	212
Exploring Problem Solving Is It Possible?	197		
		FAMILY MATH Watch Your Step	213
Problem Solving Strategies Guess and Test	198–199	CUMULATIVE REVIEW	214–215

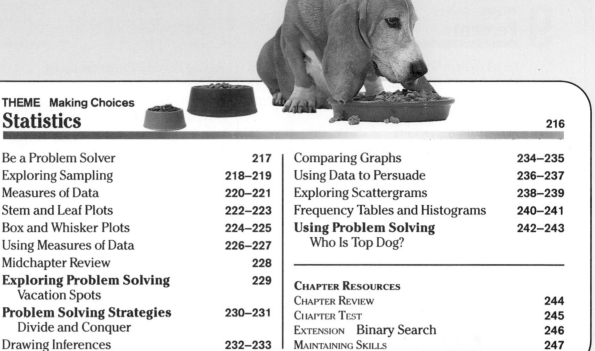

7 THEME Making Choices
Statistics 216

Be a Problem Solver	217
Exploring Sampling	218–219
Measures of Data	220–221
Stem and Leaf Plots	222–223
Box and Whisker Plots	224–225
Using Measures of Data	226–227
Midchapter Review	228
Exploring Problem Solving	229
Vacation Spots	
Problem Solving Strategies	230–231
Divide and Conquer	
Drawing Inferences	232–233

Comparing Graphs	234–235
Using Data to Persuade	236–237
Exploring Scattergrams	238–239
Frequency Tables and Histograms	240–241
Using Problem Solving	242–243
Who Is Top Dog?	

CHAPTER RESOURCES
CHAPTER REVIEW	244
CHAPTER TEST	245
EXTENSION Binary Search	246
MAINTAINING SKILLS	247

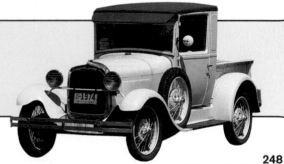

8 THEME Then and Now
Ratio and Proportion 248

Be a Problem Solver	249
Ratios and Equal Ratios	250–251
Rates	252–253
Proportions	254–255
Solving Proportions	256–257
Scale Drawing	258–259
Distance, Rate, and Time	260–261
Midchapter Review	262
Exploring Problem Solving	263
What Is the Average Speed?	
Problem Solving Strategies	264–265
Solving a Simpler Problem	
Drawing Similar Polygons	266–267
Similar Triangles	268–269

Precision and Greatest Possible	270–271
Error	
Special Ratios	272–273
Working with Right Triangles	274–275
Using Problem Solving	276–277
Interview: Calculators and	
the Museum	

CHAPTER RESOURCES
CHAPTER REVIEW	278
CHAPTER TEST	279
COMPUTER LINK Fibonacci Sequence	280–281
EXTENSION Significant Digits	282
and Accuracy	
MAINTAINING SKILLS	283

9
THEME Sports
Percent
284

Be a Problem Solver | 285
Understanding Percent | 286–287
Relating Percents, Ratios, and Decimals | 288–289
Mental Math: Percents | 290–291
Less Than 1 Percent or Greater Than 100 Percent | 292–293
Midchapter Review | 294
Exploring Problem Solving Competitive Teams | 295
Problem Solving Strategies Simulation | 296–297
Solving Percent Problems Using Mental Math | 298–299
Solving Percent Problems Using Ratios or Decimals | 300–301
Solving Percent Problems Using Proportions | 302–303

Solving Percent Problems Using Equations | 304–305
Estimating Percents | 306–307
Making Circle Graphs | 308–309
Interest | 310–311
Discount and Sale Price | 312–313
Markup and Selling Price | 314–315
Percent of Increase or Decrease | 316–317
Using Problem Solving Interview: Calculators and Sports | 318–319

CHAPTER RESOURCES
CHAPTER REVIEW | 320
CHAPTER TEST | 321
EXTENSION Mathematical Bones | 322
MAINTAINING SKILLS | 323

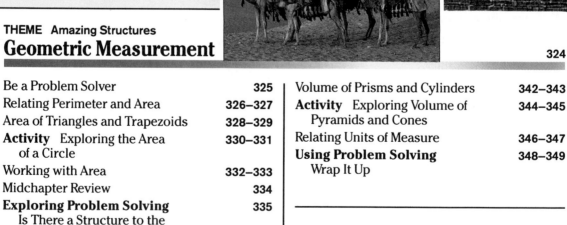

10
THEME Amazing Structures
Geometric Measurement
324

Be a Problem Solver | 325
Relating Perimeter and Area | 326–327
Area of Triangles and Trapezoids | 328–329
Activity Exploring the Area of a Circle | 330–331
Working with Area | 332–333
Midchapter Review | 334
Exploring Problem Solving Is There a Structure to the Solar System? | 335
Problem Solving Strategies Making and Using Tables | 336–337
Surface Area of Prisms | 338–339
Activity Exploring Surface Area of Cylinders | 340–341

Volume of Prisms and Cylinders | 342–343
Activity Exploring Volume of Pyramids and Cones | 344–345
Relating Units of Measure | 346–347
Using Problem Solving Wrap It Up | 348–349

CHAPTER RESOURCES
CHAPTER REVIEW | 350
CHAPTER TEST | 351
EXTENSION Möbius Strip | 352
FAMILY MATH Let's Go South | 353
CUMULATIVE REVIEW | 354–355

11 THEME What Would You Expect?
Probability

356

Be a Problem Solver	357
Probability	358–359
Activity Exploring Relative Frequency	360–361
Fundamental Counting Principle	362–363
Independent and Dependent Events	364–365
Mutually Exclusive Events	366–367
Midchapter Review	368
Exploring Problem Solving Test the Waters	369
Problem Solving Strategies Organized Listing	370–371

Factorials	372–373
Permutations	374–375
Combinations	376–377
Using Problem Solving Finding the Area of an Irregular Figure	378–379

CHAPTER RESOURCES

CHAPTER REVIEW	380
CHAPTER TEST	381
COMPUTER LINK Batter Up	382–383
EXTENSION Pascal's Triangle and Probability	384
MAINTAINING SKILLS	385

12 THEME Design
Transformations and Constructions

386

Be a Problem Solver	387
Activity Exploring Geometric Patterns	388–389
Translations and Reflections	390–391
Graphing Translations and Reflections	392–393
Rotations	394–395
Midchapter Review	396
Exploring Problem Solving Design a Logo	397
Problem Solving Strategies Logic	398–399
Activity Exploring Geometric Relationships	400–401
Congruent Triangles	402–403
Constructing Congruent Figures	404–405

Bisecting Figures	406–407
Constructing Perpendicular and Parallel Lines	408–409
Constructing Congruent Triangles	410–411
Constructing Polygons	412–413
Using Problem Solving Topology	414–415

CHAPTER RESOURCES

CHAPTER REVIEW	416
CHAPTER TEST	417
COMPUTER LINK Coordinates and Geometric Motions	418–419
EXTENSION Transformations: Expansion and Reduction	420
MAINTAINING SKILLS	421

13 THEME Traveling Around the World
Pre-Algebra: Equations and Inequalities
422

Be a Problem Solver	423
Inverses	424–425
Adding to Solve Equations	426–427
Multiplying to Solve Equations	428–429
Two-Step Equations	430–431
Combining Terms	432–433
Simplifying Equations	434–435
Midchapter Review	436
Exploring Problem Solving	437
Seeing the Sights	
Problem Solving Strategies	438–439
Logic	

Graphing on the Number Line	440–441
Inequalities	442–443
Two-Step Inequalities	444–445
Using Problem Solving Interview:	446–447
Calculators and Travelers	

CHAPTER RESOURCES

CHAPTER REVIEW	448
CHAPTER TEST	449
EXTENSION Polls, Statistics,	450
and Probability	
MAINTAINING SKILLS	451

14 THEME Ecology
Pre-Algebra: Relations, Functions, and Graphing
452

Be a Problem Solver	453
Real Numbers	454–455
Relations	456–457
Activity Exploring Functions	458–459
Midchapter Review	460
Exploring Problem Solving	461
What Are the Chances?	
Problem Solving Strategies	462–463
Alternate Solutions	
Graphing Equations	464–465
Slope	466–467
Systems of Equations	468–469

Graphing Inequalities	470–471
Using Problem Solving	472–473
Using Functions	

CHAPTER RESOURCES

CHAPTER REVIEW	474
CHAPTER TEST	475
COMPUTER LINK Functions	476–477
EXTENSION Parallel and	478
Perpendicular Lines	
FAMILY MATH What's For Dinner?	479
FINAL REVIEW	480–481

BOOK RESOURCES

EXTRA PRACTICE	482–497
PROBLEM SOLVING EXTRA PRACTICE	498–504
SELECTED ANSWERS	506–511

SKILL HINTS	512–527
GLOSSARY	528–534
TABLES, SYMBOLS	535–537
INDEX	538–544
CREDITS	545–546

The universal language of mathematics opens the door to a world of ideas.

MATHEMATICS
Exploring Your World

How does this diamond appraiser use mathematics?

Why do bees use hexagons, not triangles or squares, to construct a honeycomb?

Predict the number of cars on this highway at noon. How could you find out?

Share Your Ideas Why is mathematics an important part of our world? How will you use mathematics today?

How Will You Learn Mathematics?

You will learn mathematics in several different ways. Each way will help you become a better mathematician.

Learn by Working Cooperatively with Others

Working together

What if the digit 0 disappeared? What problems would arise? Would the entire number system need to be changed?

In your group...

- Always contribute to the best of your ability.
- Consider all ideas carefully.
- Discuss why you agree or disagree.
- Help the group reach agreement.

Learn by Making Choices

Decision-making is part of mathematics. This symbol means you will be able to make choices to solve problems.

Do you need an exact answer or an estimate? How will you find an exact answer?

- manipulatives
- mental math
- calculator
- paper and pencil

Chemistry
This helium atom has a nucleus with a positive charge of 2 and 2 electrons each with a negative charge of 1.

Learn by Using Mathematics in Other Areas

Architecture
How was mathematics used in building this bridge?

Learn by Thinking in Many Different Ways

- **Logical thinking** means putting several ideas together.

- **Visual thinking** uses pictures to explore ideas.

- **Critical thinking** encourages questioning to search for new possibilities.

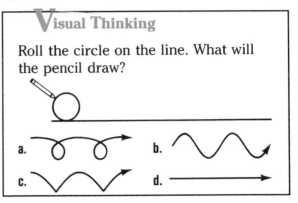

Visual Thinking

Roll the circle on the line. What will the pencil draw?

a.

b.

c.

d.

Learn by Solving Interesting Problems

Problems can be solved with many different strategies. You will decide which strategy is best: organized listing, using a drawing, working backwards, simulations, or solving a simpler problem.

THINK
EXPLORE
SOLVE
LOOK BACK

There are 7 islands. The islands are connected to each other by bridges. How many bridges can there be?

Which strategy worked best for you? Discuss your solution.

Mathematics will help you explore your world in many ways. The opportunity is yours!

SUMMING UP

Sharing What You Know

How much is a dollar worth? You probably know what you can buy for $1 in stores near you. But if you travel to another country, the value of your dollar will change, depending on that country's currency value on the international exchange. How much is a dollar worth in yen, marks, francs, dirhams, lire, or pesos? To find out, you would check the rates of exchange published in the newspaper. Discuss how mathematics is used in determining the value of a dollar.

Using Language

When you look at an exchange table, you will see a list of **decimals.** What do you think these decimals mean? Discuss how these decimals would be used to find out how many yen would be exchanged for a dollar.

Words to Know   factor, powers of 10, sequence, exponent, base, compatible numbers, decimal, estimate

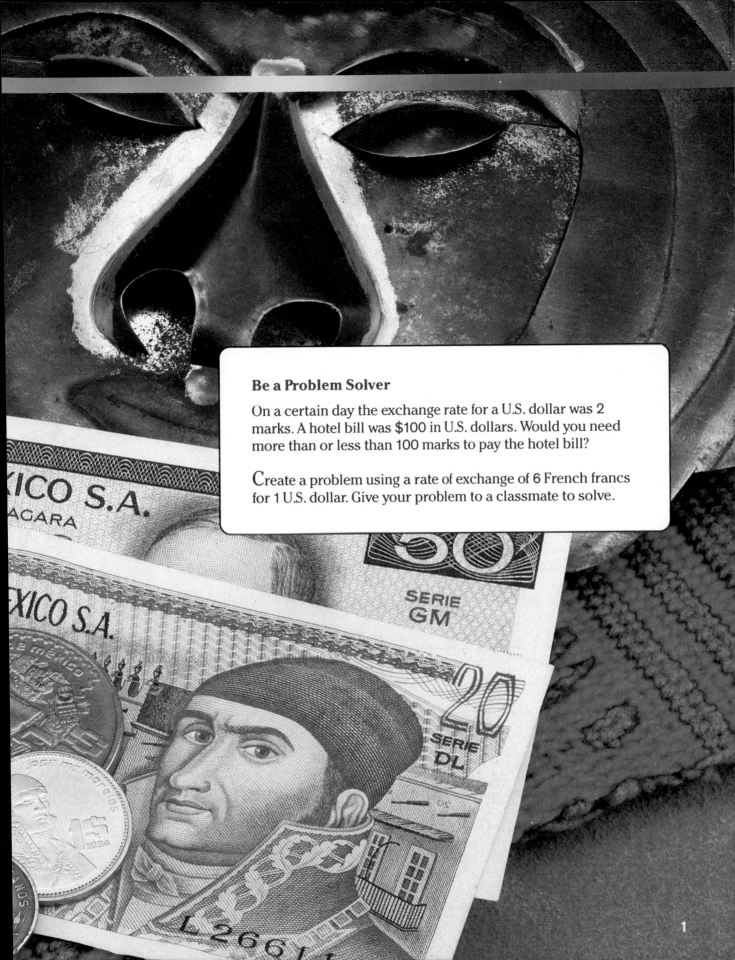

Be a Problem Solver

On a certain day the exchange rate for a U.S. dollar was 2 marks. A hotel bill was $100 in U.S. dollars. Would you need more than or less than 100 marks to pay the hotel bill?

Create a problem using a rate of exchange of 6 French francs for 1 U.S. dollar. Give your problem to a classmate to solve.

Activity

Exploring Number Patterns

For at least 600 years, mathematicians have explored the patterns in a special triangle called Pascal's triangle. How many patterns can you find?

Working together

Materials: Workmat 1, calculator

A. Look at the numbers in the first row. How can you find the numbers in the second row?

B. Test your ideas. Can you now use the numbers in the second row to find the numbers in the third row?

C. Copy the triangle. Use the pattern you find to complete the next 8 rows. You may wish to use a calculator.

D. Shade the numbers in your triangle to correspond to the pattern shown in the triangle at the right.

E. Which numbers form the pattern?

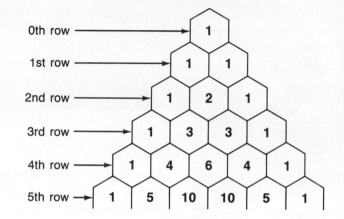

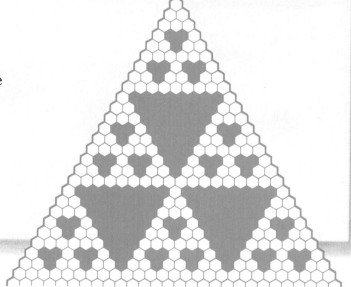

Sharing Your Results

1. Describe a pattern that will help you find the next row in Pascal's triangle.

2. Share the pattern that you found in the triangle you shaded.

2

Extending the Activity

Work on your own. Replace all even numbers with E and all odd numbers with O in the first 15 rows of Pascal's triangle.

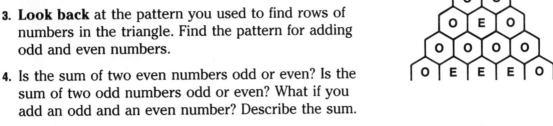

3. Look back at the pattern you used to find rows of numbers in the triangle. Find the pattern for adding odd and even numbers.

4. Is the sum of two even numbers odd or even? Is the sum of two odd numbers odd or even? What if you add an odd and an even number? Describe the sum.

5. Which rows of Pascal's triangle contain only odd numbers?

6. Describe the pattern of odd and even numbers along the diagonals.

Summing Up

7. The sum of the numbers in the second row is 4, or 2 × 2. Find the sum of the numbers in each of the next 5 rows. Express each sum as the product of a repeating factor. What product do you expect for the 8th row? Describe the pattern you have found.

8. Find another pattern in Pascal's triangle. Describe the pattern you have found and shade the triangle to display your pattern.

3

Activity

Exploring Number Sequences

Patterns and number sequences are found throughout the natural world.

Working together

A. Many patterns found in nature are based on terms of the Fibonacci sequence. Look for a pattern in the first 7 terms below. Use the pattern to find the next 3 terms.

1, 1, 2, 3, 5, 8, 13,_ ,_ ,_

B. The numbers below are called triangular numbers. Study the pattern. Draw the next three figures.

1   3   6   10

How can you use the figures to determine a rule for finding triangular numbers?

Sharing Your Results

1. Describe your rule for finding terms in the Fibonacci sequence.

2. Explain your method for finding triangular numbers.

3. If you know three numbers in a sequence, do you think you can be sure of the next term? Discuss.

4

Extending the Activity

Find the next 3 terms for each sequence. Use paper and pencil, mental math, or a calculator. Explain the rule you used for each.

4. 0, 4, 8, 12, _____, _____, _____

5. 111, 333, 999, _____, _____, _____

6. 9, 15, 21, 27, _____, _____, _____

7. 3, 12, 48, 192, _____, _____, _____

8. 1, 2, 4, 7, _____, _____, _____

9. 1, 4, 3, 6, 5, _____, _____, _____

10. 3, 15, 75, 375, _____, _____, _____

11. 4, 9, 19, 39, _____, _____, _____

Use each rule to write the next 5 terms of a sequence. Begin with 1.

12. Double each term and add 1.

13. Add 2 to the first term, add 3 to the second term, add 4 to the third term, . . .

14. Multiply each term by itself and add 1.

15. Triple each term and subtract 1.

Use patterns to predict the number of regions formed by connecting points on a circle.

16. A diameter divides the circle into 2 regions. How many regions do you think are formed by connecting 6 points? Try it and discuss your results.

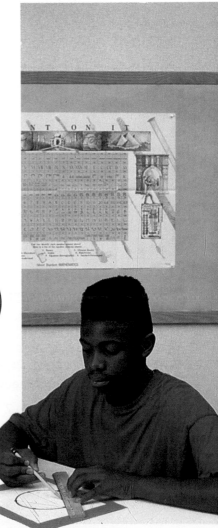

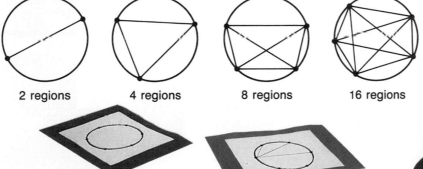

| 2 regions | 4 regions | 8 regions | 16 regions |

Summing Up

17. What is a sequence? Discuss your ideas.

18. Write several terms for a sequence. Exchange sequences with your partner and find the next 3 terms.

A chessboard has 8 rows with 8 squares in each row. What are some different ways you can write the total number of small squares on the board?

Exponents

Number patterns can occur in geometric figures as well as in designs found in nature. Look at the patterns of small squares or cubes shown below.

4 **squared** can be expressed as 4×4, 4^2, or four to the second power.

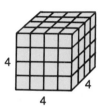

4 **cubed** can be expressed as $4 \times 4 \times 4$, 4^3, or four to the third power.

exponent
↓
$$4^3 = 4 \times 4 \times 4 = 64$$
↑   ↑ ↑ ↑
base factors

An **exponent** tells how many times the base is used as a factor.

How could you write 64×4 using exponents?

More Examples

	Read	Factors	Standard Form
5^4	Five to the fourth power	$5 \times 5 \times 5 \times 5$	625
1.5^2	One and five tenths squared	1.5×1.5	2.25
1^6	One to the sixth power	$1 \times 1 \times 1 \times 1 \times 1 \times 1$	1

For any number n, n^1 equals n. $8^1 = 8$ $4.3^1 = 4.3$ $10^1 = 10$

For any number n, except 0, n^0 equals 1. $6^0 = 1$ $2.5^0 = 1$ $10^0 = 1$

Check Your Understanding

Write each, using exponents.

1. $5 \times 5 \times 5$ **2.** $7 \times 7 \times 7 \times 7$ **3.** 5.2×5.2 **4.** two cubed

Write each as a product of factors. Then write each in standard form.

5. 4^2 **6.** 10^3 **7.** six squared   **8.** 1.2^2

Share Your Ideas Does $2 + 2$ equal 2^2? Does $2 + 2 + 2$ equal 2^3? Explain.

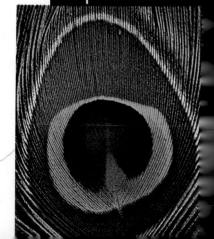

Write each, using exponents.

9. 5×5 **10.** $2.7 \times 2.7 \times 2.7$ **11.** 11 **12.** seven squared

Write each as a product of factors. Then write the number in standard form.

13. 8^3 **14.** 11^4 **15.** 12^2 **16.** 10^4 **17.** three to the third power

18. 2^6 **19.** 7^3 **20.** 25^2 **21.** 0.8^2 **22.** 5.5^2

 Write each number in standard form. Use mental math, pencil and paper, or a calculator. Explain your choices.

23. 10^5 **24.** 5^2 **25.** 0.7^2 **26.** 11^2 **27.** two to the third power

28. 2.5^2 **29.** 3^3 **30.** 16^2 **31.** 2^8 **32.** eight to the fourth power

33. $3^2 \times 5^2 \times 2^4$ **34.** $5^3 \times 10^2 \times 2^1$ **35.** $20^2 \times 0.5^2 \times 10^0$

Find n.

36. $7^n = 49$ **37.** $1^3 = n$ **38.** $n^2 = 25$ **39.** $2^n = 8$

40. $3^n = 27$ **41.** $n^2 = 100$ **42.** $1.1^0 = n$ **43.** $1.6^n = 1$

Find the least value for n to make each sentence true.

44. $3^n > 5^2$ **45.** $10^2 < 5^n$ **46.** $n^3 > 5^2$

Think and Apply

47. The game of tic-tac-toe uses 9 spaces for play. A variation of the game can be played in three dimensions, using 27 spaces. Use exponents to express 9 and 27.

48. What general statement can you make about 1 raised to any power? Give a reason.

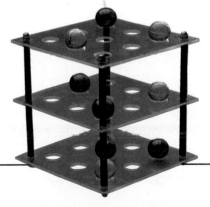

Visual Thinking

The dot patterns show the first three square numbers.

49. Use dots to show the next two square numbers.

50. Use exponents to write each number.

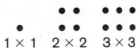

1×1 2×2 3×3

Which is greater, 3^2 or 2^3? Explain.

Ten cents and ten dollars are values in our monetary system. How are they related?

The Decimal Number System

Billions of stars, including our sun, encircle the center of the Milky Way galaxy. They rotate clockwise in a complete orbit once every 300 million years.

Three hundred million can be written as a decimal number in standard form, using our decimal place value system.

Millions			Thousands			Ones								
hundreds 100,000,000	tens 10,000,000	ones 1,000,000	hundreds 100,000	tens 10,000	ones 1,000	hundreds 100	tens 10	ones 1	tenths 0.1	hundredths 0.01	thousandths 0.001	ten-thousandths 0.0001	hundred-thousandths 0.00001	millionths 0.000001
10^8	10^7	10^6	10^5	10^4	10^3	10^2	10^1	10^0	$\frac{1}{10^1}$	$\frac{1}{10^2}$	$\frac{1}{10^3}$	$\frac{1}{10^4}$	$\frac{1}{10^5}$	$\frac{1}{10^6}$
3	0	0	0	0	0	0	0	0.						
								7.	0	0	5			

300,000,000 **read** three hundred million

7.005 **read** seven and five thousandths

Decimal numbers in standard form can be expressed in different ways. Study the examples below.

1,000,000 = one million = 1 million = 10^6

500,000 = five hundred thousand = $\frac{1}{2}$ million = **0.5** million

1,500,000 = one million, five hundred thousand = $1\frac{1}{2}$ million = **1.5** million

Check Your Understanding

Express each number as a decimal number in standard form.

1. twelve and thirteen thousandths
2. 10^3
3. $9 \times \frac{1}{10}$
4. 10^9
5. three million, thirty thousand
6. $\frac{2}{100}$
7. $2\frac{1}{2}$ billion
8. 8.5 million

Share Your Ideas Does 4.8 equal 4.800? Explain your thinking.

Write each in words.

9. 52.08   **10.** 92.015   **11.** 4,500,000   **12.** 124.5   **13.** 4,782.4782

Write each in standard form.

14. three and fifteen thousandths

15. thirty and five hundredths

16. ten to the sixth power

17. five hundred thousand, nine

Compare. Use <, >, or = for each ●.

18. 75.89 ● 75.98   **19.** 68.704 ● 68.9   **20.** 35 hundred ● 3,500

21. 53 thousand ● 52,999   **22.** 10^9 ● 999,000   **23.** 3.5 million ● 2.5 billion

Solve.

24. Identify the smallest five-digit whole number.

25. Write the decimal that is 1 less than a million.

26. Name the decimal that is halfway between 2.5 million and 3.5 million.

27. Write another name for one million two hundred fifty thousand.

Think and Apply

28. Is it possible to write the smallest decimal number? the largest decimal number? Explain your thinking.

Mathematics and History

Digits for the decimal system were used as early as 300 B.C. They have evolved over time to their present form. The symbols below show the influence of several cultures.

20th-century bankcheck	1 2 3 4 5 6 7 8 9 0
15th-century European	L 2 3 4 5 6 ʏ ꝛ 9 o
10th-century Arabic	۱ ۲ ۳ ۳ ۲ ۲ ۶ ۷ ۸ ۹
3rd-century B.C. Hindu	- = Ξ ≠ ⋔ 6 7 ら ?

29. What similarities do you see among the different symbols?

30. Which symbol has changed the most? the least?

Look back at **18–19**. Write a rule for deciding which is the greater decimal.

SUMMING UP

A bicycle seat is about 1 meter high. Name something that is about 10 meters high. about 100 meters high. about 1,000 meters high.

Mental Math: Powers of 10

A giant sequoia in Kings Canyon National Park stands about 88.4 meters high. Mount Everest is about 100 times as high. About how high would this be?

Patterns in the decimal number system can be used to multiply or divide by powers of 10.

88.4 × 10 = 884
88.4 × 100 = 8,840

Mount Everest is about 8,840 meters high.

What patterns do you see in the examples below?

$25 \times 10 = 25 \times 10^1 = 250$ $25 \div 10 = 25 \div 10^1 = 2.5$

$25 \times 100 = 25 \times 10^2 = 2,500$ $25 \div 100 = 25 \div 10^2 = 0.25$

$25 \times 1,000 = 25 \times 10^3 = 25,000$ $25 \div 1,000 = 25 \div 10^3 = 0.025$

More Examples

a. $7.53 \times 10 = 75.3$ b. $7.53 \div 10 = 0.753$

$7.53 \times 10^2 = 753$ $7.53 \div 10^2 = 0.0753$

$7.53 \times 10^3 = 7,530$ $7.53 \div 10^3 = 0.00753$

$7.53 \times 10^4 = 75,300$ $7.53 \div 10^4 = 0.000753$

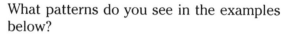
Check Your Understanding

Find each product or quotient mentally.

1. 24×10 2. $3.6 \div 10$ 3. $6.14 \div 100$ 4. 69×10^2

5. $63.9 \times 1,000$ 6. $639 \div 10^3$ 7. 0.009×10^2 8. $0.9 \div 10^3$

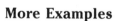
Share Your Ideas Describe how you would multiply a number by a power of ten. Describe how you would divide a number by a power of ten.

Complete each pattern.

9. $16 \times 10 = 160$
   $16 \times 100 = \underline{\hspace{1cm}}$
   $16 \times 1,000 = \underline{\hspace{1cm}}$

10. $43.5 \times 10 = \underline{\hspace{1cm}}$
    $43.5 \times 100 = 4,350$
    $43.5 \times 1,000 = \underline{\hspace{1cm}}$

11. $27 \div 10 = 2.7$
    $27 \div 100 = \underline{\hspace{1cm}}$
    $27 \div 1,000 = \underline{\hspace{1cm}}$

Find each product or quotient mentally.

12. 321×10

13. $4,209 \div 100$

14. $4,209 \times 100$

15. $832 \div 10$

16. 100×0.53

17. $0.53 \div 100$

18. $1,000 \times 38$

19. $375 \div 1,000$

20. 78.6×10

21. $843.8 \div 10^2$

22. $7,500 \times 10^3$

23. $78 \div 10^0$

24. 0.145×10^3

25. $784 \div 10^5$

26. 27.1×10^5

27. $27,200 \div 10^6$

Find n.

28. $42 \div n = 4.2$

29. $86 \times n = 8,600$

30. $10^n \times 98 = 980$

31. $n \div 10^2 = 37.7$

32. $9 \times 10^n = 9$

33. $4,319 \div 10^n = 4,319$

Think and Apply

34. Twenty thousand years ago, a meteor landed in Arizona, creating the famous Meteor Crater. Write this number, using 10^4 as a factor.

35. Fossils have shown that the first land creatures were insects that emerged from the sea 390 million years ago. Write this number in standard form. Then write it using a power of 10 as a factor.

36. Granite found at the bottom of the Grand Canyon was formed about two billion years ago. How many different ways are there to write this number, using a power of 10 as a factor?

Complete the pattern. Then describe a rule for multiplying a number by a multiple of a power of 10.

$11 \times 8 = \underline{\hspace{0.5cm}}$
$11 \times 80 = \underline{\hspace{0.5cm}}$
$11 \times 800 = \underline{\hspace{0.5cm}}$

SUMMING UP

Activity

Understanding Place Value

The sign on top of Beefburger World records the company's sales.

What if each panel can change 100,000 times before it needs replacement? How many panels required replacement to count 1 million sales?

Working together

Think about the place value of each panel to answer the questions below. Record your results.

A. How many times does the units panel change to count 100,000 sales? 1 million sales?

B. How many times does the tens panel change to count 100,000 sales? 1 million sales?

C. How many times does the hundreds panel change to count 1 million sales?

D. How many panels have been replaced after 1 million sales are recorded?

Sharing Your Results

Look back at the results you recorded.

1. How did you determine how many times a panel would be replaced to count a number of sales?

2. Compare how often each panel is replaced. What patterns did you find as you recorded your results?

3. Which panels were replaced to record the sales shown on the sign?

4. The director of advertising said over 1 million panels were replaced to record sales thus far. Was she correct?

Extending the Activity

5. **What if** each panel costs $1,000 to replace? Should the company keep the sign? Why or why not?

The director of advertising is considering using a different sign to record company sales. Look at the model sign below.

The first three panels display only digits.

6. How could the sign display 1 billion sales?
$\frac{1}{2}$ billion sales? $\frac{1}{4}$ billion sales?

7. Could the sign be altered to display $1\frac{1}{2}$ million sales without adding more panels? Explain.

Summing Up

8. Compare the advantages and disadvantages of using each sign.

9. If you were the director, which sign would you use? Write a few sentences explaining your choice.

Activity

Exploring Number Systems

Explore how addition works in a number system with a finite number of numbers.

Working together

Materials: compass, ruler, Workmats 2, 3

A. Draw a clock. Show the numbers 1 to 12 on its face.

B. Answer the following questions about clock arithmetic.
- What time is it 5 hours after 9 o'clock?
- What time is it 10 hours after 8 o'clock?

C. Clock arithmetic is arithmetic in mod 12. Use clock arithmetic to complete the mod 12 addition table below.

Why does $1 + 12 = 1$ in mod 12?

D. Draw a new clock. Use only the numbers 1 to 5 on its face.

Use this clock to complete the mod 5 addition table.

+	1	2	3	4	5	6	7	8	9	10	11	12
1	2	3	4	5	6	7	8	9	10	11	12	1
2	3											
3	4											
4	5											
5	6											
6	7											
7	8											
8	9											
9	10											
10	11											
11	12											
12	1											

+	1	2	3	4	5
1					
2					
3					
4					
5					

Sharing Your Results

Answer these questions for mod 12 and mod 5.

1. What kinds of patterns do you see?

2. Which sums are the same sums as in standard addition?

3. Use shading in your tables to show when the sum is less than either of the addends.

4. What number, when added to a second number, always produces a sum equal to the second number?

Extending the Activity

Work on your own.

5. Draw a new clock using the numbers 1 to 6. Make a mod 6 addition table.

6. Do the same for mod 4.

7. Do the same for mod 9.

Use the information in your tables to answer these questions.

8. In which tables can the sum of two even numbers be an odd number?

9. In which tables does 1 + 1 = 4 + 4? does 1 + 1 = 3 + 3? does 1 + 1 + 1 = 4 + 4 + 4?

10. What is the value of 3 + 4 in mod 6? in mod 4? in mod 9?

11. What is the value of 1 + 2 in mod 6? in mod 4? in mod 9?

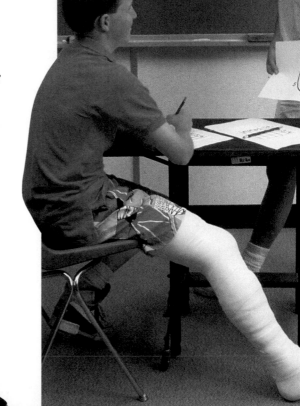

Summing Up

12. What do the five tables have in common?

13. Each table has one number that has the same property as zero has in standard addition. What is the number?

14. Under what circumstances is the sum of two numbers in a mod table different from their sum in standard arithmetic? When is it the same?

Midchapter Review

Find the next four terms in each sequence. pages 4–5

1. 1, 1, 2, 4, 3, 9, ___, ___, ___, ___

2. 16, 8, 4, 2, ___, ___, ___, ___

3. 1, 3, 9, 27, ___, ___, ___, ___

4. 3, 7, 15, 31, ___, ___, ___, ___

Use each rule to write the next four terms of a sequence. Begin with 1. pages 4–5

5. Add 4 to each term.

6. Square each term and add 1.

7. Multiply each term by 4 and subtract 2.

8. Double each term.

Write each as a product of factors. Then write the number in standard form. pages 6–7

9. 3^4 **10.** 7^2 **11.** 2^5 **12.** 23^1 **13.** 32^0 **14.** 3.5^2

Write each number in standard form. pages 8–9

15. $7 \times \frac{1}{100}$ **16.** 10^{10} **17.** 9.3 million **18.** seven and five thousandths

Find each product or quotient. pages 10–13

19. 1.34×10^3 **20.** $7.1 \div 10^2$ **21.** $983 \div 10$

22. $3.46 \div 10^3$ **23.** 658×10^4 **24.** $7{,}284 \times 10^0$

Write each number in mod 4. pages 14–15

25. 3 **26.** 27 **27.** 38 **28.** 45

Complete each sentence.

29. The sum of two odd numbers is ___.

30. The sum of an odd and an even number is ___.

31. An exponent tells the number of times the base is used as a ___.

32. Our decimal number system is based on place values that are powers of ___.

Words to Know
ten
factor
odd
product
even

Solve.

33. The diameter of the sun is 1.4 million km. Its distance from Earth is 150 million km. Write each number in standard form.

34. The seas and oceans of Earth cover about 360 million square kilometers. They contain more than 1.32 billion cubic kilometers of water. Write each number as a product, using a power of 10 as a factor.

Exploring Problem Solving

Is Business All Fun and Games?

Mrs. Weiss sells about 15 copies of Galactic Tiddleywinks a week in her computer store. She pays $15 for each game. However, there are other costs in doing business. She has to pay her employees, as well as the rent on her store. Each time she orders, she pays an employee $12 to fill out a purchase order, no matter how large the order is. In addition, it costs $.20 per game to keep one game on the shelf for each week or part of a week. This is called inventory cost.

Thinking Critically

How many games should Mrs. Weiss order at a time? When you solve problems in lessons like this, work in a group. Keep a record of your work and use it when you discuss the problem.

Analyzing and Making Decisions

1. If Mrs. Weiss orders 30 games in one order, what are her paperwork costs? What are the costs for 45 games?

2. Suppose Mrs. Weiss orders 15 games. What are her inventory costs for that week? **What if** she orders 30 games?

3. If Mrs. Weiss orders 15 games, what is the total cost of the order? Include the paperwork and inventory costs for one week.

4. If Mrs. Weiss orders 30 games, how much would her order cost? Include the paperwork and inventory cost until all 30 games sell. What would be the cost of the 15 games sold in the first week? (She sells 15 games per week).

5. Develop orders for a different number of weeks. What is the best way for Mrs. Weiss to order games? Explain.

Look Back What if she receives 20% (or $3) off the price of each game, when she orders 50 or more games? Now what is the best way for her to order?

Problem Solving Strategies

Alternate Solutions

Steve and Barbara are running the popcorn stand at the school fair. They want to raise $50 for the band. Popcorn costs $.96 for 32 ounces. One ounce of kernels will give them enough for a one-serving bag. Bags cost $1.09 for 100. All of the other materials are being donated. They think they can sell between 100 and 200 bags of popcorn. What should Steve and Barbara charge for one bag of popcorn to make a $50 profit?

Sometimes you need to find more than one solution to a problem to help you find the best answer.

Solving the Problem

CHOICES **Use a calculator where appropriate.**

Think   What is the question?

Explore   How much does the popcorn cost for a one-serving bag? How much does the paper bag cost? How much does it cost to prepare a bag of popcorn for sale? How much profit per bag do they need to make if they sell 100 bags of popcorn? 200 bags?

Solve   What should they charge per bag?

Look Back   How much profit will they make if they sell 100 bags? 200 bags?

Share Your Ideas

1. Do you think it is better to charge a lower price and try to sell more popcorn, or to charge a higher price and hope you can sell just enough to meet your goal?

2. Write a response to the following statement: "When you solve a math problem, there is always only one correct answer."

Practice

THINK
EXPLORE
SOLVE
LOOK BACK

CHOICES Solve. Use a calculator where appropriate.

Use this list to solve problems **3** and **4**.

VIDEO TAPES: COST OF MOVIES			
To Earth and Back	$24.95	Seven Lonesome Cowboys	$16.95
Adventures in Space	$19.95	And Then There Were Four	$16.95
The Last Baseball Game	$18.95	South by Southeast	$13.95
The Shrinking Caterpillar	$18.95		

3. Tamara wanted to buy 2 videos, but she only had $35 to spend. What 2 videos might she purchase?

4. The movie store ran this special for a week in September: Buy 1 movie and get the second one (of equal or lesser value) for half price. What movies might you purchase if you had $40 to spend?

Use the Course List to solve problems 5, 6, and 7.

5. Stanley is attending the community college. If Stanley has to take a course load of 10 credits, what courses might he take?

6. **What if** Stanley must take four courses? What courses might he take to earn 10 credits?

7. Annette needs to earn 12 credits during her second semester. She must take physical education and mathematics. What other courses might she take to fulfill the 12-credit requirement?

COURSE LIST	
Courses	**Credits**
Science	3
Mathematics	3
English	3
Word Processing	2
Accounting I	2
Physical Education	1
First Aid	1

Mixed Strategy Review

The mile run was divided into two races with 3 runners in each group. Below are the times recorded for each runner.

Use the table to solve problems, **8, 9, 10,** and **11.**

Runners	Time	Runners	Time
A. Burns	4 min 30 s	D. Evans	4 min 53 s
B. Chang	4 min 41 s	E. Fein	5 min 2 s
C. Don	4 min 45 s	F. Henry	5 min 10 s

8. Who might have come in first in each race?

9. Who might have come in last in each race?

10. Who might have come in 2nd in each race?

11. If the first and second place runners in each race were put together, who might be in the race?

Create **Your Own**

Write a problem for which there are at least two solutions.

Which is easier to compute mentally, 23 × 4 or (20 × 4) + (3 × 4)?

Mental Math:
Using Properties and Strategies

Sometimes it is faster, easier, and more convenient to compute using mental math.

Using properties can help you compute mentally.

a. $17 + 29 + 53 =$
$17 + 53 + 29 =$
$70 \quad + 29 = 99$

b. $3 \times 62 =$
$(3 \times 60) + (3 \times 2) =$
$180 \quad + \quad 6 \quad = 186$

> **Commutative Properties**
> $a + b = b + a \quad a \times b = b \times a$
>
> **Associative Properties**
> $(a + b) + c = a + (b + c)$
> $(a \times b) \times c = a \times (b \times c)$
>
> **Distributive Property**
> $a \times (b + c) = (a \times b) + (a \times c)$

Some other mental math strategies can also help you.

c. $426 + 72 =$
$426 + 70 + 2 =$
$496 + 2 = 498$

Thinking of 72 as 70 + 2 allows you to use numbers that are easier to add.

d. $475 - 95 =$
$480 - 100 = 380$

Adding 5 to each number does not change the answer.

What if you needed to compute $1.97 - 0.98$? Explain the strategy you would use.

Using equivalent forms can help you compute mentally.

e. $0.25 \times 48 = \frac{1}{4} \times 48 = 12$

Think $\frac{1}{4}$ of 48 equals 48 ÷ 4.

f. $8 \div 0.5 = 8 \div \frac{1}{2} = 16$

Think 8 divided into halves equals 8 × 2. **What if** you need to compute 8 ÷ 0.25?

Check Your Understanding

Compute each mentally. Explain the strategy you used.

1. $65 + 95$
2. $143 - 69$
3. 254×3
4. $16 \div 0.5$
5. $39.7 - 9.9$
6. $4.3 + 7.9 + 6.7$
7. 35×12
8. 100×0.25

Share Your Ideas Multiplying by 0.25 is the same as dividing by 4. Restate multiplying by 0.5 in terms of division.

Compute each mentally.

9. $234 + 88$

10. $511 + 97$

11. $24.8 + 13.2$

12. $185 - 87$

13. $10 - 2.87$

14. $2.63 - 1.64$

15. 231×4

16. 1.7×9

17. $5 \times 23 \times 2$

18. 60×1.5

19. $100 \div 0.25$

20. $25 \times 7 \times 4$

21. $1.8 + 5.6 + 11.2 + 3.4$

22. $56 - 47 - 33 + 24$

Compare. Use <, >, or = for each 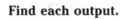.

23. 0.5×12 ⬤ 0.25×12

24. $4 \div 0.25$ ⬤ $4 \div 0.5$

25. 50×0.5 ⬤ $50 \times \frac{1}{2}$

26. 48×0.25 ⬤ 24×0.5

27. $4 \div \frac{1}{2}$ ⬤ $4 \div \frac{1}{4}$

28. $\frac{1}{2} \times 36$ ⬤ 0.25×36

Find each output.

	Rule: Multiply by 3.	
	Input	Output
29.	88	
30.	123	
31.	490	

	Rule: Divide by 0.5.	
	Input	Output
32.	9	
33.	15	
34.	28	

Think and Apply

Using money equivalents can help you compute mentally.
Look at the examples below.

a. $5 \div 0.1$ **Think** How many dimes are in $5? $5 \div \$.10 = 50$

b. $8 \div 0.25$ **Think** How many quarters are in $8? $8 \div \$.25 = 32$

c. $12 \div 0.5$ **Think** How many half dollars are in $12? $12 \div \$.50 = 24$

Use this method to compute each mentally.

35. $7 \div 0.25$

36. $16 \div 0.5$

37. $9 \div 0.1$

38. $8 \div 0.05$

Look back at **11** and **16**. Describe two different ways to compute each mentally.

SUMMING UP

Name some ways in which you will use estimation today.

Estimating Sums and Differences

There are many ways to make an estimate. Choosing a strategy depends on the situation.

- Decide how close an estimate you need.

- Consider whether an underestimate or an overestimate would be appropriate.

- Use numbers that are easy to compute mentally.

Erica has $90 to spend for school clothes. Can she buy all the items shown? Estimate to find out.

▶ Round each number to a number that is easy to compute mentally.

$23.95	→	$25
$28	→	30
$24.75	→	25
$21.99	→	+ 20
		$100

Notice that all the amounts are close to $25. So you can also estimate the total as 4 × $25.

Erica probably cannot buy all the items.

▶ Estimation can also be done by using the front digits. Estimate 8,467 − 1,523.

Think 8,000 − 1,000 = 7,000   Adjust the answer. 467 < 523
So the answer is *less than* 7,000. Why?

What if you needed to estimate 8,523 − 8,467?
Could you use the front digits?
How would you estimate?

Check Your Understanding

Estimate. Explain the method you used for each.

1. 64 + 39 + 12
2. 356 − 127
3. 14 + 13.7 + 15.6
4. 7.32 − 1.85
5. $435 + $189 + $371
6. $11.59 − $1.25

Share Your Ideas What if you estimate the answer to a subtraction problem, using just the front digits? Would the estimate be reasonable? How could you decide?

Estimate.

7. $345.12
   − 230.16

8. 5,374,238
   + 4,862,099

9. $672.28
   + 354.83

10. 546,982
    − 67,312

11. 78,543
    + 2,998

12. 9,023,114
    + 310,647

13. $1,398
    − 54

14. 75,086
    − 428

15. 658,236 + 235,089 + 543,710

16. 4,287 + 4,031 + 3,980

17. 104.31 − 79.29

18. 377.8 + 412.2 + 350 + 422

19. 5 ft 3 in.
    7 ft 2 in.
    6 ft 4 in.
    + 5 ft 11 in.

20. 12 lb 13 oz
    14 lb 7 oz
    10 lb 6 oz
    + 15 lb 4 oz

21. 4 h 20 min
    5 h 30 min
    3 h 49 min
    + 5 h 12 min

Estimate to compare. Write < or > for each ⬬.

22. 45,823 + 76,127 ⬬ 110,000

23. 4.92 + 1.87 + 1.099 ⬬ 10

24. 375,982 + 673,099 ⬬ 1 million

25. $49.98 + $19.98 + $29.98 ⬬ $100

For which situation would you need an exact number? For which is only an estimate necessary? Explain your answer.

26. reporting the number of trees destroyed in a forest fire

27. recording the number of workers on the payroll

28. advertising the circulation of a newspaper

29. advertising the price of an airline ticket

30. Emile has $234.89 in his bank account. He wants to purchase a compact disk player for $350. About how much more does he need to save to make the purchase?

31. Karen purchased two scarves at $8.75 each and three pairs of socks at $2.79 each. Will $20 be enough to buy all the items?

Visual Thinking

This segment represents 10 units.

⊢————⊣

Estimate the perimeter of each shape.

32.   33.   34.

List the estimation strategies you use for addition and subtraction. Describe a situation when each strategy would be most useful.

865 + 135 = 1,000, so 86.5 + 13.5 = 100.
What other sums can you find using this fact?

Using Decimals:
Adding and Subtracting

Martin has a five-dollar bill. He wants
to buy a hamburger, salad, and juice.
How much change should he receive?

Martin estimates to know about how much he will
spend.

$1.89 → $2
$ .89 →   1
$ .79 → +   1
              $4   Martin will spend about $4.
                       He will receive about $1 in change.

Do you think the change will be more or less than $1?
Explain.

To find the exact amount, add and then subtract.

```
  2 2
$1.89       Align the decimal points.
  .89       Write additional zeros as needed.
+  .79
 $3.57      Place the decimal point in the answer.
```

```
        9
     4 1010
  $5.00
 − 3.57
  $1.43
```

Martin should receive $1.43 in change.

More Examples

a. Add. 24 + 0.081 + 4.93

How would you
estimate the sum?

```
   24.000
    0.081
 +  4.930
   29.011
```

b. Subtract. 1.58 − 0.053

The answer will
be close to 1.58.
Why?

```
   1.580
 − 0.053
   1.527
```

Estimate first. Then compute.

1.   734.98
    + 13.05

2. $83.05
    − 19.89

3. 27.89 + 5.07 + 0.09

4. 28 − 3.54

Share Your Ideas Why is it necessary to align the
decimal points when adding or subtracting?

Practice

Estimate. Then use paper and pencil or a calculator to find the exact answer.

5.	38.95	6.	237.09	7.	52.15	8.	93.02	9.	$90.00
	+ 9.86		+ 104.38		+ 8.72		− 6.54		− 12.95

10.	201.7	11.	95.003	12.	623.07	13.	83.5	14.	7,000.2
	+ 5.654		+ 2.91		− 54.7		− 9.678		− 461.001

15. 25.9 + 101.35 + 2.193

16. 35.9 − 10.91

17. 5.7 million − 1.9 million

18. $175.23 + $53.75 + $9.89

19. 15 − 0.837

★20. 2.5 billion − 1.8 million

Place a decimal point in each whole number to make each statement true. Use estimation to help you.

21. 798 − 401 = 39.7

22. 532 + 641 = 53.841

23. 946 − 754 = 0.192

24. 507 + 281 + 695 = 33.865

25. 205 + 823 − 189 = 26.84

Think and Apply

Solve. Choose paper and pencil, mental math, or a calculator for each.

26. Annie bought 11.9 gallons of gas for her car. The tank holds 15 gallons. How much gas was in the tank before it was filled?

27. Look back at **26.** During the next 2 weeks, Annie bought 13.6 gal and 12.8 gal of gas. How much gas did she use in 3 weeks?

28. In 1896, Tom Curtis won a gold medal in the Olympic 110-meter hurdle event. His time was 17.6 seconds. Roger Kingdom's time for first place in the same event in 1988 was 12.98 seconds. Who was faster? by how many seconds?

Common Error

These problems were solved incorrectly. Find the error that was made in each. Then write the correct solution.

29. 3.57 + 98.5 ✗ 13.42

30. 24.3 − 2.05 ✗ 3.8

31. 43.99 − 28 ✗ 43.71

Create your own problem that uses addition or subtraction of decimals. Tell whether an exact answer or an estimate is necessary and solve.

SUMMING UP

25

How would you estimate the number of hours you spend in school each year? Do you think it is more than or less than 1,000 hours?

Estimating Products

The Ridgedale School band sold citrus to raise money for a trip. There were 16 pieces of fruit in each box.
If the band sold 67 boxes, about how many pieces of fruit were sold? Estimate to find out.

▶ You can estimate a product by rounding each factor to a number that is easy to compute mentally.

$$67 \rightarrow 70$$
$$\times 16 \rightarrow \times 20$$
$$\overline{1,400}$$

Is 1,400 an overestimate or an underestimate? Explain.

The band sold about 1,400 pieces of fruit.

▶ Sometimes one factor is close to a power of 10. Round only that factor and compute mentally.

Estimate.
$$475 \qquad 475$$
$$\times 92 \rightarrow \times 100$$
$$\overline{47,500}$$

Think 92 is close to 100.

This method often gives a closer estimate than rounding both factors.

More Examples

a. Estimate. 55×62.2
$$50 \times 62 = 3,100$$

Think 50×62 is half of 100×62, or 6,200

b. Estimate. 432×68.7
$$400 \times 70 = 28,000$$

This is probably an underestimate. Why?

Check Your Understanding

Estimate. Explain the method you used for each.

1. 83×69 **2.** 18×39 **3.** 5.3×4.2 **4.** 28×31 **5.** $3 \times \$7.39$

Share Your Ideas Describe a situation where an overestimate is necessary. When might an underestimate be needed?

Estimate. Explain the method you used for each.

6. 7×835 **7.** 7×8.35 **8.** 63×28 **9.** 630×38

10. 32.8×4.7 **11.** 9.5×56.8 **12.** 810×9.3 **13.** 5.9×368

14. 444×55 **15.** 25×478 **16.** 87.5×34.21 **17.** 52.66×3.98

Use an estimate to choose the actual product.

18. 32×41
  a. 1,192
  b. 1,202
  c. 1,312

19. 67×7.9
  a. 335.3
  b. 529.3
  c. 670.3

20. 63.8×22.4
  a. 1,199.32
  b. 1,429.12
  c. 14,291.2

21. 49.7×38.6
  a. 1,918.42
  b. 2,000.42
  c. 19,184.2

Estimate to compare. Write > or < for each ⬤.

22. 64×36 ⬤ $1,800$ **23.** 41×42 ⬤ $1,600$ **24.** 7.89×62.3 ⬤ 420

25. 704×55 ⬤ $42,000$ **26.** 73×2.9 ⬤ 215 **27.** $27 \times 19 \times 5$ ⬤ $2,700$

Think and Apply

28. Cheryl receives $3.85 per hour for mowing lawns. She takes approximately three hours to cut the lawn for a neighbor. If the lawn needs mowing three times in June, about how much money will she earn that month?

29. A sound system can be purchased for $800 cash or $50.95 per month for 18 months. If the system is purchased on the extended payment plan, what is the estimated total cost? About how much money is saved by paying cash?

Write a problem that you would solve by estimating a product. Solve it and describe the method you used.

SUMMING UP

> How could you determine which is the better buy—
> 3 compact disks for $20 or 1 for $7.90?

Estimating Quotients

One way to estimate quotients is to use compatible numbers. **Compatible numbers** are easy to compute mentally. In division, compatible numbers divide with a remainder of 0.

Estimate. 397.7 ÷ 82   You can estimate in more than one way.

397.7 ÷ 82   **397.7 ÷ 82**
 ↓   ↓   ↓   ↓
400 ÷ 80 = 5   360 ÷ 90 = 4

Which estimate do you think is closer to the exact answer? Why?

Estimate. **150 ÷ 0.4**

When the divisor is less than 1, change it to a whole number before estimating.

150 ÷ 0.4 = 1,500 ÷ 4   Multiply <u>both</u> numbers by 10.

Then estimate.   **1,500 ÷ 4 → 1,500 ÷ 5 = 300**

More Examples

a. Estimate.   630.8 ÷ 33.2 → 660 ÷ 33 = 20

The actual quotient is less than 20. Explain why.

b. Estimate.   3,326 ÷ 16 → 3,200 ÷ 16 = 200

The actual quotient is more than 200. Explain why.

Check Your Understanding

Estimate. Explain the method you used for each.

1. 56.9 ÷ 7   2. 841 ÷ 279   3. 65)‾1,403   4. $23.95 ÷ 3

5. 0.18)‾10   6. 12)‾$3,844   7. 439 ÷ 14   8. 85.7 ÷ 41

Share Your Ideas   What if you use 630 ÷ 30 to estimate 630.8 ÷ 33.2? Explain why decreasing the divisor gives an overestimate.

Estimate. Explain the method you used for each.

9. $6.4\overline{)48.5}$

10. $6.4\overline{)485}$

11. $810 \div 9.3$

12. $5.9\overline{)43}$

13. $454.9 \div 23.8$

14. $41.7\overline{)839.4}$

15. $33.8\overline{)147.6}$

16. $73.2\overline{)553}$

17. $63.8 \div 22.4$

18. $49.7 \div 38.6$

19. $11.8\overline{)743.9}$

20. $258.7 \div 91.4$

21. $\dfrac{95 \times 7}{8.9}$

22. $\dfrac{8 \times 1.25}{3}$

23. $\dfrac{151 \times 9.8}{10.1}$

24. $\dfrac{12 \times 56}{22 \times 28}$

Write *overestimate* or *underestimate* for each.
Try to decide without computing.

25. $15\overline{)789.2}$ is about $15\overline{)750}$.

26. $29\overline{)180}$ is about $30\overline{)180}$.

27. $9.78\overline{)367}$ is about $367 \div 10$.

28. $12.6\overline{)753}$ is about $753 \div 10$.

29. 847.9×111 is about 850×100.

30. 285.3×95.2 is about 285×100.

Think and Apply

31. Maria walked 116.7 miles as part of her exercise program. If she can walk 1 mile in 17 minutes, about how much time did she spend walking?

32. Find a supermarket register tape. Notice how many entries have 9 as the last digit. Why, do you think, does this happen? How can you estimate the total cost of an order? Would it be useful to estimate an average cost per item? Explain

33. A delicatessen item sells for $3.59 per pound. Estimate the cost per ounce and per quarter-pound.

Describe a situation where overestimating a quotient is appropriate.

Mixed Review

1. $475,852$
    $120,859$
    $+ 31,007$

2. $80,001$
    $- 14,567$

3. $4,602 \times 793$

4. $34.786 + 173.92$

5. $430 - 78.987$

6. 421×65

7. $928 \div 16$

8. $27\overline{)2,349}$

9. $5 \times 0.5 \times 50$

10. 0.178×100

Estimate.

11. $4.53 + 7.2$

12. $102.72 - 39.9$

13. $7,500 - 89.99$

14. $95.788 + 102.9$

Compare. Replace each ⬤ with <, >, or −.

15. $\frac{1}{2}$ million ⬤ $500,000$

16. 0.25×10^3 ⬤ $25,000$

17. 1^1 ⬤ 10^1

18. 1^0 ⬤ 10^0

19. 0.5×100 ⬤ $500 \div 10$

20. 10×0.25 ⬤ $10 \div 0.25$

Which is greater, 12 × 0.5 or 12 ÷ 0.5? How can you explain why?

Using Decimals: Multiplying and Dividing

The Leahys filled their gas tank before leaving for vacation. When they stopped for gas again, they had traveled 255 miles. It took 12.5 gallons to fill the tank. What was the average number of miles the car traveled per gallon?

Explain how you could estimate the gas mileage. What numbers would you use?

To find the exact answer, divide.   255 ÷ 12.5

Multiply the divisor and the dividend by the least power of 10 that makes the divisor a whole number.

$$12.5 \overline{)255.0}$$
× 10   × 10

Place the decimal point in the quotient and divide.

$$
\begin{array}{r}
20.4 \\
125 \overline{)2550.0} \\
250 \\
\hline
50\ 0 \\
50\ 0 \\
\hline
0
\end{array}
$$

The car traveled an average of 20.4 miles per gallon.

At $1.59 per gallon, what did it cost to fill the tank? To find the exact amount, multiply.

$$
\begin{array}{r}
\$1.59 \\
\times\ 12.5 \\
\hline
795 \\
3\ 18 \\
15\ 9 \\
\hline
\$19.875
\end{array}
$$

You can use an estimate to place the decimal point correctly in the product.

The Leahys paid $19.88 to fill the tank.

Check Your Understanding

Estimate first. Then find the product or quotient.

1. 12.25 × 3.8
2. 6.34$\overline{)28.53}$
3. 42.9 × 18.5
4. 3.75 × 0.25
5. 407.25 ÷ 4.5
6. 407.25 × 0.4

Share Your Ideas   What steps can you omit if you use a calculator to divide decimals? Explain.

Estimate. Then find the product or quotient.

7. $9.7\overline{)22.31}$ **8.** 6.2×6.3 **9.** 3.9×4.5 **10.** $0.54\overline{)37.26}$

11. $5.2\overline{)32.76}$ **12.** 15.4×9.7 **13.** $26.46 \div 0.42$ **14.** 15.4×0.87

15. $\$6.20 \times 63$ **16.** $0.97\overline{)543.2}$ **17.** $66.42 \div 5.4$ **18.** $45 \times \$3.90$

19. $\$.98 \times 7$ **20.** 4.05×0.27 **21.** $45.6 \div 0.8$ **22.** 93.2×47

Add, subtract, multiply, or divide. Use paper and pencil, mental math, or a calculator. Explain your choices.

CHOICES

23. 6.5×0.01 **24.** 43.2×70 **25.** 0.49×1.31 **26.** $2.79 \div 0.01$

27. 7.3×32.8 **28.** $17.9 - 2.01$ **29.** $13 + 48 + 12.52$ **30.** $79 \div 0.1$

31. $11.088 \div 0.21 + 6$ **32.** $4.25 \times 3 \div 25$ **33.** $15 \times 10.3 - 10$ **34.** $\dfrac{6.15 - 5.79}{6}$

Use an estimate to help choose the correct answer.

35. $25.8\overline{)141.126}$ **36.** $1.836 \div 1.2$ **37.** 568×0.144 **38.** 258×2.15

a. 0.547	**a.** 15.3	**a.** 8179.2	**a.** 5,547
b. 5.47	**b.** 153	**b.** 817.92	**b.** 554.7
c. 54.7	**c.** 1.53	**c.** 81.792	**c.** 5.547

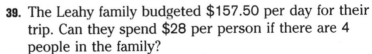

Think and Apply

Solve. Decide whether an estimate is sufficient or an exact answer is needed for each.

39. The Leahy family budgeted $157.50 per day for their trip. Can they spend $28 per person if there are 4 people in the family?

40. Mary's parents agree to deposit in her bank account $.25 for each dollar she saves. If Mary saves $60, how much will her parents deposit?

Logical Thinking

Use a calculator or paper and pencil.

41. Find a two-digit number that when squared equals the cube of the sum of its digits. Is this possible for a one-digit number? a three-digit number?

Divide 75 by 25, by 2.5, and by 0.25. Compare the quotients. Explain the pattern you observe.

SUMMING UP

Using Problem Solving

How Much Postage?

Each year Mrs. Draper sends her 10 grandchildren presents on her birthday. Each present is mailed separately. She wants to find out if sending all the presents for one address together will save her money.

FOURTH CLASS PARCEL POST ZONED RATES						
Weight, up to but not exceeding— (pounds)	Zones					
	Local	1 and 2	3	4	5	6
2	$1.63	$1.69	$1.81	$1.97	$2.24	$2.35
3	1.68	1.78	1.95	2.20	2.59	2.98
4	1.74	1.86	2.10	2.42	2.94	3.46
5	1.79	1.95	2.24	2.65	3.29	3.94
6	1.85	2.04	2.39	2.87	3.64	4.43
7	1.91	2.12	2.53	3.10	4.00	4.91
8	1.96	2.21	2.68	3.32	4.35	5.39
9	2.02	2.30	2.82	3.55	4.70	5.87
10	2.07	2.38	2.97	3.78	5.05	6.35
11	2.13	2.47	3.11	4.00	5.40	6.83
12	2.19	2.56	3.25	4.22	5.75	7.30

Here are the weights for each package.

Sue, Tom, Amy Draper (zone 3)

- 3 lb 5 oz
- 3 lb 2 oz
- 5 lb 3 oz

Ned, Ellen Draper (zone 2)

- 6 lb
- 3 lb 2 oz

A. How much will it cost her to send each of the 10 presents individually?

Bob, Joe, Lisa Draper (zone 4)

- 7 lb 7 oz
- 3 lb 4 oz
- 1 lb 3 oz

Mat, Jenny Ives (zone 6)

- 5 lb 4 oz
- 5 lb 7 oz

B. How much will it cost her to send the presents for each address together?

Sharing Your Ideas

1. How should she send the packages?

Practice

2. Mrs. Draper had trouble finding the presents for all the children, so she was late in mailing them. She could send them faster by using priority mail. How much more will it cost to send the 4 packages by priority mail than by fourth class mail?

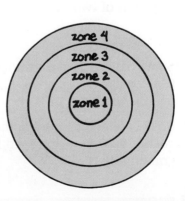

PRIORITY MAIL				
Weight, up to but not exceeding— (pounds)	Zones			
	Local, 1, 2, and 3	4	5	6
2	$2.40	$2.40	$2.40	$2.40
3	2.74	3.16	3.45	3.74
4	3.18	3.75	4.13	4.53
5	3.61	4.32	4.86	5.27
6	4.15	5.08	5.71	6.31
7	4.58	5.66	6.39	7.09
8	5.00	6.23	7.07	7.87
9	5.43	6.81	7.76	8.66
10	5.85	7.39	8.44	9.44
11	6.27	7.97	9.12	10.22
12	6.70	8.55	9.81	11.01

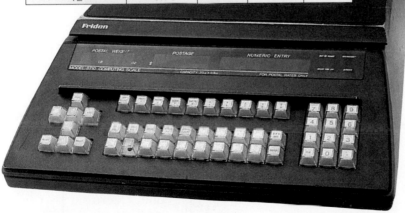

3. If Mrs. Draper used priority mail, should she send each package together or separately?

Summing Up

4. Why do you think it is more expensive to send two 2-lb boxes instead of one 4-lb box?

5. These postal zones are represented by a series of circles. Why do you think that zones are created that way?

33

Chapter Review

Find the next three terms for each sequence. pages 4–5

1. 3, 6, 12, 24, ___, ___, ___

2. $\frac{3}{4}$, $\frac{4}{5}$, $\frac{5}{6}$, $\frac{6}{7}$, ___, ___, ___

3. 2, 5, 11, 23, ___, ___, ___

4. 97, 93, 89, 85, ___, ___, ___

Write each as a product of factors. Then write in standard form. pages 6–7

5. 10^4

6. three squared

7. 2^6

8. 13^2

Write each in words. pages 8–9

9. the greatest 4-digit whole number

10. the least 10-digit whole number

Find each product or quotient. pages 10–13, 20–21

11. 1.16×10^3

12. $6,780 \div 10^2$

13. $5,329 \times 10^0$

14. 340×0.5

15. $100 \div 0.25$

16. $45 \div 0.5$

Find each sum or difference. pages 24–25

17. $7.3 + 3.9 + 9.7$

18. $58.65 - 51.55$

19. $64 + 19 + 32$

20. $\$5 - \$2.29$

21. $\$3 + \$4.75 + \$2.10$

22. 9.3 million − 7.6 million

Estimate each. pages 22–23, 26–29

23. $14.57 + 27.12$

24. 64.7×4.1

25. $37.9 \div 3.2$

26. $123 + 159 + 2,174$

27. $\$16.74 - \$5.20$

28. 42.9×21.4

Find each product or quotient. pages 30–31

29. 41×107

30. $\$8.25 \times 3$

31. $\$29.85 \div 5$

32. $64.668 \div 3.4$

Complete each statement.

33. A ___ is a list of numbers that follows a rule or pattern.

34. For any number n except 0, n^0 equals ___.

35. The sum of two even numbers is always ___.

Words to Know
one   zero
odd   even
sequence
factor

Solve. pages 17–19

36. Some oxygen in our atmosphere can be found as high as 6 miles above sea level. About how many feet above sea level is that?

37. Rose called her grandmother long-distance. If the call cost $10.26, how long did Rose talk to her grandmother?

LONG DISTANCE RATES

$4.10 for first 3 min

$.44 each additional min

Chapter Test

Find the next three terms for each sequence.

1. $1, \frac{1}{2}, \frac{1}{3}, \frac{1}{4}$, ——, ——, ——

2. 2, 10, 5, 11, 8, 12, ——, ——, ——

3. 1, 4, 9, 16, ——, ——, ——

Write each as a product of factors. Then write in standard form.

4. five cubed

5. four squared

6. six to the zero power

Write each in words.

7. the greatest 5-digit whole number

8. the least 7-digit whole number

Find each product or quotient.

9. 8.47×10^2

10. $772 \div 10^3$

11. $135.9 \div 10^0$

12. 44×0.25

13. $250 \div 0.25$

14. 26×0.5

Estimate each.

15. 409×12.6

16. $27.3 \div 4.2$

17. $116.75 - 57.40

Find each sum, difference, product, or quotient.

18. $115.73 + 12.9$

19. 16.7×5.2

20. $37.52 \div 0.7$

21. $549.3 - 278.71$

22. 116×0.4

23. $537.20 \div 3.40

Solve.

24. You have $4.50 to spend for lunch. What would you buy?

25. Sam's car gets 42.5 miles per gallon. The gas tank holds 13 gallons. About how far can he expect to travel on one tankful of gas?

MENU	
FISH SANDWICH	$2.50
SALAD	.90
SOUP	.75
MILK	.50
FRUIT	.45
PIZZA SLICE	1.25

THINK Represent each number. You may use operations and exponents.

Example. Use three 2's to name 1.

$$2 - \frac{2}{2} = 1$$

Using two 9's, name the greatest possible number; the least possible number.

EXTENSION

Magic Squares

In 1514 the German painter Albrecht Dürer created this magic square for his engraving entitled *Melencolia*.

16	3	2	13
5	10	11	8
9	6	7	12
4	15	14	1

1. Find the sum of each row, column, and diagonal in the square above. What do you notice?

2. Find the sum of the 4 numbers in the center of the square. What do you notice?

3. Multiply each entry by $\frac{1}{2}$. Is the array still a magic square? How can you tell?

4. Can you always multiply each entry of the square by the same number and still maintain a magic square? Justify your answer.

5. Add $1\frac{5}{8}$ to each entry of the square. Is the array still a magic square? If so, write the magic sum.

6. Use the operation of division to construct another magic square. Explain your procedure and find the magic sum.

Maintaining Skills

Choose the correct answer. Write A, B, C, or D.

1. Complete the 3 terms of the sequence.
   5, 6, 8, 11, _____, _____, _____

   A 14, 17, 20   C 15, 16, 20

   B 15, 20, 26   D not given

2. What is 6^4 as a product of factors?

   A $6 \times 6 \times 6 \times 6$ C $6 \times 5 \times 4 \times 3$

   B 6×4 D not given

3. What is forty and four hundredths in standard form?

   A 40.04   C 4.04

   B 40.4   D not given

4. What is the value of 10^5?

   A 10,000   C 100,000

   B 1,000,000   D not given

5. 26.8×100

   A 206.8   C 0.268

   B 268   D not given

6. $3,500 \div 10^2$

   A 0.35   C 35

   B 350,000   D not given

7. Estimate. $863.12 + $122.04

   A $1,000.00   C $900.00

   B $1,700.00   D $1,200.00

8. Estimate. $26.4 + 81 + 16.9$

   A 100   C 90

   B 1,200   D 130

9. $45.02 + 6.3$

   A 41.32   C 51.32

   B 45.65   D not given

10. Estimate.   55.3
                $\times$ 6.72

    A 420   C 4.2

    B 42   D not given

11. Estimate. $5.8\overline{)15.36}$

    A 3   C 0.3

    B 30   D 300

12. $115.02 \div 21.3$

    A 0.54   C 5.26

    B 5.4   D not given

13.   22.4
    $\times$ 8.6

    A 182.64   C 1,926.4

    B 19.264   D not given

Solve.

14. A taxi charges $1.75 for the first mile and $.15 for each additional 0.1 mile. How long a trip could Julia take for exactly $5.00?

    A 0.7 miles   C 6 miles

    B 2 miles   D not given

15. A poll was taken of all 126 eighth graders in Center Middle School to find out how many were collectors. Twice as many students were collectors as were not. How many were collectors?

    A 46   C 84

    B 42   D not given

2 Number Theory and Fractions

Sharing What You Know

Look at the numbers on the clay tablet. How are they different from the numbers you know? Primitive number systems represented numbers with different arrangements of strokes or lines. One stroke was "one" and nine strokes were "nine." Discuss how you might work calculations with a number system like this. Do you know of any other number systems where the numbers were similar to strokes?

Using Language

Words like *primitive, primary* and *prime* come from the Latin root *primus,* meaning *first.* In mathematics, a number is **prime** if it is divisible only by itself and 1. All whole numbers that are not prime can be written as the product of **prime** factors.

Words to Know   composite number, conjecture, prime factorization, prime number, counter example

Be a Problem Solver

2 is prime because it is divisible only by itself and 1. Are any other even numbers prime? If so, which ones? If not, why not?

Write a set of directions that tell how to do calculations using either Roman numerals or an abacus.

Activity

Exploring Primes

A number with exactly two factors is a **prime** number. A number with more than two factors is a **composite** number. The number 1 is neither prime nor composite.

How can you tell whether a number is prime or composite?

Working together

Explore these methods for determining whether a number is prime or composite. Use a calculator when appropriate. Record your work.

A. One way to decide if a number is prime or composite is to list the factors of the number.

Factors of 16: 1×16, 2×8, 4×4 16 is composite.
Factors of 17: 1×17 17 is prime.

Use a list of factors to find out if 91 is prime.

B. Another way to tell whether a number is prime is to use this test.

Is 5 prime?

$4 \times 3 \times 2 \times 1 = 24$ Multiply all whole numbers less than the number.
$24 + 1 = 25$ Add 1 to the product.
$25 \div 5 = 5$ 5 is prime.   Divide by the original number. If the remainder is 0, the number is prime.

Show that 7 and 11 are prime.

C. A third method is to divide by prime numbers less than or equal to the square root of the number to find out if any are factors. Use the list of primes shown.

Is 8,191 prime?   8,191 is close to 91×91.
Try to divide by primes up to 89.

PRIME NUMBERS			
2	3	5	7
11	13	17	19
23	29	31	37
41	43	47	53
59	61	67	71
73	79	83	89
97 . . .			

Sharing Your Results

1. **What if** 8, 191 has a prime factor greater than 89. Would you find it by dividing by primes less than 89? Explain.

2. Could you test 8,191 using the method in **B**? Do you think it is practical to do so? Why or why not?

3. Use any method to determine whether each is prime.

   a. 27   **b.** 41   **c.** 211   **d.** 253   **e.** 10,011

Extending the Activity

Number theorists have found rules that generate numbers, some of which are prime. None of their rules can be used to generate only prime numbers.

Work in a small group to investigate some rules they found. You may wish to use a calculator.

4. Use each rule below to find at least five numbers. Make an organized list.

   a. Choose a number. Square it and then add the original number and 41 to the result. Start with the number 1.

   b. Use 2 as a factor 2, 3, 5, 7, and 11 times. Then subtract 1 from each result.

   c. Use the list of primes on page 40. Multiply the first two primes and add 1. Then multiply the first three primes and add 1. Continue this pattern up to the product of six primes. Add 1 each time.

5. Test the numbers in each list to find out if each is prime or composite. Record your results.

6. Does any method seem to give only primes? Which one?

7. **What if** you continue to use that method. Will you continue to get only primes? Find out how many consecutive primes that method generates.

Summing Up

8. Write in your own words how to find out whether a number is prime or composite.

9. One of the greatest prime numbers known is $2^{216,091} - 1$. It was found by using a computer. Tell which rule above might have been used to find it. Give a reason.

List all the factors of 24. Then use the list to find the prime factors of 24.

Prime Factorization

Every composite number can be written as a product of prime factors. This product is called the **prime factorization** of the number.

You can use a factor tree to list the prime factors of a number.

Find the prime factorization of 102.

102
2 × 51   Use divisibility rules to find any two factors.
2 × 3 × 17   Continue finding factors until all factors are prime.

The prime factorization of 102 is 2 × 3 × 17.

How do you know that you have reached the last row of a factor tree?

Another Example

Find the prime factorization of 884.

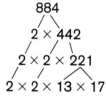

884
2 × 442
2 × 2 × 221   2 is a factor twice.
2 × 2 × 13 × 17   3, 5, 7, and 11 are not factors of 211.

$884 = 2 \times 2 \times 13 \times 17$ Write the product, using exponents.

$884 = 2^2 \times 13 \times 17$

Divisibility Rules

A number is divisible by
2 if it ends in 0, 2, 4, 6 or 8.
3 if the sum of its digits is divisible by 3.
5 if it ends in 0 or 5.
6 if it is divisible by 2 and 3.
9 If the sum of the digits is divisible by 9.
10 if it ends in 0.

Check Your Understanding

Write the prime factorization of each number that is composite. Use exponents. If a number is prime, write *prime*.

1. 30 **2.** 48 **3.** 144 **4.** 121 **5.** 31 **6.** 143

7. 56 **8.** 24 **9.** 512 **10.** 78 **11.** 53 **12.** 209

Share Your Ideas   What if you know that the prime factorization of a number is $2^2 \times 47$. What is the number?

Practice

Write the prime factorization of each composite number, using exponents. If a number is prime, write *prime*. Use mental math, paper and pencil, or a calculator.

13. 40   **14.** 63   **15.** 72   **16.** 29

17. 88   **18.** 36   **19.** 243   **20.** 91

21. 169   **22.** 253   **23.** 89   **24.** 165

25. 101   **26.** 133   **27.** 273   **28.** 391

Find *n* to make each prime factorization.

29. $3 \times 3 \times 3 \times n = 54$

30. $n \times 11^2 = 605$

31. $n \times 7^2 \times 3 = 294$

32. $875 = n \times 5^3$

33. $2^2 \times n^2 \times 5^2 = 900$

34. $n^2 \times 23 = 3,887$

Write the number represented by each prime factorization.

35. $2^3 \times 11$ **36.** $3^2 \times 41$ **37.** 5×13^2

38. $2^4 \times 3$ **39.** $5^2 \times 19$ **40.** 17×19

41. $3^3 \times 5^2$ **42.** $3^2 \times 43$ **43.** $7^2 \times 47$

Think and Apply

44. A number has 2, 5, 6, and 7 among its factors. What is the least number that has these factors?

45. To find the prime factorization of a number, Meg divides by factors from least to greatest. Jim divides by any factor. Which way do you prefer? Why?

46. Two of the numbers that open Joann's combination lock are prime factors of 437. Find the numbers.

Can a number have two different prime factorizations? Can two different numbers have the same prime factorization? Explain.

Mixed Review

1. $3,465 + 21,369 + 487$

2. $3,424 - 1,928$

3. 428×94

4. $15,133 \div 37$

5. $25 \div 1,000$

6. $5.23 + 0.984 + 21.9$

7. $0.82 - 0.093$

8. 12.3×0.078

9. $35.784 \div 0.84$

10. $57.6 \div 100$

Find *n*.

11. $2^n = 1,024$

12. $10^3 = n$

13. $5^n = 1$

14. $45 \times 10^3 = n$

15. $92 \div 10^4 = n$

16. $0.15 \times 10^n = 1,500$

17. $0.19 \div 10^n = 0.019$

18. $92.5 - n = 41.1$

19. $8.11 + n = 51.2$

20. $42 \div n = 10.5$

SUMMING UP

Is 11 a common factor of 44 and 132? Is there a greater factor common to both numbers? If so, name it.

Greatest Common Factor and Least Common Multiple

▶ The greatest common factor (GCF) of two or more numbers is the greatest number that is a factor of each.

You can use prime factorization to find the GCF of two or more numbers.

Find the GCF of 84 and 70.

$84 = 2 \times 2 \times 3 \times 7$ Write the prime factorization of each number.

$70 = 2 \times 5 \times 7$ Mark all pairs of the prime factors that are common to both.

$2 \times 7 = 14$ Multiply the common factors.

The GCF of 84 and 70 is 14.

The GCF of two or more numbers is the product of the common prime factors. If there are no common prime factors, the GCF is 1.

▶ The least common multiple (LCM) of two or more numbers is the least nonzero number that is a multiple of each.

You can use prime factorization to find the LCM of two or more numbers.

Find the LCM of 48 and 72.

$48 = 2^4 \times 3$ Write the prime factorization of each number.

$72 = 2^3 \times 3^2$ Choose the highest power of each prime factor.

$2^4 \times 3^2 = 16 \times 9 = 144$ Find the product.

The LCM of 48 and 72 is 144.

Theano teaching at the Pythagorean School in ancient Greece

Check Your Understanding

Find the GCF and the LCM of each pair of numbers.

1. 14, 35   2. 12, 48   3. 15, 28   4. 16, 36

5. 29, 7   6. 42, 60   7. 121, 88   8. 34, 38

Share Your Ideas   List all factors of 48 and 64. How could you use the list to find the GCF? Do you think it might be easier to use prime factorization? Why or why not?

The prime factorization of each number is given. Find the GCF of each pair.

9. $15 = 3 \times 5$
   $75 = 3 \times 5^2$

10. $22 = 2 \times 11$
    $26 = 2 \times 13$

11. $42 = 2 \times 3 \times 7$
    $63 = 3^2 \times 7$

The prime factorization of each number is given. Find the LCM of each pair.

12. $90 = 2 \times 3^2 \times 5$
    $135 = 3^3 \times 5$

13. $72 = 2^3 \times 3^2$
    $108 = 2^2 \times 3^3$

14. $96 = 2^5 \times 3$
    $144 = 2^4 \times 3^2$

Find the GCF and the LCM of each.

15. 30, 40
16. 12, 28
17. 12, 16
18. 6, 16
19. 49, 63

20. 8, 32
21. 12, 72
22. 12, 15
23. 75, 90
24. 12, 18

25. 6, 90
26. 25, 40
27. 14, 49
28. 26, 35
29. 19, 48

30. 43, 1
31. 14, 21
32. 8, 18, 28
33. 6, 24, 60
34. 5, 45, 22

Write *true* or *false*.

35. The GCF of 28 and 56 is 56.

36. Every multiple of 5 is also a multiple of 10.

37. Every pair of numbers has a least common factor.

38. Every pair of numbers has a greatest common multiple.

39. The LCM of two prime numbers is the product of the numbers.

40. The LCM of 17 and 51 is greater than or equal to 51.

Euclid

The Granger Collection

Think and Apply

41. Use a calculator to complete six rows of the table. Choose five pairs of numbers. Find the GCF and LCM. What do you observe about the numbers, their GCF, and their LCM?

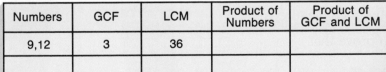

Numbers	GCF	LCM	Product of Numbers	Product of GCF and LCM
9,12	3	36		

Explain an easy way to find the LCM of two numbers if you know the GCF.

SUMMING UP

Activity

Exploring Conjectures

John says there are more boys than girls in each of the eighth grade classes. Sarah found that one class had more girls than boys.

John's statement is a conjecture. Sarah's counterexample disproves John's conjecture.

A **conjecture** is a statement that has not been proved true or false. A statement can be proved false by one example, called a counterexample. Mathematical statements cannot be proved true by examples, no matter how many you find.

Working together

Record your work as you explore conjectures.

A. Predict whether each conjecture below is true or false. Then test each conjecture with any numbers you choose. Try to find a counterexample. Record as many examples as you need.

- The sum of any two numbers is even.

- The product of any three consecutive numbers is divisible by 6.

B. Which statement were you able to prove false? What counterexample did you find?

C. Change the false statement slightly to a statement you think is true. Exchange statements with another group. Test the statements with numbers and try to find a counterexample.

Sharing Your Results

1. Explain in your own words what a conjecture is.

2. Discuss how you would try to prove that a conjecture is false.

3. **What if** you are not able to find a counterexample that disproves a statement. Is it still possible that a counterexample exists?

Extending the Activity

Work in a small group to explore conjectures about prime numbers. Record your work.

4. Copy and extend the table to ten rows.

Multiple of 6	(multiple of 6)−1	(multiple of 6)+1
6	5	7
12	11	13
18	17	19

5. Check the numbers in the table against a list of primes. What do you notice?

6. Are these conjectures true? Why or why not?
   a. Adding 1 to a multiple of 6 gives a prime number.
   b. Subtracting 1 from a multiple of 6 gives a prime number.

7. Change one of the conjectures above slightly to one you think may be true.

8. One of the best-known conjectures about primes states that any odd number greater than or equal to 7 can be written as the sum of three primes. Choose five odd numbers greater than 7. Write each as the sum of 3 primes.

9. This conjecture has not been proved true. Do you think it is true? Give a reason.

Summing Up

10. One of the following conjectures is true and the other is false. Give a counterexample for one of the statements. Tell why you think the other is true.

   a. If the product of two numbers is divisible by 2, then one of the numbers is divisible by 2.

   b. If the product of two numbers is divisible by 6, then one of the numbers is divisible by 6.

A quarter is $\frac{1}{4}$ dollar, or 0.25 dollar. List the decimal equivalents and fractional parts of a dollar for other United States coins.

Relating Fractions and Decimals

The Sumerian art shown dates to 2500 B.C. The tallest figure is about 2.5 feet tall. Express the height in fraction form.

▶ You can use place value to write a decimal as a fraction.

Express 2.5 in fraction form.

$0.5 = \frac{5}{10}$, or $\frac{1}{2}$

The height of the figure is $2\frac{1}{2}$ feet.

Another Example

Express 0.875 as a fraction in lowest terms.

$0.875 = \frac{875}{1,000}$ $\qquad \frac{875 \div 125}{1,000 \div 125} = \frac{7}{8}$ Think Divide by the GCF. $\qquad 0.875 = \frac{7}{8}$

▶ You can use division to write a fraction as a decimal. Divide the numerator by the denominator.

a. Express $2\frac{5}{8}$ as a decimal.

$$\begin{array}{r} 0.625 \\ 8)\overline{5.000} \\ \underline{4\,8} \\ 20 \\ \underline{16} \\ 40 \\ \underline{40} \\ 0 \end{array}$$

The remainder is 0.
0.625 is a terminating decimal.

$2\frac{5}{8} = 2.625$

b. Express $\frac{1}{6}$ as a decimal.

$$\begin{array}{r} 0.166 \\ 6)\overline{1.000} \\ \underline{6} \\ 40 \\ \underline{36} \\ 40 \\ \underline{36} \\ 4 \end{array}$$

The remainder is never 0. The decimal for $\frac{1}{6}$ is a repeating decimal.

$\frac{1}{6} = 0.166\frac{4}{6}$, or $0.16\frac{2}{3}$

Why does the calculator display 0.166 . . . as 0.1666667?

Check Your Understanding

Write each decimal as a fraction. Write each fraction or mixed number as a decimal.

1. 0.375 **2.** $\frac{3}{4}$ **3.** 2.35 **4.** $\frac{3}{40}$ **5.** $2\frac{3}{5}$ **6.** 5.021

Share Your Ideas   In what ways are $\frac{3}{4}$ and 0.75 the same? How are they different?

Express each decimal as a fraction in lowest terms.

7. 0.2　　　　　　　**8.** 0.35　　　　　　　**9.** 0.625

10. 0.57　　　　　　**11.** 0.29　　　　　　**12.** 1.6

13. 3.48　　　　　　**14.** 2.125　　　　　　**15.** 1.79

16. 1.45　　　　　　**17.** 4.17　　　　　　**18.** 1.05

19. 2.55　　　　　　**20.** 1.75　　　　　　**21.** 2.008

Express each fraction as a decimal. Use mental math, paper and pencil, or a calculator.

22. $\frac{1}{5}$ 　　　　　　**23.** $\frac{3}{10}$ 　　　　　　**24.** $\frac{7}{8}$

25. $\frac{17}{20}$ 　　　　　　**26.** $\frac{1}{4}$ 　　　　　　**27.** $3\frac{1}{2}$

28. $1\frac{4}{5}$ 　　　　　　**29.** $2\frac{1}{10}$ 　　　　　**30.** $4\frac{9}{20}$

31. $2\frac{19}{100}$ 　　　　　**32.** $4\frac{2}{5}$ 　　　　　　**33.** $1\frac{3}{8}$

34. $5\frac{3}{4}$ 　　　　　　**35.** $1\frac{23}{40}$ 　　　　　**36.** $2\frac{59}{80}$

Choose the correct value for n.

37. $\frac{3}{8} = n$

  a. $0.37\frac{1}{2}$

  b. 0.375

  c. both **a** and **b**

  d. none of the above

38. $0.85 = n$

  a. $\frac{85}{100}$

  b. 17 nickels

  c. both **a** and **b**

  d. none of the above

39. $5\frac{3}{50} = n$

  a. 5.06

  b. 5.60

  c. 5.006

  d. none of the above

Think and Apply

40. If you know that $\frac{1}{5} = 0.2$, you can find the decimal equivalent for $\frac{2}{5}$ by multiplying 2×0.2. Use this method to find decimals for $\frac{3}{5}$ and $\frac{4}{5}$.

41. Sumerian cuneiform writing has about 27 times as many hieroglyphs, or symbols, as our alphabet has letters. About how many symbols does cuneiform have?

Use mental math to write each fraction as a decimal.

$\frac{1}{2}$　$\frac{3}{4}$　$\frac{2}{5}$　$\frac{1}{8}$　$\frac{3}{8}$　$\frac{7}{8}$

SUMMING UP

Amy said that $\frac{2}{3}$ equals 0.66. Is she correct?

Understanding Repeating Decimals

From 1500 B.C. to the sixth century A.D., China was the sole producer of silk. One third of the silk threads in the design shown are shades of gold. What decimal part of the fabric is gold?

Use paper and pencil or a calculator to express $\frac{1}{3}$ as a decimal.

$$
\begin{array}{r}
0.333\ldots \\
3\overline{)1.000} \\
\underline{9} \\
10 \\
\underline{9} \\
10 \\
\underline{9} \\
1
\end{array}
$$

← shows that 6 repeats in the quotient.

If you continue to divide, the digits in the quotient continue to repeat. The remainder will never be zero. The decimal for $\frac{1}{3}$ is repeating, or nonterminating.

$\frac{1}{3} = 0.\overline{3}$ ← The bar is used to show the digit or digits that repeat.

$\frac{1}{3}$ is sometimes written as $0.33\frac{1}{3}$.

More Examples

a. Express $\frac{5}{6}$ as a decimal.

$$
\begin{array}{r}
0.833\ldots \\
6\overline{)5.000} \\
\underline{4\,8} \\
20 \\
\underline{18} \\
20 \\
\underline{18} \\
2
\end{array}
$$

$\frac{5}{6} = 0.8\overline{3}$

b. Express $2\frac{5}{11}$ as a decimal.

$$
\begin{array}{r}
0.4545\ldots \\
11\overline{)5.0000} \\
\underline{4\,4} \\
60 \\
\underline{55} \\
50 \\
\underline{44} \\
60 \\
\underline{55} \\
5
\end{array}
$$

$2\frac{5}{11} = 2.\overline{45}$

Write each fraction as a repeating decimal.

1. $\frac{4}{9}$ 2. $\frac{1}{6}$ 3. $\frac{1}{11}$ 4. $\frac{7}{11}$ 5. $\frac{1}{7}$

Share Your Ideas   Write $\frac{1}{3}$ as a decimal five different ways.

Express each fraction as a decimal. Use a bar for repeating decimals.

6. $\frac{7}{9}$ **7.** $\frac{3}{11}$ **8.** $\frac{5}{6}$ **9.** $\frac{1}{11}$ **10.** $\frac{2}{7}$

11. $\frac{3}{4}$ **12.** $\frac{5}{8}$ **13.** $\frac{6}{11}$ **14.** $\frac{4}{9}$ **15.** $\frac{4}{5}$

16. $\frac{9}{10}$ **17.** $\frac{2}{3}$ **18.** $\frac{5}{11}$ **19.** $\frac{1}{13}$ **20.** $\frac{3}{13}$

Compare. Use <, >, or = for each ⬤.

21. $\frac{1}{9}$ ⬤ 0.111 **22.** $\frac{1}{11}$ ⬤ 0.1 **23.** $\frac{2}{3}$ ⬤ 0.6 **24.** $\frac{1}{6}$ ⬤ 0.17

25. $\frac{1}{7}$ ⬤ 0.142857 **26.** $\frac{1}{8}$ ⬤ 0.125 **27.** $\frac{4}{9}$ ⬤ 0.445 **28.** $\frac{5}{11}$ ⬤ 0.45

List in order from least to greatest.

29. $0.\overline{3}, \frac{3}{10}, \frac{33}{100}$ **30.** $0.16, 0.17, \frac{1}{6}$ **31.** $0.875, \frac{5}{6}, 0.\overline{8}$

Think and Apply

32. Today, thirty-five countries produce silk. China leads with over one half of the total annual production. If 52,000 tons of raw silk are produced worldwide, about how many tons of silk does China produce each year?

33. Find decimals for $\frac{1}{9}, \frac{2}{9}, \ldots, \frac{8}{9}$. What pattern do you observe?

34. Find decimals for $\frac{1}{11}, \frac{2}{11}, \ldots, \frac{10}{11}$. Describe the pattern.

Consider all fractions having denominators 2 to 11. List the fractions that have repeating decimal equivalents.

SUMMING UP

51

Comparing Fractions

Equivalent fractions name equal parts of a whole or of a group. To find an equivalent fraction, multiply or divide the numerator and denominator by the same nonzero number.

$$\frac{1}{3} = \frac{1 \times 2}{3 \times 2} = \frac{2}{6} \qquad \frac{3}{9} = \frac{3 \div 3}{9 \div 3} = \frac{1}{3}$$

Find the value of n to make the fractions equivalent.

$$\frac{5}{15} = \frac{n}{30}$$
$$n = 10$$

Think $15 \times 2 = 30 \qquad n = 10$
$5 \times 2 = 10$

Equivalent fractions have cross products that are equal.

$2 \times 12 = 3 \times 8$
$24 = 24$

▶ You can compare fractions by using any of the following methods.

a. Find cross products.

Compare $\frac{4}{5}$ and $\frac{5}{6}$

$4 \times 6 < 5 \times 5$, so $\frac{4}{5} < \frac{5}{6}$.

b. Find like fractions.

Compare $\frac{5}{8}$ and $\frac{2}{3}$.

$\frac{15}{24} < \frac{16}{24}$, so $\frac{5}{8} < \frac{2}{3}$.

c. Find decimal equivalents.

Compare $\frac{4}{5}$ and $\frac{3}{4}$.

$0.80 > 0.75$, so $\frac{4}{5} > \frac{3}{4}$.

d. Use number sense.

Compare $\frac{5}{11}$ and $\frac{3}{11}$.

$5 > 3$, so $\frac{5}{11} > \frac{3}{11}$.

Explain how you would compare $\frac{7}{9}$ and $\frac{7}{11}$.

Check Your Understanding

Find the value of n to make the fractions equivalent.

1. $\frac{4}{12} = \frac{n}{24}$ **2.** $\frac{5}{35} = \frac{1}{n}$ **3.** $\frac{15}{42} = \frac{5}{n}$ **4.** $\frac{n}{36} = \frac{14}{72}$ **5.** $\frac{12}{n} = \frac{1}{3}$

Compare. Use <, >, or = for each ⬤.

6. $\frac{2}{9}$ ⬤ $\frac{4}{9}$ **7.** $\frac{12}{15}$ ⬤ $\frac{24}{30}$ **8.** $\frac{6}{21}$ ⬤ $\frac{13}{49}$ **9.** $\frac{12}{50}$ ⬤ $\frac{37}{15}$ **10.** 0.3 ⬤ $\frac{1}{3}$

Share Your Ideas Explain how you would order $\frac{5}{6}$, $\frac{4}{7}$, and $\frac{5}{8}$ from least to greatest.

Find the value of *n* to make the fractions equivalent.

11. $\frac{8}{12} = \frac{n}{24}$ **12.** $\frac{n}{3} = \frac{6}{9}$ **13.** $\frac{11}{16} = \frac{n}{32}$ **14.** $\frac{n}{7} = \frac{15}{21}$

15. $\frac{3}{15} = \frac{n}{5}$ **16.** $\frac{12}{16} = \frac{3}{n}$ **17.** $\frac{4}{14} = \frac{n}{21}$ **18.** $\frac{5}{25} = \frac{n}{35}$

Compare. Use <, >, or = for each ⬤

19. $\frac{4}{7}$ ⬤ $\frac{3}{7}$ **20.** $\frac{9}{12}$ ⬤ $\frac{3}{4}$ **21.** $\frac{4}{15}$ ⬤ $\frac{9}{30}$ **22.** $\frac{7}{8}$ ⬤ $\frac{7}{11}$

23. $\frac{11}{16}$ ⬤ $\frac{3}{4}$ **24.** $\frac{3}{4}$ ⬤ $\frac{25}{32}$ **25.** $\frac{10}{18}$ ⬤ $\frac{25}{45}$ **26.** $\frac{5}{9}$ ⬤ $\frac{5}{8}$

27. $\frac{1}{2}$ ⬤ $\frac{17}{32}$ **28.** 0.75 ⬤ $\frac{3}{4}$ **29.** $\frac{5}{6}$ ⬤ 0.875 **30.** $\frac{38}{15}$ ⬤ $\frac{26}{10}$

List in order from least to greatest.

31. $\frac{2}{3}, \frac{5}{8}, \frac{66}{100}$ **32.** $\frac{4}{9}, \frac{4}{7}, \frac{5}{11}$ **33.** $\frac{7}{8}, \frac{8}{10}, \frac{8}{9}$ **34.** $0.1, \frac{1}{11}, 0.\overline{1}$

Think and Apply

35. The classification system used in libraries makes it possible to place a book between any two books. What numbers could be assigned to books between A304.1 and A304.2?

36. **What if** libraries used fractions to place books in order.

a. What numbers could be assigned to books between $11\frac{7}{15}$ and $11\frac{11}{15}$?

b. What numbers could be assigned to books between $5\frac{1}{10}$ and $5\frac{2}{10}$?

If the library had multiple copies of a book, the books might be numbered $4\frac{3}{5}, 4\frac{6}{10}, 4\frac{9}{15}, \ldots$

c. What number would be on the eighth copy of book $99\frac{2}{7}$?

d. What number would be on the first copy of book $35\frac{18}{24}$?

Use a number line to show that $\frac{2}{3} < \frac{5}{6}$.

SUMMING UP

Midchapter Review

Write the prime factors of each composite number. If a number is prime, write *prime*. pages 42–43

1. 42   **2.** 150   **3.** 61   **4.** 176   **5.** 209

Find the GCF of each pair of numbers. pages 44–45

6. 15, 24   **7.** 45, 105   **8.** 14, 42   **9.** 3, 144

Find the LCM of each pair of numbers. pages 44–45

10. 5, 15   **11.** 6, 9   **12.** 32, 48   **13.** 8, 12

Write *true* or *false*. If false, give a counterexample. pages 46–47

14. The product of two even numbers is even.

15. The quotient of two even numbers is even.

Write each as a fraction or mixed number in lowest terms. pages 48–49

16. 0.2   **17.** 0.46   **18.** 0.125   **19.** 3.75   **20.** 5.95

Write each as a decimal. Use a bar for repeating decimals. pages 48–51

21. $\frac{1}{3}$ **22.** $\frac{5}{8}$ **23.** $\frac{5}{6}$ **24.** $\frac{2}{9}$ **25.** $\frac{9}{10}$

Compare. Use <, >, or = for each ⬤. pages 52–53

26. $\frac{7}{8}$ ⬤ $\frac{3}{4}$ **27.** $\frac{9}{10}$ ⬤ $0.\overline{9}$ **28.** 2.7 ⬤ $2\frac{2}{3}$ **29.** $\frac{7}{8}$ ⬤ 0.875

Choose the correct word to complete each statement.

30. If a number has more than two factors, it is a ___ number.

31. A statement that may be true is called a ___.

Words to Know
composite
conjecture
counterexample
prime

Solve.

32. Mary finished $\frac{2}{3}$ of her homework. Jim has to complete $\frac{1}{4}$ of the same assignment. Who has less work left to do?

33. Bob ordered $2\frac{3}{4}$ pounds of cheese at the delicatessen. The scale shows weight to two decimal places. What weight shows on the scale?

Exploring Problem Solving

What Is Puzzling You?

You are a designer for a toy company. You have been asked to create some new jigsaw puzzles that picture the 48 adjoining states in the United States of America.

Thinking Critically

You are to create two puzzles. One will have four pieces and will be for younger children. A second one will have 15 pieces and will be for older children. Use Workmat 4 to help you decide how to design the puzzle.

UNITED STATES

Analyzing and Making Decisions

1. Start by designing the puzzle with four pieces. Look at the map. What boundaries will help you divide it into four pieces? Try several ideas.

2. Share your final design for the puzzle with four pieces. Explain why you chose that design.

3. Your puzzle with 15 pieces should have boundaries along state lines. Each piece should be as close to the same size as possible. What states should be just one piece?

4. Which states might share a puzzle piece with one other? Which states need to share a puzzle piece with two or more states?

5. Experiment to make your puzzle with 15 pieces. Show the puzzle you like the best.

Look Back What if you wished to color both of your puzzles so that no two pieces that touch are of the same color? Could you use two different colors? three different colors? four different colors?

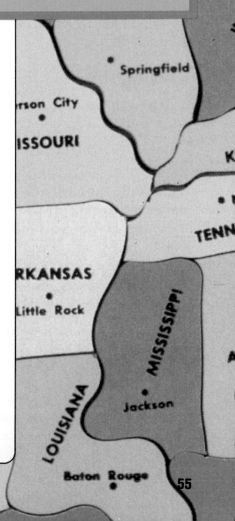

Problem Solving Strategies

Too Much or Too Little Information

Last January Sarah joined the Historical Book Club. When
she joined, she received 3 books free of charge. She paid
$2.00 for postage and handling of the free books. Sarah
agreed to buy 3 more books during the year at the regular
book-club price plus $1.93 for postage and handling of
each book. If she bought 7 books in a year, she would
receive a free bonus book. She bought these books during
the year.

March	2 books	$10.95 each
July	1 book	$14.95 each
October	3 books	$12.95 each

What was the average cost per book that Sarah received
from the club? What would the average cost have been if
she had bought 7 books and received a free bonus book?

Sometimes too little or too much information is given.
Knowing what the question is can help you decide what
information you need.

Solving the Problem

 **Use a calculator where appropriate. If the necessary
information is missing, tell what information is needed.**

Think   What are the questions?

Explore   How many books did Sarah receive? How much
did she pay for postage and handling? How much did all
the books cost? What was her total cost for all the books?
If she had bought a seventh book, how much would it have
cost?

Solve   What was the average total cost per book for the
books Sarah received from the club? If she had bought 7,
what would the average cost be?

Look Back   Explain why your answer for the average cost
for a book makes sense.

Share Your Ideas

1. What is the least amount that the seventh
   book can cost and increase the average
   cost of a book?

Practice

Solve. Use a calculator where appropriate.
 If necessary information is missing, tell what information is needed.

2. Sandra has to write a report on ancient civilizations. She read a 200-page book on ancient Greece in 5 hours. She has found a 160-page book on ancient Rome. How long will it take her to read it?

3. Germaine wanted to listen to 2 tapes on Rome. His cassette player broke half-way through the first tape. Then he borrowed Sandra's tape player and finished listening to both tapes. How long did it take Germaine to listen to the 2 tapes?

4. Enrico joined a record club in September. During the first year he bought 6 records at an average cost of $6.50 per record. He paid an additional $1.93 for postage and handling per record. How much did he pay for postage and handling for all 6 records?

5. During the second year Enrico bought 3 compact discs, 2 cassette tapes, and 1 more compact disc. The total cost, including shipping and handling was $52.68. What was the cost of the 2 cassette tapes?

Mixed Strategy Review

> growth call Mr. Rap   555-8769
>
> **MUSEUM WORKERS WANTED**
> PART TIME WORK
> HOURLY RATES
> $7 PER HOUR WEEKDAYS
> $5 PER HOUR WEEKENDS
> please call 555-7676
>
> ─────────────────
> NURSES WANTED
> Busy hospital needs exp'd nurses

6. Clarissa works part time at the museum. She wants to earn $70 to $75 per week. For what times might she ask to work?

7. One week Sam earned $70 at the museum. When might he have worked?

8. During the summer Thomas works at the museum five days a week. For his lunch in the cafeteria, he can pay $1.50 every day, or he can pay $7 a week. How might he buy his lunch in the cafeteria? Explain.

9. **Look back** at **8**. If a monthly lunch pass costs $26, how many days would Tom have to buy his lunch in the cafeteria to make buying a pass worthwhile?

Create
Your Own

Use the information in the Museum Workers Help Wanted sign to write a problem with too much information.

Estimating Sums and Differences

Amy traveled to Greece. She spent $2\frac{1}{4}$ hours of the flight reading. For the remaining $2\frac{3}{5}$ hours, she watched a movie. About how long was the flight?

Estimate $2\frac{1}{4} + 2\frac{3}{5}$.

$$
\begin{array}{l}
2\frac{1}{4} \longrightarrow \ \ 2 \\
2\frac{3}{5} \longrightarrow + \ 2\frac{1}{2} \\
\hline
\quad\ 4\frac{1}{2} \longleftarrow \text{estimate}
\end{array}
$$

Think $2\frac{1}{4}$ is close to 2 since $\frac{1}{4}$ is close to 0.

$2\frac{3}{5}$ is close to $2\frac{1}{2}$ since $\frac{3}{5}$ is close to $\frac{1}{2}$.

Is this a reasonable estimate?

The flight was about $4\frac{1}{2}$ hours long.

You can use these methods to estimate sums and differences.

a. Compare the numerator and denominator.
Is the fraction closer to 0, $\frac{1}{2}$, or 1?

Estimate $4\frac{7}{8} - \frac{1}{7}$.

$$
\begin{array}{cc}
\downarrow & \downarrow \\
5 & - \ 0 = 5
\end{array}
$$

Think $4\frac{7}{8}$ is about 5 since $\frac{7}{8}$ is close to 1.

$\frac{1}{7}$ is about 0 since $\frac{1}{7}$ is close to 0.

Explain why 5 may or may not be a reasonable estimate.

b. Think of common fractions that are easy to compute mentally. Use denominators such as 4, 5, or 10.
Estimate $5\frac{7}{11} + 3\frac{8}{9}$.   Think $\frac{7}{11}$ is close to $\frac{7}{10}$. $\frac{8}{9}$ is close to $\frac{8}{10}$.

$\frac{7}{10} + \frac{8}{10} = \frac{15}{10}$, or $1\frac{1}{2}$.

$5 + 3 + 1\frac{1}{2} = 9\frac{1}{2}$ So, $5\frac{7}{11} + 3\frac{8}{9}$ is about $9\frac{1}{2}$.

Check Your Understanding

Tell whether each fraction is closer to 0, $\frac{1}{2}$, or 1.

1. $\frac{2}{5}$ **2.** $\frac{1}{9}$ **3.** $\frac{11}{13}$ **4.** $\frac{3}{14}$ **5.** $\frac{55}{100}$ **6.** $\frac{35}{50}$

Estimate each sum or difference.

7. $1\frac{3}{5} + 1\frac{2}{3}$ **8.** $4\frac{7}{8} - \frac{1}{6}$ **9.** $2\frac{6}{11} + 3\frac{1}{3}$ **10.** $17\frac{1}{7} - 6\frac{7}{8}$

Share Your Ideas   Sam estimates that $\frac{4}{7}$ is close to $\frac{1}{2}$ because 4 is about half of 7. Tom claims that $\frac{4}{7}$ is close to $\frac{1}{2}$ because 2×4, or 8, is close to 7. Are they both correct? Explain.

Tell whether each fraction is closer to 0, $\frac{1}{2}$, or 1.

11. $\frac{1}{5}$ **12.** $\frac{2}{3}$ **13.** $\frac{2}{5}$ **14.** $\frac{5}{8}$ **15.** $\frac{3}{7}$ **16.** $\frac{2}{9}$

17. $\frac{5}{6}$ **18.** $\frac{7}{15}$ **19.** $\frac{15}{50}$ **20.** $\frac{51}{100}$ **21.** $\frac{79}{100}$ **22.** $\frac{55}{91}$

Estimate each sum or difference.

23. $13\frac{2}{3}$
$+\ 5\frac{1}{2}$

24. $24\frac{1}{5}$
$-\ 6\frac{3}{4}$

25. $7\frac{5}{6}$
$+\ 1\frac{1}{8}$

26. $4\frac{3}{4}$
$-\ 4\frac{2}{9}$

27. $7\frac{1}{3}$
$+\ 4\frac{2}{7}$

28. $19\frac{1}{8}$
$-\ 11\frac{5}{6}$

29. $6\frac{1}{3}$
$+\ 7\frac{7}{10}$

30. $10\frac{7}{15}$
$-\ 5\frac{3}{7}$

31. $15\frac{1}{2}$
$-\ 9\frac{9}{10}$

32. 12.5
$-\ 1\frac{15}{31}$

33. $27\frac{1}{3}$
$-\ 5.02$

34. 0.95
$-\ \frac{19}{20}$

35. $8\frac{4}{5} - 5\frac{1}{3}$ **36.** $17\frac{2}{3} - 15\frac{1}{6}$ **37.** $8\frac{4}{7} + 15\frac{1}{2}$ **38.** $17\frac{2}{3} + 9\frac{1}{3}$

39. $8\frac{1}{10} + 9\frac{7}{8}$ **40.** $25 - 14\frac{5}{9}$ **41.** $27\frac{1}{3} - 5.8$ **42.** $9.23 - 2\frac{15}{20}$

Think and Apply

43. The first Olympics were held in Greece, in 776 B.C. The modern games began in Athens, in 1896 A.D. About how many centuries apart are the two dates?

DATA 44. The first Olympic game was a foot race of about 200 yards. In the modern Summer Olympic Games, there are 22 sports, including track and field. Find data to show which event in the modern games most closely resembles the original event.

45. Sam needs two pieces of wire to complete a project. The lengths needed are $3\frac{1}{4}$ in. and $1\frac{7}{8}$ in. If he has 5 in. of wire, does he have enough?

46. A carpenter cuts $4\frac{3}{4}$ ft from a board that is $10\frac{1}{2}$ ft long. How much is left? Can she cut two more pieces that are each $2\frac{7}{8}$ ft long?

47. A rectangular table measures $6\frac{3}{4}$ ft in length and $3\frac{7}{8}$ ft in width. Estimate the perimeter of the table.

48. A recipe calls for $2\frac{1}{3}$ c of whole-wheat flour and $\frac{3}{4}$ c of oat bran. If Bob wants to double the recipe, about how much of each ingredient does he need?

When you estimate fractions, what methods do you use to get a good estimate? Describe one of your methods.

SUMMING UP

Adding Fractions and Mixed Numbers

The ancient Britons who built Stonehenge dragged huge stones weighing as much as 45 tons a distance of 20 miles. Pairs of stones topped with a lintel stone are called trilithons. The stones of one trilithon measure about $21\frac{2}{3}$ feet high and the lintel measures $2\frac{1}{2}$ feet. Find the total height of the trilithon.

Estimate first. $21\frac{2}{3} + 2\frac{1}{2} \longrightarrow 22 + 2 = 24$

$\frac{1}{2}$ was rounded down because the first fraction was rounded up.

Then find the exact sum.

▶ To add fractions or mixed numbers, first find equivalent fractions using the LCD. Add the fractions, then add the whole numbers. If needed, divide the numerator and denominator by the GCF to write the answer in lowest terms.

$$21\frac{2}{3} = 21\frac{4}{6}$$
$$+ \ 2\frac{1}{2} = \ 2\frac{3}{6}$$
$$23\frac{7}{6} = 24\frac{1}{6}$$

$\frac{7}{6} = 1\frac{1}{6}$

$23 + 1\frac{1}{6} = 24\frac{1}{6}$

Think

The height of the trilithon is $24\frac{1}{6}$ feet.

More Examples

a.
$$\frac{3}{14} = \frac{15}{70}$$
$$+ \frac{7}{10} = \frac{49}{70}$$
$$\frac{64}{70} = \frac{32}{35}$$

b.
$$5\frac{5}{6} = 5\frac{5}{6}$$
$$+ 1\frac{1}{2} = 1\frac{3}{6}$$
$$6\frac{8}{6} = 7\frac{2}{6} = 7\frac{1}{3}$$

Check Your Understanding

Estimate first. Then add. Write each answer in lowest terms.

1. $\frac{1}{2}$
$+\frac{5}{6}$

2. $\frac{1}{6}$
$+\frac{2}{5}$

3. $9\frac{4}{5}$
$+7\frac{1}{10}$

4. $8\frac{5}{6}$
$+3\frac{1}{2}$

5. $9\frac{1}{2}$
$+8\frac{3}{5}$

Share Your Ideas Look back at example **b**. **What if** the problem is rewritten as $\frac{35}{6} + \frac{3}{2}$. Is the sum the same? Why?

Practice

Estimate first. Then add. Write each answer in lowest terms.

6. $10\frac{2}{3}$
   $+19\frac{3}{4}$

7. $6\frac{3}{5}$
   $+9\frac{7}{10}$

8. $4\frac{5}{6}$
   $+5\frac{3}{4}$

9. $14\frac{7}{8}$
   $+1\frac{1}{2}$

10. $23\frac{2}{3}$
    $+9\frac{5}{6}$

11. $18\frac{1}{2}$
    $+3\frac{1}{6}$

12. $20\frac{5}{6}$
    $+4\frac{1}{4}$

13. 28
    $+26\frac{2}{3}$

14. $36\frac{1}{3}$
    $+4\frac{5}{6}$

15. $63\frac{3}{4}$
    $+9\frac{5}{8}$

16. $12\frac{3}{8} + 17\frac{5}{6}$

17. $21\frac{3}{4} + 31\frac{3}{5}$

18. $8\frac{2}{9} + 5\frac{7}{9} + \frac{22}{27}$

19. $7\frac{1}{3} + 8\frac{2}{3} + 5\frac{3}{4}$

20. $4\frac{2}{9} + 2\frac{5}{6} + 7\frac{11}{12}$

21. $9\frac{7}{10} + 5\frac{1}{6} + 8\frac{4}{5}$

Compare. Use <, >, or = for each ●.

22. $\frac{3}{4} + \frac{3}{4}$ ● $1\frac{1}{2}$

23. $\frac{1}{2} + 2\frac{1}{3}$ ● 3

24. $5\frac{2}{3} + 6\frac{1}{3}$ ● 12

25. $10\frac{1}{2} + 8\frac{1}{4}$ ● 19

26. $22\frac{5}{6} + 4\frac{1}{5}$ ● 27

27. $3\frac{7}{10} + 7\frac{1}{2}$ ● $11\frac{1}{5}$

28. $5\frac{7}{20} + 13\frac{1}{4}$ ● $19\frac{3}{5}$

29. $12\frac{1}{2} + 10\frac{11}{20}$ ● $8\frac{3}{5} + 14\frac{1}{2}$

30. $19\frac{5}{6} + 9\frac{2}{9}$ ● $8\frac{5}{7} + 20$

Think and Apply

31. **Look back** at **22–30**. Some problems may be easier to solve by thinking of money. Find two that you can solve by thinking of United States coins. Explain how the coins relate to the fractions and the sum.

32. The circle of trilithons at Stonehenge has a circumference of about 314 feet. What is the diameter of the site? ($C = 3.14d$)

Logical Thinking

33. The sum of two fractions is $\frac{31}{40}$. Both numerators are prime but not the same prime. The GCF of the denominators is 1. Name the fractions.

You can rewrite $\frac{1}{3} + \frac{1}{6}$ as $\frac{2}{6} + \frac{1}{6}$. **What if** you write the fractions as $\frac{4}{12} + \frac{2}{12}$. Is the sum the same? Explain.

SUMMING UP

61

Express this idea in your own words.

$$1 = \frac{2}{2}, \frac{3}{3}, \frac{4}{4}, \frac{5}{5}, \ldots$$

Subtracting Fractions and Mixed Numbers

Archaeologists think there may have been as many as 1,400 small sphinxes located along the road leading to the Great Sphinx. Suppose that two sphinxes were unearthed at $13\frac{2}{3}$ yards and $19\frac{1}{4}$ yards from the beginning of the road. How many yards apart were the sphinxes?

Estimate first.

$$19\frac{1}{4} - 13\frac{2}{3} \longrightarrow 19 - 14 = 5 \quad \text{The difference is about 5.}$$

Then find $19\frac{1}{4} - 13\frac{2}{3}$.

Write equivalent fractions, using the LCD.	Rename if you cannot subtract.	Subtract. Write the answer in lowest terms.
$19\frac{1}{4} = 19\frac{3}{12}$ $- 13\frac{2}{3} = 13\frac{8}{12}$	$19\frac{3}{12} = 18\frac{15}{12}$ $- 13\frac{8}{12} = 13\frac{8}{12}$	$18\frac{15}{12}$ $- 13\frac{8}{12}$ $5\frac{7}{12}$

The sphinxes were located $5\frac{7}{12}$ yards apart.

Another way to subtract fractions and mixed numbers is to change to improper fractions first.

$$15\frac{3}{10} = \frac{153}{10} = \frac{153}{10}$$
$$- \ 2\frac{1}{2} = \frac{5}{2} = \frac{25}{10}$$
$$\frac{128}{10} = 12\frac{8}{10} = 12\frac{4}{5}$$

Compare this method to the one shown above.

Do both use a common denominator? renaming?

Check Your Understanding

Estimate. Then subtract. Write each answer in lowest terms.

1. $9\frac{1}{2}$
 $- 4\frac{2}{3}$

2. $12\frac{1}{5}$
 $- 7\frac{4}{5}$

3. $6\frac{3}{4}$
 $- 4\frac{5}{6}$

4. 3
 $- 1\frac{3}{8}$

5. $9\frac{1}{6}$
 $- 4\frac{1}{2}$

Share Your Ideas Look back at **5**. Which method did you use to solve it? Tell why you prefer that method.

Estimate. Then subtract. Write each answer in lowest terms.

6. $6\frac{2}{3}$
$-\ 2\frac{5}{6}$

7. $13\frac{1}{9}$
$-\ 5\frac{5}{9}$

8. $26\frac{1}{5}$
$-\ 8\frac{2}{3}$

9. $16\frac{1}{2}$
$-\ 4\frac{7}{8}$

10. $25\frac{5}{6}$
$-\ 8\frac{3}{10}$

11. $8\frac{2}{3}$
$-\ 4\frac{1}{2}$

12. 52
$-\ 18\frac{3}{4}$

13. $16\frac{1}{5}$
$-\ 3\frac{1}{4}$

14. $7\frac{1}{6}$
$-\ 1\frac{7}{10}$

15. $6\frac{15}{16}$
$-\ 2\frac{31}{32}$

Find n.

16. $7 - 2\frac{2}{3} = n$

17. $11\frac{1}{2} + 8 = n$

18. $16\frac{1}{2} - 4\frac{1}{4} = n$

19. $15\frac{5}{8} - 10\frac{7}{8} = n$

20. $9\frac{1}{4} - 5\frac{1}{2} = n$

21. $8\frac{1}{2} + 6\frac{1}{2} = n$

22. $11\frac{1}{2} + n = 13$

23. $n + 9\frac{1}{4} = 15$

Find each input or output.

Rule: Add $2\frac{3}{4}$.

	Input	Output
24.	$7\frac{1}{2}$	
25.	$3\frac{3}{8}$	
26.		$9\frac{1}{4}$
27.		$8\frac{7}{8}$

Rule: Subtract $1\frac{1}{3}$.

	Input	Output
28.	$5\frac{1}{4}$	
29.	7	
30.		$6\frac{7}{8}$
31.		$9\frac{2}{3}$

Think and Apply

32. The Greek sphinx shown was carved about 540 B.C. The Egyptian Great Sphinx was carved about 2600 B.C. Which is older, the Egyptian sphinx or the Greek sphinx?

33. Centuries ago the Egyptians used a measurement called a cubit. If a cubit is approximately 18 in., about how many cubits would measure 50 ft?

Common Error

- Look at Jim's paper.

- What is Jim's error?

- Correct each answer.

34. $11\frac{1}{7} = 10\frac{11}{7}$
$-\ 2\frac{5}{7} = \ \ 2\frac{5}{7}$
$8\frac{6}{7}$ ⟵ incorrect ⟶

35. $7\frac{3}{4} = 6\frac{16}{8}$
$-\ 3\frac{7}{8} = 3\frac{7}{8}$
$3\frac{9}{8}$

To subtract 2.9 from 34.2, you must rename a one as 10 tenths. How is this like renaming to subtract mixed numbers? How is it different?

SUMMING UP

Is the value of a fraction changed if you multiply it by 1? $\frac{2}{2}$? $\frac{3}{3}$? If you divide it by 1? $\frac{2}{2}$? $\frac{3}{3}$? Explain.

Multiplying Fractions

Jim is making a model of the aqueducts of ancient Rome. He bought $\frac{7}{8}$ yard of plasterboard to make the base of the model. He used $\frac{2}{3}$ of the board. What part of a yard of plasterboard did he use?

Find $\frac{2}{3} \times \frac{7}{8}$.

To multiply fractions, multiply numerators and multiply denominators. You can simplify factors before multiplying by dividing a numerator and a denominator by a common factor.

$$\frac{2}{3} \times \frac{7}{8} = \frac{\overset{1}{\cancel{2}}}{3} \times \frac{7}{\underset{4}{\cancel{8}}} = \frac{7}{12}$$

Jim used $\frac{7}{12}$ yard of plasterboard.

Look back at the example. Is the answer reasonable? If you multiply two fractions that are between 0 and 1, is the answer greater or less than 1? Explain.

More Examples

a. Find $\frac{6}{7}$ of $\frac{3}{16}$.

$$\frac{\overset{3}{\cancel{6}}}{7} \times \frac{3}{\underset{8}{\cancel{16}}} = \frac{9}{56}$$

b. $\frac{1}{2} \times \frac{3}{4} \times \frac{6}{7} = n$

$$\frac{1}{\underset{1}{\cancel{2}}} \times \frac{3}{4} \times \frac{\overset{3}{\cancel{6}}}{7} = \frac{9}{28}$$

What if you do not divide by a common factor? Explain what would happen.

Check Your Understanding

Multiply. Write each answer in lowest terms.

1. $\frac{3}{4} \times \frac{1}{2}$ **2.** $\frac{2}{5} \times \frac{3}{8}$ **3.** $\frac{7}{12} \times \frac{3}{5}$ **4.** $\frac{5}{8} \times \frac{2}{25}$

5. $\frac{2}{3}$ of $\frac{6}{11}$ **6.** $\frac{4}{5}$ of $\frac{1}{8}$ **7.** $\frac{5}{6}$ of $\frac{3}{4}$ **8.** $\frac{3}{10} \times \frac{5}{6} \times \frac{8}{9}$

Share Your Ideas When you multiply two fractions that are between 0 and 1, is the product greater than each of the factors or less than each of the factors? Explain.

Multiply. Write each answer in lowest terms.

9. $\frac{2}{3} \times \frac{4}{5}$ **10.** $\frac{3}{5} \times \frac{1}{6}$ **11.** $\frac{2}{11} \times \frac{2}{3}$ **12.** $\frac{1}{4} \times \frac{2}{3}$

13. $\frac{1}{2} \times \frac{3}{4}$ **14.** $\frac{5}{6} \times \frac{1}{4}$ **15.** $\frac{3}{8} \times \frac{1}{2}$ **16.** $\frac{3}{4} \times \frac{5}{12}$

17. $\frac{2}{3} \times \frac{5}{8}$ **18.** $\frac{4}{5} \times \frac{10}{16}$ **19.** $\frac{3}{8} \times \frac{4}{15}$ **20.** $\frac{5}{8} \times \frac{7}{8}$

21. $\frac{3}{5}$ of $\frac{1}{3}$ **22.** $\frac{2}{7}$ of $\frac{1}{2}$ **23.** $\frac{3}{4}$ of $\frac{5}{12}$ **24.** $\frac{5}{8}$ of $\frac{1}{10}$

25. $\frac{3}{5} \times \frac{7}{12} \times \frac{5}{21}$ **26.** $\frac{5}{16} \times \frac{4}{10} \times \frac{10}{11}$ **27.** $\frac{2}{7} \times \frac{91}{104} \times \frac{4}{13}$ **28.** $\frac{4}{13} \times \frac{65}{80} \times \frac{3}{7}$

29. $\frac{3}{4} \times \frac{1}{2} \times \frac{4}{9}$ **30.** $\frac{2}{5} \times \frac{1}{4} \times \frac{3}{8}$ **31.** $\frac{7}{12} \times \frac{3}{8} \times \frac{6}{7}$ **32.** $\frac{2}{5} \times \frac{1}{2} \times \frac{3}{4}$

 Find each input or output. You may wish to use a calculator.

Rule: Multiply by $\frac{1}{2}$.

	Input	Output
33.	$\frac{1}{3}$	
34.	$\frac{2}{5}$	
35.	$\frac{3}{7}$	
36.	$\frac{7}{8}$	

Rule: Multiply by $\frac{5}{8}$.

	Input	Output
37.	$\frac{2}{3}$	
38.	$\frac{3}{5}$	
39.	$\frac{1}{17}$	
40.	$\frac{4}{5}$	

Rule: Multiply by $\frac{2}{3}$.

	Input	Output
41.	$\frac{5}{12}$	
42.	$\frac{51}{52}$	
43.		$\frac{1}{3}$
44.		$\frac{2}{9}$

Think and Apply

45. Jane is making programs for the project exhibit. She needs $\frac{3}{4}$ sheet of paper for the cover and $\frac{1}{3}$ sheet of paper for each of two inside pages. How much paper does she need to make 48 programs?

46. **What if** Jane makes the two inside pages using $\frac{2}{3}$ sheet of paper instead of $\frac{1}{3}$ sheet each? Will the answer be the same? How many sheets will she need? Explain.

47. Find one half of $\frac{3}{5}$ of 0.22 seconds.

48. Find one third of $\frac{4}{5}$ of 0.75 pounds.

If you divide all common factors when you multiply fractions, is the product always in lowest terms? Explain why or why not.

SUMMING UP

The drawing shows $2\frac{1}{4}$. Use the drawing to show that $2\frac{1}{4}$ equals $\frac{9}{4}$.

Multiplying Mixed Numbers

Kayaks used today are similar to those used by Aleut and Inuit cultures thousands of years ago. Azazruk and Cidaq spend $2\frac{3}{4}$ hours traveling to Unimak Island and $1\frac{1}{3}$ times as long on the return trip. How long is the return trip?

Find $2\frac{3}{4} \times 1\frac{1}{3}$.

$\frac{11}{4} \times \frac{4}{3} =$ Write mixed numbers as improper fractions.

$\frac{11}{\overset{}{\underset{1}{\cancel{4}}}} \times \frac{\overset{1}{\cancel{4}}}{3} =$ Simplify factors. Then multiply.

$\frac{11}{3} = 3\frac{2}{3}$ Express as a mixed number.

The return trip took $3\frac{2}{3}$ hours.

Estimate to be sure that the answer makes sense.

$2\frac{3}{4} \times 1\frac{1}{3} \longrightarrow 3 \times 1 = 3$

If you multiply two mixed numbers, is the product greater or less than the factors?

More Examples

a. $3\frac{3}{8} \times 5\frac{1}{3} = n$

$\frac{\overset{9}{\cancel{27}}}{\underset{1}{\cancel{8}}} \times \frac{\overset{2}{\cancel{16}}}{\underset{1}{\cancel{3}}} = \frac{18}{1} = 18$

$n = 18$

b. $\frac{1}{4} \times 168 = n$

$\frac{1}{\underset{1}{\cancel{4}}} \times \frac{\overset{42}{\cancel{168}}}{1} = 42$

$n = 42$

Multiply. Write each answer in lowest terms.

1. $1\frac{3}{4} \times 2\frac{1}{5}$ 2. $3\frac{2}{3} \times \frac{3}{5}$ 3. $4\frac{5}{6} \times 1\frac{3}{4}$ 4. $\frac{4}{5} \times 35$

5. $1\frac{1}{2} \times 2\frac{3}{5}$ 6. $4\frac{2}{3} \times 1\frac{1}{7}$ 7. $\frac{1}{4} \times 72$ 8. $6\frac{1}{4} \times 5$

Share Your Ideas The product $3\frac{4}{5} \times 8\frac{1}{5}$ is between 24 and 36. Is the product closer to 24 or 36? How do you know?

Multiply. Write each answer in lowest terms.

9. $1\frac{3}{5} \times \frac{10}{17}$ **10.** $\frac{2}{3} \times 5\frac{2}{7}$ **11.** $3\frac{1}{4} \times 8$ **12.** $2\frac{5}{6} \times 8\frac{3}{5}$

13. $\frac{7}{8} \times 56$ **14.** $6\frac{3}{7} \times 8\frac{4}{9}$ **15.** $4\frac{2}{3} \times 12\frac{3}{4}$ **16.** $27 \times \frac{4}{9}$

17. $1\frac{2}{3} \times 4\frac{3}{5}$ **18.** $2\frac{1}{2} \times 3$ **19.** $5\frac{5}{12} \times 24$ **20.** $4\frac{2}{3} \times 1\frac{1}{4}$

21. $5\frac{1}{7} \times \frac{1}{36}$ **22.** $3\frac{3}{5} \times 2\frac{1}{3}$ **23.** $6\frac{2}{7} \times 3\frac{2}{11}$ **24.** $9 \times 15\frac{2}{3}$

Add, subtract, or multiply. Write each answer in lowest terms.

25. $8\frac{1}{4} \times 2\frac{1}{2}$ **26.** $8\frac{1}{4} + 2\frac{1}{2}$ **27.** $15 \times \frac{2}{3}$ **28.** $10\frac{1}{8} - 2\frac{3}{4}$

29. $1\frac{2}{3} \times 18$ **30.** $6\frac{1}{3} + 5\frac{3}{10}$ **31.** $25.5 \times 6\frac{2}{3}$ **32.** $5\frac{1}{3} \times 1.875$

Write the next three numbers in each sequence.

33. $1\frac{1}{7}, 1\frac{3}{7}, 1\frac{5}{7},$ ___, ___, ___   **34.** $4\frac{1}{8}, 4\frac{1}{4}, 4\frac{3}{8},$ ___, ___, ___   **35.** $12\frac{1}{2}, 2.5, 0.5,$ ___, ___, ___

36. An ancient Alaskan stone lamp provided light by burning whale oil. Its height was about $\frac{1}{7}$ of its circumference. If the lamp measured 22 inches around, estimate the height of the lamp.

37. A typical Inuit snowhouse has a circular base with a diameter of 15 ft. It is made of blocks that are 3 ft long, 2 ft high, and $\frac{2}{3}$ ft thick. How many blocks are used around the base of the snowhouse?

38. An eighth-grade math class has 32 students. Which of the following cannot be true?

   a. $\frac{1}{2}$ are boys.   **b.** $\frac{1}{4}$ have an A.

   c. $\frac{1}{5}$ have blond hair.   **d.** $\frac{7}{8}$ are present.

A product is less than one factor and greater than the other. Describe its factors.

Compare these problems.
How are they alike? $\frac{27}{55} \times 23\frac{1}{9}$ $\frac{1}{2} \times 24$
How are they different?

Estimating Products

Bob is reading a translation of the *Odyssey* by Homer. He has about $\frac{1}{4}$ of the book left to read. If the book contains 374 pages, about how many pages does Bob have left to read?

Estimate $\frac{1}{4} \times 374$.

$\frac{1}{4} \times 374$

$\downarrow$

$\frac{1}{4} \times 360 = 90$

$\frac{1}{4} \times 374$ is about 90.

Choose a number that is easy to multiply mentally.

Think 360 is close to 374.
360 is divisible by 4.

Bob has about 90 more pages to read.

More Examples

a. Estimate $\frac{5}{11} \times 138$.

Think $\frac{5}{11}$ is close to $\frac{5}{10}$, or $\frac{1}{2}$.
138 is close to 140

$\frac{5}{11} \times 138$

$\downarrow$ $\downarrow$

$\frac{1}{2} \times 140 = 70$

$\frac{5}{11} \times 138$ is about 70.

b. Estimate $5\frac{4}{9} \times 212$.

Think $\frac{4}{9}$ is close to $\frac{3}{9}$, or $\frac{1}{3}$.
212 is close to 210.

$5\frac{4}{9} \times 212 \rightarrow 5\frac{1}{3} \times 210$

$5\frac{1}{3} \times 210 =$

$(5 \times 210) + (\frac{1}{3} \times 210) =$

$1{,}050 + 70 = 1{,}120$

$5\frac{4}{9} \times 212$ is about 1,120.

Check Your Understanding

Estimate each product.

1. $\frac{5}{9} \times 124$ **2.** $\frac{8}{9} \times 95$ **3.** $3\frac{2}{21} \times 199$ **4.** $2\frac{12}{39} \times 60$

Share Your Ideas   Is there more than one reasonable estimate for a problem? Estimate $\frac{5}{12} \times 355$, using two different compatible number pairs.

Estimate each product.

5. $\frac{5}{11} \times 60$

6. $\frac{12}{37} \times 90$

7. $\frac{15}{21} \times 120$

8. $\frac{9}{46} \times 51$

9. $\frac{41}{50} \times 26$

10. $\frac{17}{33} \times 421$

11. $1\frac{4}{7} \times 31$

12. $2\frac{11}{33} \times 30$

13. $3\frac{15}{61} \times 79$

14. $\frac{20}{31} \times 12$

15. $\frac{10}{28} \times 57$

16. $2\frac{12}{17} \times 122$

Name the compatible numbers that were used to estimate each product.

	Estimate
17. $\frac{17}{30} \times 199$	100
18. $\frac{11}{18} \times 258$	160
19. $2\frac{5}{9} \times 50$	125
20. $5\frac{7}{8} \times 2\frac{1}{4}$	12
21. $2\frac{5}{8} \times 2\frac{3}{8}$	$6\frac{1}{4}$
22. $1\frac{1}{3} \times 1\frac{1}{3}$	$1\frac{1}{2}$

Think and Apply

23. Homer's *Odyssey* is an epic poem about Odysseus, who spent ten years trying to return home. It is divided into 24 books, with an average of 500 lines per book. About how many lines long is the *Odyssey*?

24. Stock in Manuscripts Unlimited is selling at $67\frac{5}{8}$ per share. Estimate the cost of 70 shares of stock.

25. Five people go to lunch and agree to split the cost. The bill of $37.00 includes tax. They decide to leave $5.50 as a tip for the server. Find each person's share of the total cost.

26. What if Jan forgot her money. What might the group do? Describe two different options.

Explain three ways to get good estimates for $2\frac{3}{11} \times 107$.

Mixed Review

1. $9.78 + 15.072$

2. $21.5 - 4.51$

3. 607.9×4.5

4. $37.2 \div 18.6$

5. $18.6 \div 37.2$

6. 12.15×10^3

7. $0.448 \div 10^2$

8. $49.8 + 5\frac{1}{2}$

9. $15.2 - 7\frac{3}{8}$

10. $56.3 \times 2\frac{1}{3}$

Write as a fraction or mixed number in lowest terms.

11. 0.25

12. 0.125

13. 3.5

14. 11.8

15. 2.17

Write each as a decimal.

16. $\frac{3}{4}$

17. $\frac{2}{3}$

18. $6\frac{3}{8}$

19. $\frac{7}{9}$

20. $5\frac{9}{10}$

Dividing Fractions and Mixed Numbers

How many groups of 3 fourths are in 6?

Do you think there are more than or fewer than 6?

One way to find out is to draw a diagram.

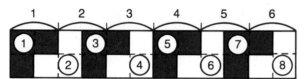

Divide each unit into fourths.
How many groups of 3 fourths are there in 6 units?

To solve the problem without a diagram, find $6 \div \frac{3}{4}$.

To divide by a fraction, multiply by its reciprocal.

$$6 \div \frac{3}{4} = 6 \times \frac{4}{3} = \frac{24}{3} = 8$$ Compare this method to the one above.

Is the answer reasonable?
Did you expect it to be greater than 6?

More Examples

a. $12\frac{1}{2} \div 3\frac{1}{4}$

$\frac{25}{2} \div \frac{13}{4} = \frac{25}{\underset{1}{2}} \times \frac{\overset{2}{4}}{13} = \frac{50}{13} = 3\frac{11}{13}$

b. $3\frac{1}{3} \div 10$

$\frac{10}{3} \div 10 = \frac{10}{3} \div \frac{10}{1} = \frac{\overset{1}{10}}{3} \times \frac{1}{\underset{1}{10}} = \frac{1}{3}$

Check Your Understanding

Divide. Write each answer in lowest terms.

1. $4 \div \frac{1}{3}$ **2.** $\frac{7}{8} \div \frac{1}{3}$ **3.** $3\frac{1}{2} \div \frac{2}{5}$ **4.** $3\frac{1}{8} \div 2\frac{1}{2}$ **5.** $14\frac{2}{3} \div 1\frac{1}{11}$

Share Your Ideas Tell what the quotient represents when you divide 30 by $\frac{3}{5}$. Do you think that the quotient will be greater or less than 30? Explain.

Divide. Write each answer in lowest terms.

6. $4 \div \frac{1}{5}$ **7.** $\frac{3}{4} \div \frac{1}{4}$ **8.** $2\frac{1}{2} \div \frac{1}{2}$ **9.** $\frac{7}{3} \div \frac{1}{3}$

10. $\frac{1}{3} \div \frac{3}{4}$ **11.** $\frac{2}{5} \div \frac{1}{7}$ **12.** $4\frac{2}{3} \div 6\frac{1}{2}$ **13.** $5\frac{1}{3} \div \frac{3}{4}$

14. $5\frac{1}{2} \div 2\frac{1}{4}$ **15.** $2\frac{7}{8} \div 1\frac{3}{4}$ **16.** $\frac{1}{12} \div 2\frac{1}{4}$ **17.** $6\frac{1}{2} \div \frac{1}{8}$

18. $3.5 \div \frac{1}{8}$ **19.** $\frac{2}{5} \div 1.8$ **20.** $3\frac{3}{4} \div 1.75$ **21.** $3.75 \div 5\frac{3}{4}$

Find *n*.

22. $5\frac{1}{2} \div 2 = n$ **23.** $9 \div 2\frac{1}{4} = n$ **24.** $8\frac{1}{3} \div 5\frac{5}{6} = n$ **25.** $14\frac{9}{11} \div 14\frac{9}{11} = n$

26. $4\frac{4}{5} \div 1.2 = n$ **27.** $6\frac{1}{4} \div 0.5 = n$ **28.** $n \div \frac{1}{5} = 20$ **29.** $n \div \frac{1}{2} = 32$

Find the missing numbers in each sequence.

30. $5\frac{1}{3}$, 6, $6\frac{2}{3}$, ____, ____

31. $15\frac{1}{2}$, $13\frac{3}{4}$, 12, ____, ____

32. $\frac{1}{2}$, $\frac{1}{4}$, $\frac{1}{8}$, ____, ____

33. $13\frac{1}{2}$, $4\frac{1}{2}$, $1\frac{1}{2}$, ____, ____

34. $2\frac{2}{3}$, $1\frac{1}{3}$, $\frac{2}{3}$, ____, ____

35. $\frac{1}{100}$, ____, 1, ____, 100

Think and Apply

Use the floor plan shown to answer 36–37.

36. The shorter wall is divided into 4 equal workstations. How wide is each workstation?

37. Machines $4\frac{1}{2}$ ft long are to be placed along the longer wall. There must be at least $1\frac{1}{2}$ feet between each machine and any wall. How many machines fit? Is any space unused?

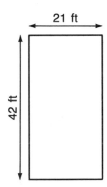

21 ft

42 ft

Test Taker

Sometimes relating fractions and decimals to money can help you to choose correct answers on a test.

38. $4\frac{3}{4} + 2\frac{1}{2}$

Think $\$4.75 + \$2.50$

   a. $7\frac{1}{8}$
   b. $7\frac{3}{8}$
   c. $7\frac{1}{4}$
   d. not given

39. $5\frac{1}{2} - 2\frac{3}{10}$

Think $\$5.50 - \$2.30$

   a. $2\frac{9}{10}$
   b. $3\frac{1}{5}$
   c. $3\frac{1}{4}$
   d. not given

40. $7 \div \frac{1}{4}$

Think How many quarters in $\$7.00$?

   a. $1\frac{3}{4}$
   b. $\frac{29}{4}$
   c. 28
   d. not given

Estimate whether each answer is less than 1 or greater than 1. Explain your thinking.

a. $5\frac{1}{3} \div \frac{7}{8}$ **b.** $\frac{7}{8} \div 5\frac{1}{3}$

SUMMING UP

Using Problem Solving

What Is the Secret?

A company is working on a project to date some recently discovered artifacts. The company wants to assign ID numbers so that any two employees can enter the project room, and so that no one person can enter alone. By entering two different ID numbers the code can be activated. How might ID numbers be assigned?

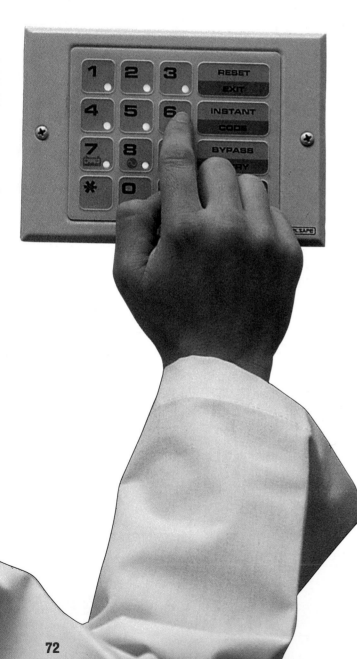

A. On one project the code was 1 2 3. One person was given the ID number 872-13. Another was given 134-7. When they went to the project room, they keyed their ID numbers into the computer. The computer subtracted the terms of their ID numbers as shown below and then divided the two differences to check the code.

$$872 - 134 = 738 \qquad \frac{738}{6} = 123$$
$$13 - 7 = 6$$

B. What if another person is given the ID number 11-6? Will this person be able to enter the project room with either of the other two people in **A**? Explain?

C. You want to assign an ID number to another person who can enter with either of the two ID numbers in **A**. Try to find an ID number to give the new person.

Sharing Your Ideas

1. **Look back** at **C**. Were you able to find an ID number for a 4th person? If so, how? If not, why not?

2. Another project uses these ID numbers. What is the code for this project?

   428-25

   326-19

Practice

You are in charge of a secret project. You must give ID numbers to several people on the project.

3. Select a three-digit code that allows people into the project room.

4. List a division problem that will give you that code.

5. Can you make two ID numbers that will give the numbers in your division problem when their corresponding terms are subtracted?

6. Try to make at least four ID numbers that, when used with another ID number, will give the code.

Summing Up

7. How did you choose your ID numbers?

8. **What if** the secret code were 1? What ID numbers would you assign to these people?

9. Could you assign ID numbers so the code would be 0?

10. Fred tried using a rule and a set of input/output boxes to make ID numbers. Do you think this would work? Explain.

Rule: Multiply by 14 and add 4.

Input	5	6
Output	74	?

ID 74–5

Chapter Review

Write the prime factorization of each composite number.
Use exponents. If a number is prime, write *prime*. pages 42–43

1. 84
2. 23
3. 243
4. 667
5. 289

Find the GCF and LCM for each. pages 44–45

6. 6, 24
7. 14, 21
8. 35, 84
9. 16, 64, 256

Write each as a fraction or mixed number in lowest terms. pages 48–49

10. 0.3
11. 0.48
12. 2.40
13. 3.512
14. 12.04

Write each fraction as a decimal. pages 48–51

15. $\frac{2}{5}$
16. $\frac{7}{20}$
17. $\frac{3}{8}$
18. $\frac{5}{7}$
19. $\frac{3}{4}$

Write each fraction in lowest terms. pages 48–49

20. $\frac{3}{15}$
21. $\frac{42}{49}$
22. $\frac{14}{67}$
23. $\frac{34}{119}$
24. $\frac{56}{256}$

Compare. Use <, >, or = for each ⬤. pages 52–53

25. $\frac{24}{36}$ ⬤ $\frac{10}{15}$
26. $\frac{11}{15}$ ⬤ $\frac{14}{22}$
27. $\frac{7}{29}$ ⬤ $\frac{3}{12}$

Add or subtract. Write each answer in lowest terms. pages 60–63

28. $2\frac{3}{4}$
    $+ 1\frac{1}{4}$

29. $3\frac{1}{2}$
    $+ 4\frac{2}{3}$

30. $6\frac{1}{3}$
    $- 2\frac{2}{3}$

31. 7
    $- 1\frac{2}{35}$

32. $7\frac{7}{10}$
    $- 2\frac{13}{14}$

Multiply or divide. Write each answer in lowest terms. pages 64–71

33. $3\frac{1}{5} \times 2\frac{1}{4}$
34. $5\frac{1}{3} \times 1\frac{7}{8}$
35. $3\frac{5}{6} \times 2\frac{3}{7}$
36. $3 \div \frac{1}{5}$
37. $\frac{3}{4} \div 1\frac{2}{3}$
38. $2\frac{5}{6} \div 1\frac{1}{2}$

Solve. pages 55–57

39. Jerry is making bookcase shelves that are $2\frac{1}{4}$ feet long. How many shelves can he make from a board that is 12 feet long? What length is left?

40. Danielle bought 25 shares of stock in Classical Archaeology for $21\frac{7}{8}$. If she later sold the stock at $23\frac{1}{4}$, how much profit did she make?

Chapter Test

Write each composite number as a product of its prime factors. Use exponents. If a number is prime, write _prime_.

1. 91   **2.** 84   **3.** 72

Find the GCF and LCM of each pair of numbers.

4. 10 and 15   **5.** 16 and 24

Write each fraction in lowest terms.

6. $\dfrac{8}{24}$ **7.** $\dfrac{26}{39}$

Compare. Use <, >, or = for each ⬤.

8. $\dfrac{20}{28}$ ⬤ $\dfrac{16}{20}$ **9.** $\dfrac{3}{15}$ ⬤ $\dfrac{7}{35}$ **10.** $\dfrac{3}{7}$ ⬤ $\dfrac{8}{21}$

Write each fraction as a decimal.

11. $\dfrac{7}{10}$ **12.** $\dfrac{5}{11}$ **13.** $\dfrac{1}{3}$ **14.** $\dfrac{5}{8}$

Add or subtract. Write each answer in lowest terms.

15. $6\dfrac{3}{4}$ **16.** $4\dfrac{1}{6}$ **17.** $5\dfrac{10}{26}$

     $+\ 2\dfrac{1}{3}$ $-\ 2\dfrac{3}{8}$ $-\ 1\dfrac{3}{39}$

Multiply or divide. Write each answer in lowest terms.

18. $4\dfrac{2}{3} \times 2\dfrac{3}{7}$ **19.** $7\dfrac{1}{2} \times 5\dfrac{2}{3}$ **20.** $15 \times \dfrac{2}{3}$

21. $4 \div \dfrac{3}{4}$ **22.** $\dfrac{3}{5} \div 4$ **23.** $8\dfrac{2}{3} \div 6\dfrac{1}{2}$

24. A fashion designer buys $5\dfrac{3}{4}$ yards of material at $9.98 per yard. He needs $2\dfrac{1}{2}$ yards to make a jacket and $2\dfrac{7}{8}$ yards to make matching slacks. Does he have enough material? If so, how much material would be left?

25. Amy is traveling to Greece to visit the Acropolis. She spends $\dfrac{3}{5}$ of the flight time reading about the Athenian culture of ancient Greece. If the flight takes $6\dfrac{3}{4}$ hours, about how long does she read?

THINK   Simplify each. Then order from least to greatest.

     a. $4 \div \dfrac{1}{2}$ **b.** $16\dfrac{1}{2} \times 0.5$ **c.** $7\dfrac{1}{3} + \dfrac{5}{6}$ **d.** $8\dfrac{2}{3} - \dfrac{5}{9}$

Computer Link

Euclidean Algorithm

There are many different ways to find the greatest common factor (GCF) of two numbers. One way that works well on a computer is the Euclidean Algorithm.

Use these steps to find the GCF of two numbers.

1) Divide the greater number by the lesser number.
2) If the remainder is not zero, divide the remainder into the previous divisor. Repeat until the remainder is 0.
3) The last divisor is the GCF of the two numbers.

Find the GCF of 36 and 96.

$$
\begin{array}{r} 2 \\ 36\overline{)96} \\ 72 \\ \hline 24 \end{array}
\qquad
\begin{array}{r} 1 \\ 24\overline{)36} \\ 24 \\ \hline 12 \end{array}
\qquad
\begin{array}{r} 2 \\ 12\overline{)24} \\ 24 \\ \hline 0 \end{array}
$$

GCF

AT THE COMPUTER

Materials: Logo

A. The REMAINDER function returns the remainder when the first number input is divided by the second number.

```
PR REMAINDER 14 7    Prints 0.
PR REMAINDER 14 4    What number prints?
```

B. Define the procedure GCF that finds the greatest common factor of two numbers. Enter GCF 96 144. What is the greatest common factor of 96 and 144?

```
TO GCF :N1 :N2
MAKE "R REMAINDER :N2 :N1
IF :R = 0 [OUTPUT :N1]
OUTPUT GCF :R :N1
END
```

C. Enter each command to find the greatest common factor for each pair of numbers.

- GCF 16 18
- GCF 49 54
- GCF 144 216
- GCF 312 512

Sharing Your Results

```
GCF
R = remainder N2 divided by N1
If R = 0 then stop
        else N2 = previous divisor
             N1 = R
             call GCF
```

1. The Euclidean Algorithm is defined recursively by these statements. Explain how it fits the definition of recursion.

2. Every recursive procedure must have a stopping condition. What is the stopping condition for GCF? How do you know GCF will stop for every pair of numbers?

recursion a process that repeats itself using previous results

Extending the Activity

The product of any two numbers D1 and D2 equals the product of their LCM and GCF.

$$\text{LCM} \times \text{GCF} = \text{D1} \times \text{D2}$$
$$\text{So LCM} = \frac{\text{D1} \times \text{D2}}{\text{GCF}}$$

The LCM of the denominators of two fractions is the LCD for the fractions.

3. Analyze the procedure ADD that adds two fractions. Explain how the value of LCD is computed. What are NUM1 and NUM2?

Input the numerator and denominator of each fraction in order.

```
TO ADD :N1 :D1 :N2 :D2
MAKE "D GCF :D1 :D2
MAKE "LCD :D1 * :D2 / :D
MAKE "NUM1 :LCD / :D1 * :N1
MAKE "NUM2 :LCD / :D2 * :N2
MAKE "NUM :NUM1 + :NUM2
PRINT :NUM
PRINT "_____
PRINT :LCD
PRINT []
PRINT [PLEASE WRITE IN SIMPLEST FORM]
END
```

4. Use the procedure ADD to find each sum. Enter the numerator and denominator of each fraction in order.

a. $\frac{1}{2} + \frac{1}{6}$ **b.** $\frac{3}{4} + \frac{7}{8}$ **c.** $\frac{3}{16} + \frac{10}{88}$ **d.** $\frac{43}{216} + \frac{75}{512}$

5. How can you use the procedure ADD to add mixed numbers? to subtract fractions or mixed numbers?

6. Use ADD to find each sum or difference.

a. $3\frac{1}{2} + 7\frac{2}{5}$ **b.** $24\frac{2}{3} + 19\frac{8}{9}$ **c.** $5\frac{1}{6} - 2\frac{5}{8}$ **d.** $5\frac{1}{3} - 4\frac{3}{4}$

Summing Up

7. Explain how you can use the GCF procedure to reduce a fraction to lowest terms.

Continued Fractions

A numerical expression such as $\dfrac{1}{2 + \dfrac{1}{3 + \frac{1}{4}}}$ is called a

simple continued fraction. Notice that the numerator of each fraction in this expression is 1. You can simplify the expression as shown below.

$$\dfrac{1}{2 + \dfrac{1}{3 + \frac{1}{4}}} = \dfrac{1}{2 + \dfrac{1}{\frac{13}{4}}} = \dfrac{1}{2 + \frac{4}{13}} = \dfrac{1}{\frac{30}{13}} = \dfrac{13}{30}$$

Think $\quad \dfrac{1}{\frac{13}{4}} = 1 \div \dfrac{13}{4} = \dfrac{4}{13}$

Simplify each continued fraction.

1. $\dfrac{1}{3 + \dfrac{1}{6 + \frac{1}{9}}}$ **2.** $\dfrac{1}{4 + \dfrac{1}{6 + \frac{1}{8}}}$ **3.** $\dfrac{1}{2 + \dfrac{1}{3 + \dfrac{1}{5 + \frac{1}{7}}}}$

Any improper fraction can be changed into a simple continued fraction. Study the example below.

$$\dfrac{712}{35} = 712 \div 35 \quad = 20 + \dfrac{12}{35}$$
$$= 20 + \dfrac{1}{\frac{35}{12}}$$
$$= 20 + \dfrac{1}{2 + \frac{11}{12}}$$
$$= 20 + \dfrac{1}{2 + \dfrac{1}{\frac{12}{11}}}$$
$$= 20 + \dfrac{1}{2 + \dfrac{1}{1 + \frac{1}{11}}}$$

Write each of these fractions as a simple continued fraction.

4. $\dfrac{56}{19}$ **5.** $\dfrac{107}{21}$ **6.** $\dfrac{12}{29}$

Maintaining Skills

Choose the correct answer. Write A, B, C, or D.

1. What is the value of 2.2^3?

   A 6.6

   B 10.648

   C 8.8

   D not given

2. Compare. 42.89 ⬤ 42.98

   A $<$

   B $>$

   C $=$

   D not given

3. Find n. $63 \div n = 0.063$

   A 10

   B 1,000

   C 100

   D not given

4. Estimate. $68,492 + 32,811 + 42,586$

   A 14,000

   B 1,400,000

   C 140,000

   D 80,000

5. $401.7 - 25.803$

   A 385.903

   B 1,978.6

   C 375.897

   D not given

6. Estimate. 7×8.45

   A 60

   B 6

   C 600

   D 0.6

7. 0.03×7.2

   A 0.216

   B 7.25

   C 2.16

   D not given

8. $0.1504 \div 3.2$

   A 0.0047

   B 0.047

   C 0.052

   D not given

9. What is the prime factorization of 45?

   A $3 \times 5 \times 5$

   B $2 \times 3 \times 5$

   C 5×9

   D not given

10. What is the LCM of 16 and 8?

    A 48

    B 24

    C 16

    D not given

11. What is $\frac{3}{8}$ as a decimal?

    A 0.275

    B 0.33

    C 0.375

    D not given

12. Compare. $\frac{3}{4}$ ⬤ $\frac{4}{5}$

    A $<$

    B $>$

    C $=$

    D not given

13. $2\frac{2}{3} + 4\frac{2}{5}$

    A $6\frac{4}{15}$

    B $6\frac{1}{15}$

    C $7\frac{1}{15}$

    D not given

Solve.

14. Each color marker in a game has a different point value. Black is 2 points, green is 3 points, and red is 5. Colin has a score of 55 points. He has 12 green markers. How many red markers could he have?

    A 1

    B 6

    C 2

    D not given

15. Mark has 24 customers on his lunch route. Three times as many customers prefer sandwiches as prefer soup. How many customers prefer soup?

    A 12

    B 6

    C 18

    D not given

3 Pre-Algebra: Expressions and Equations

THEME   Businesses That Serve Us

Sharing What You Know

Have you ever put money into a vending machine and had nothing come out? Or has the machine given you your choice and also returned your money? Whether your experiences with vending machines were frustrating or funny, you may not have thought about the companies that stock these machines. What information do they need to keep track of so that you can buy the products you want? Can you think of ways that these companies use mathematics to provide you with their products?

Using Language

The number of items sold each day from a vending machine will vary. In mathematics we call that number a **variable**. A mathematical formula uses letters to represent **variables**. For example, a vending machine company can calculate its total sales (T) by multiplying the number of items sold (n) by the price of the item (p), or $T = n \times p$. Could the company use this formula if items had different prices? Can you think of ways that you use variables every day?

Words to Know   equation, expressions, numerical expression, solution, variable, algebraic expression, inverse operation, evaluate, formula

Be a Problem Solver

Snacks in a vending machine sell for 50¢ or 75¢ each. For each of two weeks 60 items were sold, yet one week the company received $40 and the next week it received only $30. How can you explain this difference?

Take a poll of your class to determine what products should be made available in vending machines in school. Then write a letter to the editor of the school newspaper that argues for installing vending machines that sell these products.

The expression 4 + 6 means six more than four. What other phrases can you think of that mean 4 + 6?

Writing Expressions

The township library charges a 15-cent fine each day for overdue books. What expression can you write to represent the fine on a book that is 5 days overdue? 10 days overdue?

▶ A **numerical expression** represents a single value.

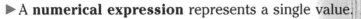

15 × 5		15 × 10
daily fine number of days		daily fine number of days

What expression represents the fine on a book overdue any number of days?

15d   15d means 15 × d

The **variable** d represents any number of days.

▶ An **algebraic expression** represents a value that can change. The value of 15d changes as the value of d changes.

More Examples

Phrase	Expression
three less than a number x	$x - 3$
twice the product of 11 and 5	$2(11 \times 5)$
5 more than twice a number y	$2y + 5$
16 decreased by a number r	$16 - r$
a number n squared divided by 5	$n^2 \div 5$

Check Your Understanding

Write an expression for each.

1. five more than twenty   **2.** a number x increased by 5   **3.** twice 7

Write each as a phrase.

4. $2y$ **5.** $16 \div c$ **6.** d^3 **7.** $1.5 - p$ **8.** $\frac{5}{r^2}$

Share Your Ideas   Is $n - 5$ the same as $5 - n$? Explain.

Write an expression for each.

9. 4 more than 7

10. 8 less than 49

11. 5 times a number b

12. a number x divided by 2 cubed

13. 50 increased by a number a

14. a number t decreased by 10

15. 25 minus a number y squared

16. the sum of 7 and a number d

17. the quotient of a number x and 4

18. two cubed divided by a number x

19. the product of 5 and a number a

20. 2 more than 5 times a number n

21. the sum of a number n and its square

22. the sum of 2 consecutive numbers

Write each as a phrase.

23. $4s$

24. $\dfrac{h}{60}$

25. $n + 1$

26. $2x + 5$

27. $5 - 2x$

28. $4x + 10$

29. $12(5 - d)$

30. $21 \div (7 - x)$

31. $\dfrac{a + b}{2}$

32. $4(p + 1)^2$

Write an expression for each.

33. the number of cups in n ounces

34. the number of ounces in n cups

35. the number of sides in n octagons

36. the number of vertexes in t triangles

37. the number of dimes in d dollars

38. the number of meters in k kilometers

Think and Apply

39. If n is even, how would you represent two consecutive odd numbers? Use an example to explain.

40. Investigate the fines at your local library. Write an expression for the fine on two books overdue.

Mathematics and History

The first multiplication symbol was invented by William Oughtred in 1631. The symbol he used resembled an X. Some sixty years later, Gottfried Leibniz introduced the raised dot to indicate multiplication. Multiplication can also be shown without using any symbol at all. Study the examples shown.

$$7 \times 5 = 7 \cdot 5 = 7(5)$$

$$a \times b = ab$$

$$5 \times (6 + n) = 5(6 + n)$$

Write each expression another way.

41. 5×32

42. $6 \times n$

43. $(1 - n) \times (6 + x)$

Describe a situation where an algebraic expression would be needed.

SUMMING UP

Why are parentheses used in this expression?
9(3 + 4.8)

Evaluating Expressions

Mark and his father went cross-country skiing in Jackson, New Hampshire, during the holidays. How much did they spend to rent the skis for 3 days? You can write an expression to show the cost.

adult's rental + child's rental

$3 \cdot 15 \quad + \quad 3 \cdot 12$

SKI RENTAL PRICES – Daily
$15.00 Adults
$12.00 Children

To **evaluate,** or find the value of an expression, follow this order of operations.

1. Work with exponents.

2. Multiply and divide from left to right. $\qquad 3 \cdot 15 + 3 \cdot 12 =$

3. Add and subtract from left to right. $\qquad 45 \quad + \quad 36 \quad =$

They spent $81 to rent the skis. $\qquad\qquad 81$

When parentheses are used in an expression, first follow the order of operations within the parentheses. When a division bar is used, follow the order of operations above and below the division bar before dividing.

a. $420 - (7 + 3)^2 \cdot 2 =$ $\qquad$ Work inside parentheses.

$420 - \quad 10^2 \quad \cdot 2 =$ $\qquad$ Simplify exponent.

$420 - \quad 100 \quad \cdot 2 =$ $\qquad$ Multiply.

$420 - \qquad 200 \quad =$ $\qquad$ Subtract.

$\qquad\qquad 220$

b. $64\left(\dfrac{(7 + 5)}{(7 - 1)}\right) - 2 =$ $\qquad$ Work above and below division bar.

$64\left(\dfrac{12}{6}\right) - 2 =$ $\qquad$ Divide.

$64(2) - 2 =$ $\qquad$ Multiply.

$128 - 2 =$ $\qquad$ Subtract.

$\qquad 126$

Check Your Understanding

Evaluate each expression.

1. $12 + 8 \div 4$

2. $(12 + 8) \div 4$

3. $9 \cdot 7 - \dfrac{12 + 8}{5}$

4. $16 \div 4^2$

5. $72 + (4 \cdot 7 + 3)$

6. $(6 + 3)^2 - 12 \div 4$

Share Your Ideas $\quad 16 + 8 \div 4 \cdot 3 \qquad$ Rewrite this expression using parentheses. How many different values can you express?

Evaluate each expression. Use paper and pencil, mental math, or a calculator.

7. $3 + 9 \cdot 7$

8. $7(3 + 9)$

9. $4^2 - (5 - 3)$

10. $4^2 - 5 - 3$

11. $3 \cdot 5 - 1 \cdot 5$

12. $25 \cdot 5 + 20 \div 2$

13. $25(5 + 15) \div 10$

14. $20^2 - 19 \cdot 21$

15. $(29 + 31) \div (17 + 13)$

16. $(18 + 2) \div (15 - 11)$

17. $(2 + 4^2) \div 6 \cdot 3$

18. $2 + 3 \cdot 3^2 + 1$

Use parentheses to make each sentence true.

19. $5 + 7 - 4 \div 2 = 10$

20. $10 \div 5 - 3 \div 5 = 1$

21. $2 + 10 - 4 \div 2 = 4$

22. $3 \cdot 12 \div 4 + 8 = 3$

23. $17 \div 8 \div 2 + 6 = 1.7$

24. $6 + 8 \div 7 \cdot 2 = 1$

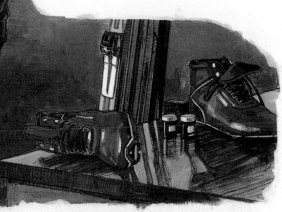

Write an expression for each and then evaluate it.

25. the admission charge for 2 adults at $6 each and 4 children at $3 each

26. the number of animals in 3 exhibits, each of which has 4 adults and 3 young

27. the cost of three drinks at seventy-five cents each and four snacks at one dollar each

Think and Apply

28. Use the key sequence shown below to determine whether or not your calculator follows the order of operations.

Enter $\boxed{2} \boxed{+} \boxed{3} \boxed{\times} \boxed{5} \boxed{=}$

If the display shows 17, then the calculator follows the order of operations. If yours does not, write the key sequence you can use to get the correct answer.

29. Mark skied 4 miles, 3 miles, and 2.5 miles in 3 days. Does the expression $4 + 3 + 2.5 \div 3$ represent the average distance he skied each day? Why or why not?

Common Error

Was the order of operations followed in each? If not, evaluate correctly.

30. $3 + 7 \cdot 8 \overset{?}{=} 80$

31. $2^2 + 10 \div 2 \overset{?}{=} 7$

32. $9 \div 3 - 1 \div 2 \overset{?}{=} 2\frac{1}{2}$

Explain why parentheses are needed in some expressions.

SUMMING UP

Can you evaluate the expression $3y + 15$? Explain why or why not.

Evaluating Expressions with Variables

Volunteers worked with naturalists from the Environmental Education Center to build a boardwalk through the Great Swamp in Somerset County, New Jersey. If they extended the walkway 250 feet each day, how much was built in 5 days? in 12 days?

$250d$ represents the length of boardwalk built in d days. To find the length built in 5 days, substitute 5 for the variable d. Then evaluate the expression.

$250d = 250(5) = 1{,}250$

The volunteers built 1,250 feet of boardwalk in 5 days.

How would you find the length built in 12 days?

What if the lumber cost $2 per foot? What expression could you write to find the cost for any number of feet? for 1,250 feet?

More Examples

Evaluate each.

a. $y^2 - 6$ (Let $y = 5$.)
$5^2 - 6 =$
$25 - 6 =$
  19

Remember to use the order of operations.

b. $25 - ab \div 5$ (Let $a = 5$ and $b = 2$.)
$25 - (5)(2) \div 5 =$
$25 - 10 \div 5 =$
  23

Check Your Understanding

Evaluate each expression. Let $a = 5$, $b = 4$, and $c = 10$.

1. $9c$
2. $4a - 6$
3. $b^2 + 10$
4. $c \div 2 + 7$
5. ab
6. $\dfrac{ab}{c}$
7. $15 \div (a + c)$
8. $\dfrac{a}{c} + 6$

Share Your Ideas   Let $d = 10$. Compare the expressions d^2 and $10d$. How do these expressions compare when d is greater than 10? less than 10?

Evaluate each expression. Let $n = 3$, $x = 5$, and $y = 2$.

9. $3x + 7$ **10.** $45 \div x$

11. $3n - 2$ **12.** $x^2 + 11$

13. $y^3 \div y$ **14.** $(x + y) \div 7$

15. $10n \div xy$ **16.** $y \div 2 - 1$

 Find each output. Use paper and pencil, mental math, or a calculator.

	Input	Output
	n	$3n^2$
17.	5	
18.	2	
19.	10	

	Input	Output
	r	$\dfrac{3r - 2}{2}$
20.	4	
21.	10	
22.	8	

Think and Apply

23. One evening there were 4 times as many ducks as geese on the pond behind the Center. Write an expression to show the total number of birds. Let g represent the number of geese. Evaluate the expression for $g = 16$.

24. Admission to the wildlife art exhibit is $2 for adults and $.50 for children. Write an expression to show the total amount of money collected. Evaluate it for 140 adults and 43 children.

25. Study the perimeter of each figure. Write an expression to determine the perimeter for a figure with n triangles in a row.

  1   2   3   4

   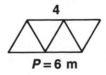

$P = 3$ m $P = 4$ m $P = 5$ m $P = 6$ m

For $d = 0$ to 10, which expression has the greater value? Explain.
a. $3d$ or $3 + d$ **b.** $5d$ or $8d$

Mixed Review

1. $\begin{aligned} &\frac{3}{5} \\ +\,&\frac{1}{4} \\ \hline \end{aligned}$

2. $\begin{aligned} &\frac{1}{2} \\ -\,&\frac{1}{6} \\ \hline \end{aligned}$

3. $\frac{2}{3} - \frac{1}{9}$

4. $1\frac{5}{6} + 4\frac{1}{2}$

5. $\frac{7}{8} \times \frac{2}{5}$

6. $\frac{1}{3} \div \frac{1}{4}$

7. $1\frac{3}{4} \times 2\frac{1}{3}$

8. $2\frac{3}{8} \div 1\frac{1}{4}$

9. $10\frac{1}{2} \times 5\frac{2}{3}$

10. $14\frac{1}{3} - 5\frac{1}{6}$

Write each as a decimal.

11. $\frac{4}{5}$

12. $\frac{3}{8}$

13. $\frac{7}{10}$

14. $3\frac{7}{8}$

15. $4\frac{1}{6}$

16. $3\frac{1}{3}$

17. $11\frac{5}{9}$

18. $\frac{17}{100}$

19. $8 \div 30$

20. $7 \div 16$

SUMMING UP

Six more than some number is 18. $x + 6 = 18$
How are these sentences alike? How are they
different?

Writing Equations

The Chesterfield Bike Shop charged Amy $26 for repairs.
The bill included a charge for labor and $6 for parts. Write
an equation to represent the total charge.

▶ An **equation** is a mathematical sentence with an
equal sign.

The total charge of $26 includes parts and labor.

Let m represent the charge for labor.

An equation says that two
expressions represent the
same number.

$$\underbrace{6 \ + \ m}_{\text{total charge}} = \underset{\uparrow \text{ total charge}}{26}$$

Another Example

Jack spent 20 hours working in the shop. He assembled 6
bikes and helped customers for 5 hours. You can write an
equation to represent the time he spent working.

$$\underset{\underset{\text{on 1 bike}}{\uparrow \text{ time spent}}}{6n} \ + \ 5 = \underset{\uparrow \text{ total time}}{20}$$

What does $6n$ represent?

What does $6n + 5$ represent?

Check Your Understanding

Write an equation for each.

1. The sum of 12 and 9 is 21.

2. Five less than a number x is 18.

3. Six muffins cost $3.60.

4. The cost of 2 cards plus $.12 tax is $2.12.

Write a statement for each.

5. $3(2 + 5) = 21$ 6. $b - 19 = 37$ 7. $2x - 4 = 6$

Share Your Ideas   Create your own statement. Write
an equation to express it mathematically.

Chesterfield Bike Shop

CUSTOMER'S ORDER NO.

NAME   DATE
ADDRESS   Amy Lowell   19

SOLD BY   CASH   CHECK   CHARGE   ON ACCT.   MDSE. RETD.   PAID OUT

QUAN.   DESCRIPTION   PRICE   AMOUNT
          Repairs
                                                  $26.00

No. 19111   ALL claims and returned goods MUST be accompanied by this bill   Total $26.00
          Rec'd by

THANK YOU

Write an equation for each.

8. Three more than 27 is 30.

9. A number n times 27 equals 270.

10. Seven squared plus a number n is 72.

11. A number b plus 3.5 is 19.2.

12. A number n divided by 3.9 is 5.

13. 5 less than a number x is 16.

14. Five tapes cost $29.75.

15. Four caps plus $.60 tax cost $10.60.

Match each statement in column A with an equation in column B.

A	B
16. The sum of 3 and 10 more than 3 is 16.	**a.** $\frac{3}{4}n = 12$
17. Five less than the sum of 12 and 17 is 24.	**b.** $3 + 30n - 63$
18. Three more than the sum of 15 and a number is 29.	**c.** $3 + 13 = 16$
19. Twelve is the difference between a number and $\frac{3}{4}$.	**d.** $3 + 15 + n = 29$
20. Three more than the product of a number and 30 is 63.	**e.** $s^2 = 16$
21. The perimeter of a square is 16 centimeters.	**f.** $n - \frac{3}{4} = 12$
22. The area of a square is 16 square centimeters.	**g.** $4s = 16$
23. Twelve dollars was three fourths of the money spent.	**h.** $12 + 17 - 5 = 24$

Write a statement for each equation.

24. $x + 17 = 34$

25. $x - 17 = 34$

26. $15y = 45$

27. $\frac{n}{16} = 2.5$

20. $\frac{48}{n} = 6$

29. $23 - n = 17$

Think and Apply

30. Write an equation to represent the area of the garden. The total area is 55 square feet.

31. **What if** the section of tomatoes is to be fenced separately? Write an expression for the total fencing needed.

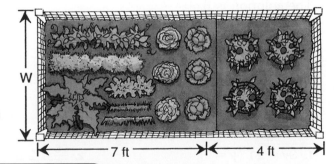

Are these sentences the same? Why or why not?
Three less than a number n times five is 42. $42 = 3 - 5n$

SUMMING UP

Solving Equations

▶ To solve an equation, find a value for the variable that makes the equation true. You can use the guess-and-test strategy to choose values to substitute for the variable.

$2x + 5 = 13$ Which values would you choose to solve this equation?

Let $x = 6$.
$$2x + 5 = 13$$
$$2(6) + 5 = 13$$
$$12 + 5 = 13$$
$$17 \neq 13$$

Let $x = 4$.
$$2x + 5 = 13$$
$$2(4) + 5 = 13$$
$$8 + 5 = 13$$
$$13 = 13$$

The solution is 4.

Another Example

Find the solution. $\frac{x}{2} + 7 = 11$

(Let $x = 6$.) $\frac{x}{2} + 7 = 11$
$$\frac{6}{2} + 7 = 11$$
$$3 + 7 = 11$$
$$10 \neq 11$$

(Let $x = 8$.) $\frac{x}{2} + 7 = 11$
$$\frac{8}{2} + 7 = 11$$
$$4 + 7 = 11$$
$$11 = 11$$

The solution is 8.

Check Your Understanding

Substitute the given value in the equation.
Then tell whether it is a solution.

1. $3y = 21$ $(y = 7)$

2. $\frac{26}{r} = 2$ $(r = 13)$

3. $z - 7 = 12$ $(z = 15)$

Share Your Ideas   Explain what the solution to an equation represents.

Substitute the given value in the equation. Then tell whether it is a solution.

4. $n + 9 = 15$ $(n = 15)$

5. $w - 4 = 10$ $(w = 12)$

6. $\frac{v}{25} = 5$ $(v = 5)$

7. $\frac{25}{v} = 5$ $(v = 5)$

8. $13m = 39$ $(m = 3)$

9. $t - 7 = 18.9$ $(t = 19.9)$

Use the number facts to solve mentally. Check by substitution.

10. $x + 10 = 30$

11. $y - 3 = 21$

12. $19 = 5 + a$

13. $7 = b - 2$

14. $3h = 270$

15. $15 = 5z$

16. $\frac{250}{r} = 2.5$

17. $375 = 3.75c$

18. $4t + 1 = 17$

19. $3x - 2 = 10$

20. $2y + 2 = 12$

21. $5y + 2 = 17$

Write an equation for each. Then match it with the solution.

22. A number m divided by 6 equals 5.

a. 7

23. Four more than a number w is 12.

b. 8

24. Five less than a number n is 11.

c. 12

25. Two times a number y is 24.

d. 30

26. Twelve less than the product of five squared and some number x is 33.

e. 1.8

27. The quotient of 42 and twice a number y equals 3.

f. 16

Think and Apply

28. A restaurant orders 3 cans of olive oil, 15 pounds of beef, and 2 boxes of sausages. The delivery receipt shows a total of 36 pounds of meat. How much did each box of sausages weigh? Write an equation. Substitute the values 10, 10.5, and 11 to find the solution.

30. A banquet is planned for 50 people. The restaurant charges $1,500 for the food. How much is that per person? Write an equation and use number facts to solve it.

29. For some equations, a solution will be any number you choose. For example, $x \cdot 1 = x$ is true for all numbers. Tell which of the equations below can have any number as a solution.

a. $y + 0 = y$ **b.** $6x + 18 = 6(x + 3)$

c. $z + 1 = 2z$ **d.** $r + r + r = 3r$

Visual Thinking

31. Add a square to the figure below so that the area is 6 square units and the perimeter remains 12 units.

Find all possible solutions for each equation.

a. $7n = 0$ **b.** $3n - 3 = 0$ **c.** $\frac{n}{1} = n$

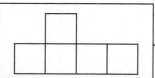
SUMMING UP

Midchapter Review

Write an expression for each. pages 82–83

1. six times seven

2. six more than seven

3. six less than seven

4. one-sixth of a number r

5. the number of hours in d days

6. the number of days in h hours

Evaluate each expression. pages 84–85

7. $3 + 6 \times 5$

8. $3 \times 6 + 5^2$

9. $3 \div 6 + 5$

10. $3 \times 5 - 6$

11. $(3 + 5) \times 6$

12. $3 + 5 + 5 \times 6 \div 3$

Evaluate each. Let $a = 3$ and $b = \frac{1}{2}$. pages 86–87

13. $3a - 10b$

14. $10a - 3b$

15. $a^2 + 6b$

16. $a^2 - 2a$

17. ab^2

18. $3b(a + \frac{1}{3})$

Write an equation for each. Then use number facts to solve. pages 88–91

19. 12 more than a number x is 15.

20. The product of 7 and a number d is 28.

21. The square of 5 minus a number x is 19.

22. A number n divided by 4 squared is 2.

Use a vocabulary word from the box to complete each sentence.

23. The value of a variable that makes an equation true is the ___.

24. 30×5 is a ___ expression.

25. A ___ represents a value that can change.

26. ___ expressions include one or more variables.

27. An ___ says that two ___ are equal.

Words to Know
equation
expressions
numerical
solution
variable
algebraic

Solve.

28. Don paid $12 for 4 equal lengths of lumber. What was the cost of each piece?

29. The cost of a dog shampoo increased by $3 to $15. What was the original cost?

30. Sue worked 4 hours, 2.5 hours, and 5.5 hours in 3 days. What was the average number of hours she worked each day? How much did she earn?

Exploring Problem Solving

Which Is More Money?

Jerry and Henry each earned $30 a day. They were given a choice of how to receive a raise in pay. They could receive a raise each week of $1 per week, or a raise each day of $.05 per day. Jerry chose the weekly raise, and Henry chose the daily raise.

Thinking Critically

Who made the better choice of how to take a raise? Use a calculator as you work with your group.

Analyzing and Making Decisions

1. How much will each person have made at the end of the first 5-day work week?

2. How much more will Henry be making on the second Monday compared to the 1st Monday?

3. Make a chart of Henry's and Jerry's salaries for several weeks. What do you see happening?

4. Who made the better choice? Explain.

Look Back   Can you change the amount of one of the raises so that it makes no difference which raise you choose? Explain.

93

Problem Solving Strategies

Simulation

Michael bought T-shirts for $4.00 each. He sold 100 shirts at $11.00 each. He made $7.00 on each shirt, or a total profit of $700. Then Michael experimented. He lowered the price to $10 each, and he sold 200 T-shirts. "Aha!" thought Michael. "My profit on each shirt went down, but my total profit went up! Suppose that each time I lowered the price $1.00 I sold 100 more T-shirts. There must be a price that gives me the greatest total profit." What is the selling price that will give Michael the greatest profit?

A simulation permits us to investigate real situations without actually experiencing them. The action can be done by using a drawing, a table, or manipulatives.

Solving the Problem

 Use a calculator where appropriate.

Think   What does Michael want to find out?

Explore   How much does it cost Michael to buy one T-shirt? How many shirts did he sell at $11 a shirt? at $10 a shirt? How much profit did he make each time? If he lowers the price $1, how many more shirts does he sell? Simulate the situation by making a table that shows costs, income, and profit. What would happen if Michael kept dropping the price by $1?

Solve   At what selling price does Michael make the most profit?

Look Back   What pattern do you see? Use the pattern to help you find out if your answer makes sense.

Share Your Ideas

1. **What if** Michael sold the shirts for $4 each? How many shirts would he sell? How much money would he make?

2. **What if** he sold 200 more shirts each time that he lowered his price by $1? At what price should he sell them to make the most profit? Explain.

Practice

CHOICES **Solve. Use a calculator where appropriate.**

3. Raj and Kate help to clean seats at the community theater. There are two sections. Each section has 8 rows with 5 seats in each row. It takes Raj about 10 seconds to clean one seat. It takes Kate about 15 seconds to clean one seat. If they work together, how long will it take them to clean all the seats?

4. When Park School is closed due to weather conditions, the principal calls 4 people who work at the school. These 4 people each call 3 people, and those 3 each call 2 more people. Each of those 2 people in turn call 1 person. How many people have been contacted?

5. The Smithtown Fire Department has held their annual Fall Harvest Festival parade. There were 2 fire engines in the parade. The police chief's car was behind one of the fire engines. The rescue squad was in front of the county park service's float, but behind the police chief's car. The road department's band was in front of a fire engine, but behind the park service. What was the order of the units in the parade?

6. At the Festival there was a tug-of-war contest. If a team lost 1 match, they were out of the contest. If 16 teams entered, how many matches did a team win in order to be the champion? How many matches were there altogether?

Mixed Strategy Review

7. Five eighth-grade students have volunteered as patient care-givers at the hospital in their town. They give a total of 40 hours of service every week. How many hours does each student work?

8. The Morris County Library has about 200,000 books on its shelves. Each week it receives about 365 books and discards an equal number. About how many new books will the library receive this year?

9. About how many books will it have on the shelves by the end of the year?

Create Your Own

Write a problem about the library for which you can simulate the action.

Adam walked 3 blocks south and 2 blocks east to get from his house to the bank. How could you describe his return route home?

Inverse Operations

The balance in Adam's bank account was $15. He deposits $20. If he withdraws $20 next week, what will be the balance in his account? You can use the number line to picture this situation.

Start at 15.

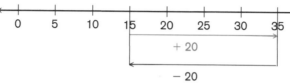

Add 20.
Subtract 20.
What is the result?

$15 + 20 - 20 = 15$ The balance will be $15.

▶ Addition and subtraction are **inverse operations.** Each one "undoes" the other.

▶ Multiplication and division are inverse operations.

$$6 \times 2 \div 2 = 6 \qquad 124 \div 4 \times 4 = 124$$

The chart shows the result of performing an operation and its inverse.

Expression	Inverse Operation	Result
$4 + 5$	$- 5$	$4 + 5 - 5 = 4$
12×6	$\div 6$	$12 \times 6 \div 6 = 12$
$x - 1$	$+ 1$	$x - 1 + 1 = x$
$y \div 3.2$	$\times 3.2$	$y \div 3.2 \times 3.2 = y$

Check Your Understanding

Name the inverse of each operation.

1. add 7   **2.** subtract 8   **3.** divide by 7   **4.** triple a number

Write the inverse operation for each.

5. $x + 5$ **6.** $\frac{z}{8}$ **7.** $8y$ **8.** $c + 10$ **9.** $p - 12$

Share Your Ideas   Describe a situation that involves inverse operations. How can you be sure that inverse operations have occurred?

Name the inverse of each operation.

10. subtract 18   **11.** divide by 5   **12.** add 9   **13.** multiply by 6

14. decrease by 12   **15.** increase by 18   **16.** double n **17.** twice 8

Write the inverse of the operation performed on each variable.

18. $y + 22$ **19.** $y - 34$ **20.** $\frac{y}{8}$ **21.** $5y$

22. $r - 7$ **23.** $14p$ **24.** $x \div 11$ **25.** $16 + d$

26. $t + 16$ **27.** $3r$ **28.** $\frac{1}{3}y$ **29.** $\frac{4}{5}x$

Find each missing operation. Write +, −, ×, or ÷ to make each sentence true.

30. $y + 22 \ \square\ 22 = y$ **31.** $t - 34 \ \square\ 34 = t$ **32.** $5x \ \square\ 5 = x$

33. $\frac{y}{8} \ \square\ 8 = y$ **34.** $12 \ \square\ x - 12 = x$ **35.** $13 \ \square\ r \div 13 = r$

Think and Apply

Write an algebraic expression for each situation. Identify the operation and name the inverse.

36. Elaine paid twice as much for the blouse.

37. The team lost 15 yards on the play.

38. Gasoline prices tripled during the shortage.

39. Gary is half as old as Mark.

40. Emily improved her running time by 3 seconds.

Test Taker

You can improve your test scores by using estimation when a computation is long or complicated.

Use estimation to help choose the correct answer for each.

41. 6.74×4.1

    a. 31.494   **c.** 27.634

    b. 22.344   **d.** 276.34

42. $8\frac{2}{3} - 3\frac{4}{5}$

    a. $4\frac{13}{15}$ **c.** $7\frac{1}{15}$

    b. $3\frac{1}{5}$ **d.** $11\frac{6}{15}$

43. Evaluate. $6 \times 3.2 + 2 \times 4.7$

    a. 39.7   **c.** 120

    b. 160   **d.** 28.6

Describe the result of performing an operation and its inverse. Use $y \div 3 \cdot 3$ as an example.

SUMMING UP

$5 = 5$ If you add or subtract the same number on both sides of the equation, would the equation still be true? Explain.

Solving Addition and Subtraction Equations

An equation says that two expressions are equal.

If you add or subtract a number on one side of an equation, you must do the same on the other side to keep the expressions equal.

$$22 - 7 = 15$$
$$22 - 7 + 7 = 15 + 7$$
$$22 = 22$$

▶You can use inverse operations to solve an equation. Find a value for x that makes the equation true.

$x - 27 = 53$ **Think**   What is the inverse of subtracting 27?

$x - 27 + 27 = 53 + 27$ Add 27 to *both* sides.

$x = 80$ **Solution**

Check $80 - 27 = 53$ Replace x with 80 in the
$53 = 53$ original equation.

Another Example

$1.6 + y = 2.7$ **Think**   What is the inverse of adding 1.6?

$1.6 + y - 1.6 = 2.7 - 1.6$ Subtract 1.6 from both sides.

$y = 1.1$ **Solution**

Check $1.6 + 1.1 = 2.7$ Replace y with 1.1 in the
$2.7 = 2.7$ original equation.

Check Your Understanding

Solve each and check.

1. $157 + x = 233$
2. $x - 157 = 233$
3. $y + 13.2 = 145$
4. $t - 7 = 41$
5. $r + 0 = 153$
6. $2 + y = 4.7$
7. $0 = x - 7$
8. $n + 4.3 = 8$

Share Your Ideas   How does using the inverse operation help you find a solution to an addition or subtraction equation?

Solve each and check.

9. $d + 102 = 183$

10. $f + 47 = 103$

11. $b - 63 = 45$

12. $103 = x + 6$

13. $t - 82 = 25.86$

14. $y + 27.5 = 53.2$

15. $140 = n - 37$

16. $18 = h - 88.9$

17. $p + 43 = 108$

18. $165 = d + 13.9$

19. $24 + r = 91$

20. $6.9 = x + 4.3$

21. $62 + 31 = t - 5$

22. $100 + x = 21 \times 5$

23. $\frac{1}{3} + r = \frac{3}{4}$

24. $v - \frac{1}{4} = \frac{2}{3}$

Write an equation for each. Then solve and check.

25. Eighteen subtracted from w is 135.

26. Thirteen more than y is 51.

27. Add 12 to x and the sum is 133.8.

28. When 11.34 is subtracted from y, the difference is 28.

29. A number x more than $\frac{3}{4}$ is $2\frac{1}{2}$.

30. Forty-one plus 29 equals y more than 5.

31. The sum of 16 and t is 5 times 4.

Think and Apply

Write an equation. Then solve.

32. To find her profits at the end of the day, Maria subtracts her costs from her sales of tortillas. If her profits were $35.75 and her costs were $29.25, what were her sales that day?

33. Joe spent $20 at the restaurant. The bill was $16 plus $.96 tax. How much was the tip?

Look back at **25.** Explain how you used an inverse operation to solve the equation.

Mixed Review

1. $\frac{1}{2} + \frac{1}{4}$

2. $0.5 \cdot 320$

3. $375 + 827$

4. $950 - 55$

5. $12 \div 0.25$

6. $73 \div 100$

7. 2.1×10^3

8. $3,542 - 273$

9. 16×0.5

10. $5.27 \cdot 2.1$

Estimate.

11. $3.89 + 47.5$

12. $\frac{3}{4} + \frac{7}{8}$

13. $387 \cdot \frac{3}{4}$

14. $73.4 \cdot 48.99$

15. $387 \div 4$

16. $8,731 - 8,429$

Write *true* or *false*.

17. 3 tenths $= 0.3$

18. 1.2 million $= 1\frac{1}{5}$ million

19. $6^2 = 12$

20. $12 \div 0.5 > 12 \cdot 0.5$

SUMMING UP

What is the inverse of multiplying by 10? of dividing by 43?

Solving Multiplication and Division Equations

An equation says that two expressions are equal.

If you multiply or divide by a number on one side of an equation, you must do the same on the other side to keep the expressions equal.

$$3 \cdot 25 = 75$$
$$3 \cdot 25 \div 25 = 75 \div 25$$
$$3 = 3$$

▶ You can use inverse operations to solve an equation.

Find a value for x that makes the equation true.

$16x = 400$	**Think** What is the inverse of multiplying by 16?
$\frac{16x}{16} = \frac{400}{16}$	Divide *both* sides of the equation by 16.
$x = 25$	**Solution**
Check $16 \cdot 25 = 400$	Replace x with 25 in the original equation.
$400 = 400$	

Another Example

$w \div 1.5 = 6.4$	**Think** What is the inverse of dividing by 1.5?
$w \div 1.5 \cdot 1.5 = 6.4 \cdot 1.5$	Multiply by 1.5 on *both* sides.
$w = 9.6$	**Solution**
Check $9.6 \div 1.5 = 6.4$	Replace w with 9.6 in the original equation.
$6.4 = 6.4$	

Check Your Understanding

Solve each equation and check.

1. $x \div 7 = 22$ **2.** $3y = 18$ **3.** $4t = 148$ **4.** $\frac{x}{11} = 90$

5. $7r = 22.4$ **6.** $12y = 612$ **7.** $\frac{z}{5} = 10.2$ **8.** $x \div 1.8 = 21.6$

Share Your Ideas How does using the inverse operation help you find a solution to a multiplication or division equation?

Solve each equation and check.

9. $500 = 25w$

10. $\frac{w}{2} = 25$

11. $18y = 162$

12. $\frac{y}{9} = 18$

13. $12 = 24n$

14. $\frac{x}{3} = 72$

15. $7y = 112$

16. $17 = w \div 4$

17. $56 = \frac{x}{4}$

18. $12.5y = 100$

19. $r \div 6 = 13$

20. $21 = 21x$

21. $5y = 0$

22. $16 + r = 51$

23. $7.5 = t - 3$

24. $1.3x = 6.5$

25. $\frac{s}{0.15} = 30$

26. $2.8 = 2x$

27. $\frac{x}{4.1} = 1$

28. $2t = 6.2$

29. $\frac{1}{3}x = 15$

30. $4k = \frac{3}{8}$

31. $16 + 30 = x - 4$

32. $2t = 5 + 4.2$

Write an equation for each. Then solve and check.

33. The product of a number x and 23 is 161.

34. A number n divided by 5 equals 1.

35. The quotient when a number n is divided by 12 is 9.

36. The product of a number t and 3.9 is 70.2.

37. Twice a number w equals 114.

38. Seventeen is the sum of a number y and 1.5.

39. The difference between a number r and 6.5 equals 4.3.

40. The product of a number y and $\frac{3}{4}$ is 12.

41. The product of 10 and a number r equals $\frac{1}{2}$.

42. Seven times three equals the quotient of a number p and 0.7.

Write an equation for each and solve.

43. A concession stand charges $1.25 for a slice of pizza. If one slice is one-eighth of the entire pie, how much does the entire pie cost?

44. A basketball player earned three times as much money this year as last. If his contract this year was for $1.2 million, how much money did he earn last year?

Create a problem for the equation $\frac{x}{8} = 12$. Then explain how you would solve it.

SUMMING UP

How many rods does 1 cube equal? Explain.

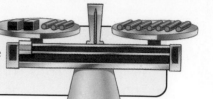

Solving Two-Step Equations

The Shirt Works sells personalized T-shirts. This week they sold 85 shirts. That is 5 more than twice the number of shirts sold last week. How many were sold last week?

Let n = number of shirts sold last week.

$2n + 5 = 85$ What does $2n + 5$ represent?

To solve an equation using more than one operation, follow these steps.

- Use the inverse of addition or subtraction and simplify.

- Use the inverse of multiplication or division and simplify.

$$2n + 5 = 85$$
$$2n + 5 - 5 = 85 - 5$$
$$2n = 80$$
$$\frac{2n}{2} = \frac{80}{2}$$
$$n = 40$$

Check Replace the variable with 40 in the original equation.

$$2(40) + 5 = 85$$
$$80 + 5 = 85$$
$$85 = 85$$

40 shirts were sold last week.

Another Example

Find y.

$$\frac{y}{5} - 3 = 10$$
$$\frac{y}{5} - 3 + 3 = 10 + 3$$
$$\frac{y}{5} = 13$$
$$5 \cdot \frac{y}{5} = 13 \cdot 5$$
$$y = 65$$

Check $\frac{65}{5} - 3 = 10$
$$13 - 3 = 10$$
$$10 = 10$$

Check Your Understanding

Solve each equation and check your results.

1. $3y - 7 = 14$

2. $\frac{x}{2} + 5 = 13$

3. $25 + \frac{x}{4} = 85$

4. $6r + 9 = 51$

Share Your Ideas Which operation would you use first to solve each equation? **a.** $\frac{x}{2} = 46$ **b.** $2x - 7 = 46$ **c.** $2x = 46$ **d.** $2x + 7 = 46$

First tell what must be done to both sides of the equation. Then solve and check.

5. $3n + 12 = 72$

6. $\frac{n}{5} - 3 = 14$

7. $33 = 3y - 12$

8. $53 = 8 + 3w$

9. $\frac{z}{5} - 6 = 8$

10. $4k - 9 = 27$

11. $\frac{m}{2} - 7 = 12$

12. $16 = \frac{z}{4} - 12$

13. $5w + 8 = 23$

14. $3y + 2 = 44$

15. $17 = 2x + 5$

16. $11 = 2d + 1$

17. $2t + 5 = 5$

18. $10y - 20 = 0$

19. $5.5 + 4x = 99.5$

20. $\frac{x}{2.5} + 8 = 20$

Write an equation for each statement. Then solve.

21. 52 is twice a number n.

22. 12 is 6 less than twice a number b.

23. 4 more than twice a number x is 24.

24. 8 is 4 less than a number n.

25. Two thirds of a number y is 52.

26. 5 more than half a number x is 16.2.

Think and Apply

Write an equation for 27–28. Then solve.

27. Tim is 6 years old. He is 1 year older than one-sixth the age of his mother. How old is Tim's mother?

28. The eighth grade class is spending $125 to buy a new flag for the school. The class has $30 in its treasury and the students are donating the rest. How much money will each of the 25 students need to contribute?

29. Fourteen cubes are on one side of a scale that is balanced. The other side contains two cubes and two triangles. Two cylinders are needed to balance three triangles. How many cubes are needed to balance one cylinder?

Explain the steps you would use to solve the following equations.

a. $3y = 33$ **b.** $y - 12 = 33$ **c.** $3y - 12 = 33$

SUMMING UP

Formulas

The fare for a taxicab ride is based on the distance traveled. The table shows the cost of a ride for each distance.

Miles	1	2	3	4
Cost	$2.20	$2.90	$3.60	$4.30

A **formula** can be used to express the relationship between the distance and the cost.

$$c = \$1.50 + \$.70d$$

minimum charge
cost   distance in miles

Fare $1.50 + $.70 per mile

What is the cost for a 5-mile ride?

$c = \$1.50 + \$.70d$ Write the formula.

$c = \$1.50 + \$.70(5)$ Substitute 5 for d.

$c = \$1.50 + \$3.50$ Simplify to solve.

$c = \$5$ The cost for a 5-mile ride is $5.

What if you know the cost is $6.40? How could you find the distance?

$c = \$1.50 + \$.70d$ Write the formula.

$\$6.40 = \$1.50 + \$.70d$ Substitute $6.40 for c.

$\$6.40 - \$1.50 = \$1.50 + \$.70d - \$1.50$ Use inverse operations

$\$4.90 = \$.70d$ and simplify to solve.

$\$4.90 \div \$.70 = \$.70d \div \$.70$

$7 = d$ The distance is 7 miles.

Check Your Understanding

A formula for calculating the tip on a restaurant check is $t = 0.15b$. (t = tip; b = bill) Use the formula to complete the chart.

Share Your Ideas   A formula relates two or more variables. Write a formula of your own and explain the relationship it shows.

	Bill	Tip
1.	$2.20	
2.	$3.60	
3.	$4.00	
4.	$7.80	

Practice

CHOICES Use paper and pencil, mental math, or a calculator. Evaluate each formula for the given values.

5.

x	$4x + 6 = d$
3	
5	
7	

6.

y	$y^2 - 3 = r$
4	
6	
8	

7.

p	$\frac{p}{3} \cdot 5 = t$
6	
3.9	
1.8	

8.

s	$A = s^2$
4.5	
10.7	
40	

9.

h	$a = \frac{10 + h}{2} - 4$
42	
52	
7.2	

10.

r	$\frac{1}{2}r^2 + 30 = x$
8	
12	
20	

Substitute the given values in each formula and evaluate.

$P = 2l + 2w$ Perimeter = 2(length) + 2(width)

11. $l = 1.7$ cm; $w = 4.3$ cm

12. $l = 4$ cm; $w = 1.3$ cm

13. $l = 2\frac{1}{2}$ m; $w = 12$ m

$V = Bh$ Volume = Base $\times$ height

14. $B = 1.2$ m^2; $h = 0.4$ m

15. $B = 16$ cm^2; $h = 34$ cm

16. $V = 130$ m^3; $B = 40$ m^2

Choose the formula that expresses each relationship.

17.

t	1	2	3	4
x	4	8	12	16

a. $t = 4x$

b. $x = 4t$

c. $x = t + 3$

18.

s	3	6	9	12
t	7	10	13	16

a. $t = s - 4$

b. $t = 4s$

c. $t = 4 + s$

19.

y	2	3	4	5
z	6	6.5	7	7.5

a. $y = \frac{z}{3}$

b. $z = 2y - 1$

c. $z = \frac{y}{2} + 5$

Think and Apply

The graph shows the hours Maria works at the grocery store and the money she earns.

20. Make a chart that shows the salary earned for the hours worked.

21. Create a formula that relates the hours and the salary.

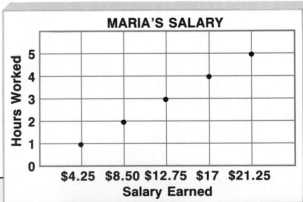

MARIA'S SALARY

Look back at **21.** Think of two ways to use the formula you created.

SUMMING UP

105

Using Problem Solving

Concrete Functions

Patterns can be formed by a rule acting on an input. How does each output relate to its corresponding input?

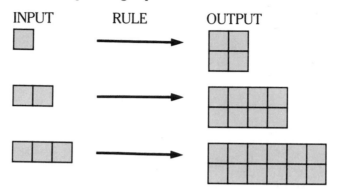

INPUT   RULE   OUTPUT

Working together

Materials: tiles or counters, graph paper

Find the rule to describe the pattern above.

A. Study the pattern. What would happen if the input were 4, 5, or 6 cubes? Show these inputs with your cubes or counters. Make a chart to show the pattern that you discover.

Input	1	2	3	4	5	6
Output	4	8	12			

What do you think the function rule is?

B. Make a graph using each ordered pair (input, output) from the input and output chart. Connect your points.

C. Make a rule. Exchange it with a friend. Your partner should select 5 inputs, find their outputs, and graph the results.

Sharing Your Ideas

1. What would your output be for the pattern in **A** if the input were 0?

2. How did you find the function rule?

3. What did your graph in **B** look like?

Extending Your Thinking

4. Record a pattern with the following rule in a chart:
Multiply the input by 1.
Graph the pattern.

5. Now record and graph patterns using the following rules.
Compare the graphs.

    a. Multiply input by 2.

    b. Multiply input by 4.

    c. Divide input by 2.

6. Record patterns using the following rules and then graph
the patterns. Compare these graphs with your graph in **4**.

    a. Multiply input by 1, and then subtract 1.

    b. Multiply input by 1, and then add 1.

Summing Up

7. How did the graphs change as you
multiplied your input by 2, then by 4?
What happened when you divided by 2?

8. How did the graph change when you
multiplied by 1 and subtracted 1?
multiplied by 1 and added 1?

9. What do you think the graph of this rule
would look like: $2x + 1$?

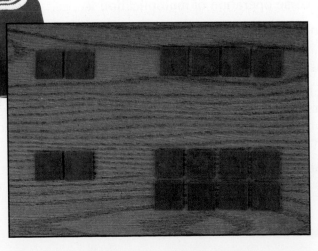

Chapter Review

Write an expression or equation for each. pages 82–83, 88–89

1. the number of eggs in x dozen

2. The product of a number x and 8 is 37.

3. 4.2 is three more than twice 0.6

4. the number of wheels in x tricycles

Evaluate each expression. pages 84–85

5. $18 - 8 \div 2$

6. $4 \cdot 7 - \dfrac{6}{2}$

7. $4^2 + 8 \cdot 7 - 6$

Evaluate by substitution. Let $a = 5$, $b = 10$, and $c = 2$. pages 86–87

8. $12.5b$

9. $\dfrac{68}{c}$

10. $4\dfrac{a}{b}$

11. $4 + ab$

Substitute the given value for the variable. Tell whether or not the value is a solution. pages 90–91

12. $2x + 6 = 10$ ($x = 2$)

13. $\dfrac{x}{5} = 35$ ($x = 7$)

14. $4x - 5 = 35$ ($x = 10$)

Solve each equation. pages 96–103

15. $4g = 80$

16. $f - 18 = 49$

17. $\dfrac{n}{11} = 7$

18. $52 = m + 25$

19. $\dfrac{x}{2} + 5 = 47$

20. $2.6h = 104$

Write an equation for each. Then solve. pages 98–103

21. A number y divided by 3 is 5.

22. Seven less than $\dfrac{1}{2}$ a number x is 18.

23. Twice a number r is 18.8.

24. A number p less 24 equals $12\dfrac{1}{4}$.

Evaluate each formula for the given value. pages 104–105

25. $p - 3.4 = q$ ($p = 17.5$)

26. $2x + 15 = t$ ($x = 0.3$)

27. $10(12 - r) = x$ ($r = 5$)

Complete each statement.

28. The inverse operation of subtraction is ____.

29. The inverse operation of multiplication is ____.

30. A number sentence with an equal sign is called a(n) ____.

Words to Know
expression
equation
division
addition
multiplication

Solve. pages 93–95

31. Alicia has 3 walls and a table on which to display posters and books on art, travel, and history. If posters cannot be displayed on the table, in how many different ways can she arrange the 4 types of items?

32. Sid had $20 in his cash drawer before he sold 7 tuna salads. He now has $31.20. How much did each salad cost?

Chapter Test

Write an expression or equation for each.

1. the number of ounces in p pounds

2. Twelve more than twice a number y is 144.

3. Two-fifths more than a number x is $5\frac{7}{10}$.

Evaluate each expression.

4. $(\frac{1}{3} + \frac{1}{2}) \times (24 - 6)$

5. $47 - 3 \cdot 4 + 3^2$

6. $(4 \cdot 7 - 6) \div 2$

Substitute the given value for the variable. Tell whether or not the value is a solution.

7. $2x + 5 = 15 \ (x = 3)$

8. $\frac{5}{r} = 20 \ (r = 0.25)$

9. $3z - 5 \cdot 2 = 8 \ (z = 6)$

10. $(\frac{4}{x} + 3) \div 5 = 1 \ (x = 2)$

Solve each equation.

11. $3f = 81$

12. $\frac{m}{12} = 7$

13. $3x + 12 = 24$

14. $57 = f + 29$

15. $5.6n = 16.8$

16. $\frac{y}{3} - 11 = 9$

Write an equation for each. Then solve.

17. The sum of a number y and 15 is 134.

18. Twice a number r is 178.

19. The difference between a number x and 12 is 11.8.

Evaluate each formula for the given value.

20. $x + 13 = y \ (x = 64)$

21. $\frac{b}{3.5} - c \ (b = 7)$

22. $\frac{6y}{10} = d \ (y = 5)$

23. $12.5 - w = r \ (w = 4.1)$

Solve.

24. Bob jogged 10 km east, 2 km south, 6 km west, 5 km north, and then 4 km west. Where is he relative to where he started?

25. A plumber charges $20 to make a house call plus $15 an hour. How long will she work for $57.50? Write an equation and solve.

THINK   Use the guess-and-test strategy to solve the equation $3x = 2x + x$. Can you find a solution? Why or why not?

EXTENSION

An Exasperating Expression

Use a calculator to evaluate the expression below. Use the list at the bottom of the page to find a value for each variable.

$$\frac{f \cdot \dfrac{e}{ah} + \left(\dfrac{j - g}{L}\right)^{k} - m^{i} + nb}{\left(q - \dfrac{c}{o}\right)^{p-r} - \dfrac{d}{a}}$$

a = the number of inches in a foot

b = the number of days in a week

c = the number of weeks in a year

d = the sum of the angles in a triangle

e = the number of items in a gross

f = the greatest number on the Richter Scale

g = the number of watts in a kilowatt

h = the number of karats in pure gold

i = the longitude of Greenwich, England

j = the 24-hour time for 3:00 P.M.

k = the number of pennies equal to a quarter

L = the value of the Roman numeral D

m = normal body temperature in degrees Celsius

n = the number of cups in a pint

o = the number of bushels in a peck

p = the number of sides on a pentagon

q = the number of days in September

r = the number of seasons in a year

Family Math

In the first three chapters of our mathematics book, we studied whole numbers, decimals, fractions, number theory, and equations.

Find the Missing Number

An equation always has an equals sign. Equations are written in arithmetic and in algebra.

Arithmetic Equation	Algebra Equation
$5 + 4 = 9$	$n + 4 = 9$
Five plus four equals nine.	Some number (n) plus 4 equals 9.

A solution to an algebra equation is a number that makes the left side of the equation equal to the right side. Since $5 + 4 = 9$, the solution to the equation above is $n = 5$.

Here is another example.
$$(4 + 6) \times n = 40$$
$$10 \times n = 40$$
$$n = 4$$
Check $10 \times 4 = 40$

Solve some equations with your family. First, copy the numbers shown and then cut out each one. Match a number to each equation. Use each number once.

0	1	2	3	4
5	6	7	8	9

1. $\boxed{n} - 6 = 3$

2. $6 + \boxed{n} = 6$

3. $2 \times \boxed{n} = 14$

4. $\boxed{n} \div 4 = 2$

5. $\boxed{n} \times 1 = 1$

6. $6 - 0 = \boxed{n}$

7. $(\boxed{n} + 2) \div 3 = 2$

8. $4 \times (\boxed{n} - 2) = 12$

9. $10 \times (3 - \boxed{n}) = 0$

10. $4 \times \boxed{n} = 16 - 8$

Can you think of a situation in which you can use an equation? For example: There are 20 in our family, including aunts and uncles. Twelve are 18 years old or over. How many are under 18?

$$12 + n = 20 \qquad \text{Solution: } n = 8$$

Have each family member make up one situation. Then have the others write and solve an equation for the situation.

Cumulative Review

Choose the correct answer. Write A, B, C, or D.

1. What is the value of 3^3?

    A 12   **C** 27

    B 9   **D** not given

2. Find n. $8^n = 64$

    A 2   **C** 8

    B 4   **D** not given

3. Compare. 3.5 billion ● 18.4 million

    A $<$ **C** $=$

    B $>$ **D** not given

4. $87,300 \div 10^5$

    A 0.873   **C** 0.0873

    B 87.3   **D** not given

5. Estimate. $241.35 - 126.92$

    A 40   **C** 100

    B 350   **D** 200

6. $92.42 - 16.56$

    A 84.14   **C** 7.584

    B 75.84   **D** not given

7. $\begin{array}{r} 5.06 \\ \times\ 3.1 \\ \hline \end{array}$

    A 15.686   **C** 1.636

    B 156.86   **D** not given

8. $6.164 \div 9.2$

    A 0.064   **C** 0.648

    B 0.67   **D** not given

9. What is the prime factorization of 60?

    A $2^2 \times 3^2 \times 5$ **C** $2^2 \times 3 \times 5$

    B $2 \times 3^2 \times 5$ **D** not given

10. What is the GCF of 24 and 56?

    A 16   **C** 4

    B 14   **D** not given

11. What is the LCM of 7 and 9?

    A 18   **C** 63

    B 1   **D** not given

12. What is $2\frac{3}{4}$ written as a decimal?

    A 2.75   **C** 2.34

    B 0.275   **D** not given

13. What is $\frac{1}{6}$ written as a decimal?

    A $0.\overline{6}$ **C** 0.61

    B $0.1\overline{66}$ **D** not given

14. Compare. $\frac{3}{8}$ ● $\frac{5}{8}$

    A $<$ **C** $=$

    B $>$ **D** not given

15. What is $\frac{48}{64}$ in lowest terms?

    A $\frac{6}{8}$ **C** $\frac{5}{8}$

    B $\frac{3}{4}$ **D** not given

16. $\frac{4}{5} \times 6\frac{2}{3}$

    A $6\frac{8}{15}$ **C** $5\frac{1}{3}$

    B 8   **D** not given

Choose the correct answer. Write A, B, C, or D.

17. Which expression means 7 more than 5?

   A $7 + 12$ **C** $5 + 7$

   B $5 + 9$ **D** not given

18. Evaluate. $5 + 2 \times 6 - 4$

   A 38   **C** 14

   B 13   **D** not given

19. Evaluate $2x^2$ for $x = 6$.

   A 64   **C** 24

   B 72   **D** not given

20. Which equation shows a number, n, plus 3 is 8?

   A $n + 3 = 8$ **C** $8 - 3 = n$

   B $3 + 8 = n$ **D** not given

21. Solve for y. $y - 18 = 45$

   A $y = 27$ **C** $y = 63$

   B $y = 53$ **D** not given

22. Solve for m. $41 = 41m$

   A $m = 2$ **C** $m = 41$

   B $m = 0$ **D** not given

23. Solve for k. $32 = 6k - 16$

   A $k = 8$ **C** $k = 288$

   B $k = 2\frac{2}{3}$ **D** not given

24. What is the value of t for $x = 3$?
$t = 4x + 7$

   A $t = 14$ **C** $t = 19$

   B $t = 11$ **D** not given

Solve.

25. Freda took $17.50 to the theme park. The admission was $5.50. She bought tickets for 3 rides at $1.75 each. How many more tickets at $1.75 each can she buy?

   A 3   **C** 6

   B 4   **D** not given

26. Jessie needs 3 fence posts. The total height of the 3 posts is 12.4 m. The fence posts differ in height by no less than 0.1 m and no more than 0.3 m. Which of the following could be the height of the tallest post?

   A 4.8 m   **C** 5.1 m

   B 4.4 m   **D** not given

Solve. If there is not enough information, tell what is missing.

27. Alice is a gymnast who works out $2\frac{1}{2}$ hours each day. During that time she spends $\frac{1}{2}$ hour on the balance beam, $\frac{1}{2}$ hour on the horse, and $\frac{1}{2}$ hour on floor exercises. About how long does she practice each week?

   A 17.5 hours   **C** 28 hours

   B 7 hours   **D** not given

28. Scott has written two articles for the school paper. He needs to cut 25 words from his first article and 45 words from the second. How many words do both articles contain?

   A 70 words   **C** 1,125 words

   B need number of words in original articles   **D** not given

4 Geometry

THEME   Geometry Shapes Our World

Sharing What You Know

What similarities do you see in these structures? Which ones were constructed by people? The ancient Romans used arches to make their aqueducts, bridges, and buildings strong. They also constructed arches to honor strong leaders. A modern version of a triumphal arch is the Gateway Arch in St. Louis, rising 630 feet above the Mississippi River. The arch marks St. Louis as the symbolic gateway to the West. What are some structures near your home that use arches for strength? Where might you find an arch that honors a strong leader?

Using Language

Examine the arches. How are they similar? In mathematics, part of the circumference of a circle is called an **arc.** Discuss how an arch and an arc are alike. How are they different?

Words to Know transversal, hexagon, corresponding angles, supplementary angles, complementary angles, adjacent angles, octagon, skew lines, parallel lines, central angle, rectangular prism, inscribed angle, trapezoid, parallelogram, cube

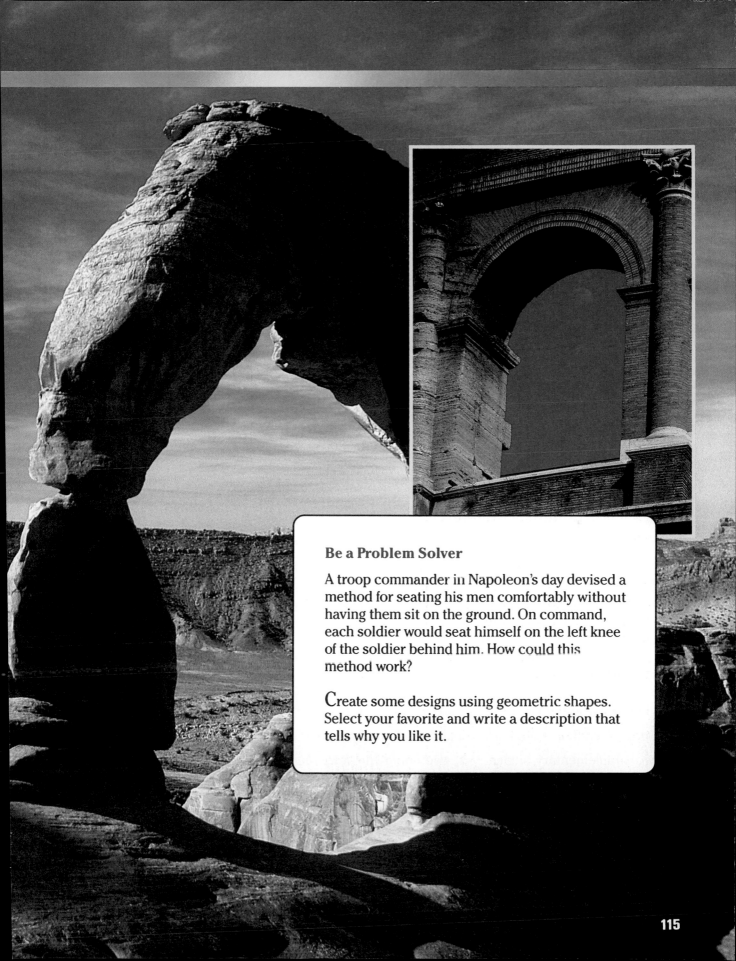

Be a Problem Solver

A troop commander in Napoleon's day devised a method for seating his men comfortably without having them sit on the ground. On command, each soldier would seat himself on the left knee of the soldier behind him. How could this method work?

Create some designs using geometric shapes. Select your favorite and write a description that tells why you like it.

Are these two angles congruent? Explain why or why not.

Angles and Intersecting Lines

A pair of scissors can model intersecting lines. Intersecting lines form pairs of angles.

A pair of opposite angles formed by intersecting lines are called **vertical angles**.

∠ABC and ∠DBE are vertical angles.

Use a protractor to measure ∠ABC and ∠DBE. What do you notice?

m∠ABC = m∠DBE, so ∠ABC ≅ ∠DBE.

↑ means *measure of*　　　　　└ means *is congruent to*

Name another pair of vertical angles.

Name a pair of angles that have a common ray, a common vertex, and interiors that do not overlap.

Angles with these properties are called **adjacent angles**. ∠CBE and ∠ABD are not adjacent. Explain why.

▶ Two angles are **supplementary** if the sum of their measures is 180°.

▶ Adjacent angles formed by two intersecting lines are supplementary.

▶ Two angles are **complementary** if the sum of their measures is 90°.

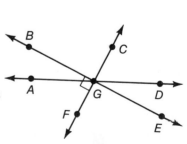

vertex of ∠ABD

interior of ∠CBE

ray, $\overrightarrow{BE}$

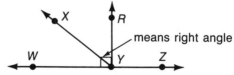

means right angle

∠WYX and ∠XYZ are supplementary.
∠WYX and ∠XYR are complementary.
∠WYZ is a straight angle

Check Your Understanding

Use the figure at the right. Name pairs of angles for each.

1. a pair of vertical angles and a pair of adjacent angles

2. two supplementary angles　　3. two complementary angles

Estimate the measure of each angle. Check with a protractor.

4. ∠AGB　　　5. ∠BGC　　　6. ∠CGD　　　7. ∠DGF

Share Your Ideas　∠XYZ and ∠RYT are vertical angles. They are also supplementary. How is this possible?

Use the figure at the right. $\overleftrightarrow{SV}$ and $\overleftrightarrow{RU}$ intersect to form right angles.

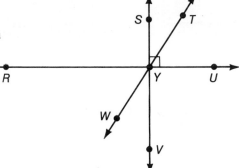

8. Name two pairs of vertical angles and two pairs of adjacent angles.

9. Name a pair of adjacent angles that are not also supplementary.

10. Name a pair of complementary angles.

Find the missing measures.

11.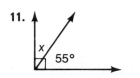

12.

13.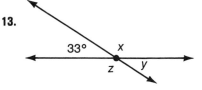

14.

15.

Draw the complement and the supplement of each angle. If one does not exist, explain why not.

16. $75°$ 17. $28°$ 18. $90°$ 19. $103°$

Write *true* or *false*. Explain your thinking.

20. The measure of the supplement of an angle is always greater than the measure of its complement.

21. An angle can never be congruent to its supplement.

22. If an angle is adjacent to its supplement, a straight angle is formed.

Think and Apply

23. Angles 1 and 2 together form a straight angle, so m∠1 + m∠2 = 180°. The same is true for angles 2 and 3. m∠2 + m∠3 = 180°. How can you use these two facts to show that vertical angles have equal measures?

24. An angle and its complement have the same supplement. What is the measure of the angle? What is the measure of its supplement?

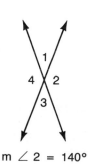

m ∠ 2 = 140°

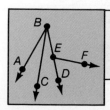

Explain why these angles are not adjacent.
∠ABC and ∠ABD
∠CBD and ∠DEF

SUMMING UP

Parallel Lines and Transversals

A farmer plows his field in parallel rows. Why is this design often chosen for planting?

▶ Two lines that lie in the same plane and do not intersect are **parallel**.

$$\overleftrightarrow{RW} \parallel \overleftrightarrow{TX}.$$

↑
means is parallel to

▶ Two lines that do not lie in the same plane and do not intersect are **skew**.

Describe how you can use cardboard and two pencils to model skew lines.

▶ A **transversal** is a line that intersects two or more lines at different points.

$\overleftrightarrow{YZ}$ is a transversal to $\overleftrightarrow{RW}$ and $\overleftrightarrow{TX}$.

Two parallel lines intersected by a transversal form pairs of congruent angles.

Alternate interior angles	$\angle c \cong \angle f$; $\angle d \cong \angle e$
Alternate exterior angles	$\angle a \cong \angle h$; $\angle b \cong \angle g$
Corresponding angles	$\angle a \cong \angle e$; $\angle b \cong \angle f$; $\angle c \cong \angle g$; $\angle d \cong \angle h$

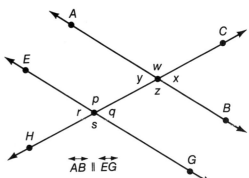

Check Your Understanding

Use the figure at the right.

1. Name one pair of each: alternate interior angles, alternate exterior angles, and corresponding angles.

2. If $m\angle y = 60°$, find the measure of all the other angles. Explain your thinking.

Share Your Ideas   Describe how to locate alternate interior angles, alternate exterior angles, and corresponding angles for a pair of parallel lines.

$\overleftrightarrow{AB} \parallel \overleftrightarrow{EG}$

In each figure below identify the alternate interior angle and the corresponding angle for ∠x.

✓ **3.**

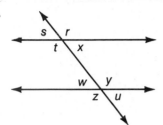

4.

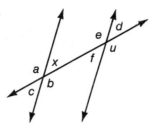

5.

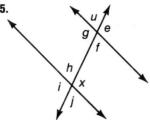

6. Use the figures for 3–5. Identify the alternate exterior angle and the corresponding angle to ∠u.

Find the missing measures.

✓ **7.**

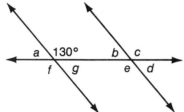

8.

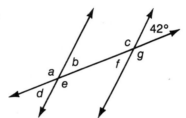

9.

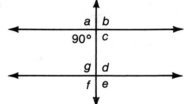

Write *true* or *false*. Explain your answers.

10. Alternate interior angles are always acute.

11. Alternate exterior angles are never on the same side of a transversal.

12. Any pair of adjacent angles on the same side of the transversal are supplementary.

13. A surveyor wants to know whether the boundaries $\overline{LM}$ and $\overline{NO}$ of the lot *LMNO* are parallel. What angles should he measure? Explain.

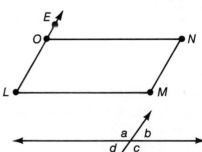

14. Three parallel lines are cut by a transversal as shown. Explain why ∠a ≅ ∠x.

15. Using the same figure as in **14**, how could you convince someone that ∠a and ∠w are supplementary?

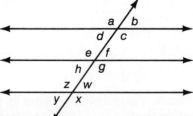

Two lines are intersected by a transversal. Describe two ways you might use to show the lines are parallel.

SUMMING UP

Tricycle, quadruped, pentathlon, hexadecimal, decathlon—what do these words mean? How are the meanings related to mathematics?

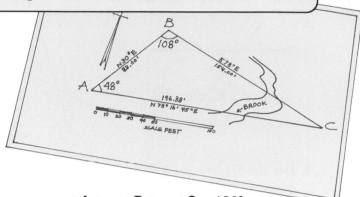

Angles and Polygons

A surveyor needs to know the measures of the angles of this triangular lot. Can the measure of $\angle ACB$ be found without measuring?

▶ The sum of the measures of the angles in any triangle is 180°.

If you know the measures of two angles of a triangle, you can find the measure of the third angle.

The third angle of the triangular lot measures 24°.

$$m\angle A + m\angle B + m\angle C = 180°$$
$$48° + 108° + n = 180°$$
$$156° + n = 180°$$
$$n = 24°$$
$$m\angle C = 24°$$

Regular polygons have congruent sides and congruent angles. Which of the polygons shown appear to be regular polygons?

The dotted lines are **diagonals.** Polygons can be separated into nonoverlapping triangular regions by drawing all the diagonals from one vertex.

Study and complete the table.

What relationship is there between the number of sides and the number of triangles formed?

▶ The sum of the measures of the angles of a polygon is the product of the number of triangles formed and 180°.

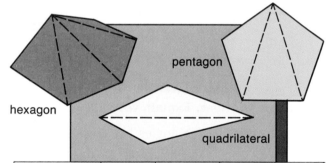

hexagon
pentagon
quadrilateral

Polygon	Number of Sides	Number of Triangles	Sum of Angle Measures
Triangle	3	1	180°
Quadrilateral	4	2	2 · 180 = 360°
Pentagon	5	3	3 · 180 = 540°
Hexagon	6	4	4 · 180 = 720°
Heptagon	7	5	5 · 180 = 900°
Octagon	8		
Nonagon	9		
Decagon	10		

Check Your Understanding

1. Two angles of a triangle have measures 38° and 112°. What is the measure of the third angle?

2. What is the sum of the angles in a 14-sided polygon?

Share Your Ideas What is the measure of each angle of a regular triangle? of a regular quadrilateral? Explain.

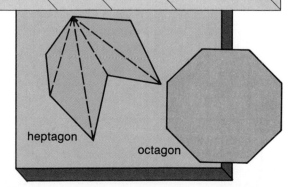

heptagon
octagon

Which of the following figures can be extended to form a triangle? Explain.

3.  61°   90°

4.  69°   111°

5. 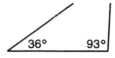 36°   93°

6. 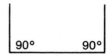 90°   90°

Find the missing angle measure in each polygon.

7. 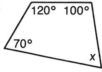 120° 100° 70° x

8. x 130° 140° 80° 80°

9. 40° 40° 90° x 90°

10. 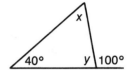 x 40° y 100°

For each regular polygon, find the sum of the angle measures and the measure of each angle.

11. 5 sides   **12.** 6 sides   **13.** 10 sides   **14.** 18 sides

Think and Apply

The figure shows the **exterior angles** in one direction of a regular hexagon.

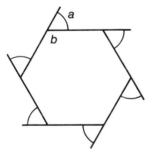

Each exterior angle and the interior angle adjacent to it make a straight angle.
$m\angle a + m\angle b = 180°$

15. What is the size of each angle of the hexagon?

16. What is the size of each exterior angle?

17. What is the sum of all the exterior angles?

18. Try the same thing for a regular pentagon and a regular octagon. What can you say is true about the exterior angles of a regular polygon?

Logical Thinking

19. How many triangles are in this figure? Make an organized list to keep track of the count.

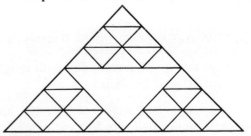

Write a formula for finding the sum of the angle measures of a polygon with *n* sides.

SUMMING UP

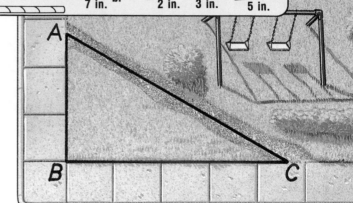

Triangles

This corner of the town park has a well-worn path across the playground. Why do you think this happened?

Measure sides $\overline{AB}$, $\overline{BC}$, and $\overline{CA}$. What do you notice?

▶ The sum of the lengths of any two sides of a triangle is greater than the length of the third side. $\overline{AB} + \overline{BC} > \overline{AC}$

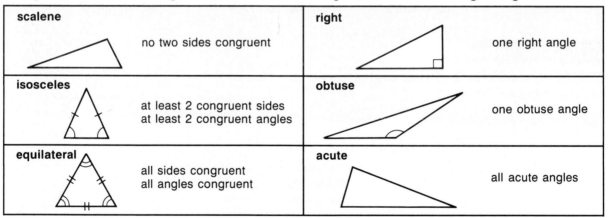

Triangles classified according to sides		Triangles classified according to angles	
scalene	no two sides congruent	**right**	one right angle
isosceles	at least 2 congruent sides, at least 2 congruent angles	**obtuse**	one obtuse angle
equilateral	all sides congruent, all angles congruent	**acute**	all acute angles

Is there a relationship between side length and angle measure? Work in a group. Draw some scalene triangles. Record the length of each side and the measure of its opposite angle. Order the sides of each triangle from least to greatest. What do you notice about the opposite angles?

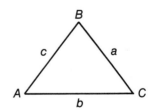

∠ B is opposite side b

Check Your Understanding

1. Can a triangle have sides with lengths of 5 cm, 4 cm, and 10 cm? Explain.

2. A triangle has angles of 30°, 42°, and 108°. Which angle will be opposite its longest side?

Share Your Ideas A triangle has been classified as a right equilateral triangle. Is this possible? Explain.

Measure the sides and the angles to classify each triangle in two ways.

3.

4.

5.

Draw each triangle with vertices *A*, *B*, and *C*. Classify each triangle as acute, right, or obtuse; scalene, isosceles, or equilateral.

6. side *AB* = 3 cm; side *BC* = 4 cm; side *AC* = 5 cm

7. side *AB* and side *BC* = 7 cm; side *AC* = 8 cm

8. side *AB* = 12 cm; side *BC* = 12 cm; m∠B = 60°

For each triangle, find or describe the missing measures.

9.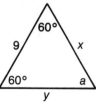

10.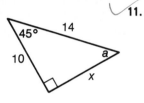

11.

12.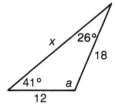

Select the correct answer.

13. A triangle has angle measures of 38°, 52°, 90°.
The longest side is opposite the ___ angle.

  a. 38°   **b.** 52°   **c.** 90°

14. A triangle with sides of 8 cm and 12 cm could have
a third side of ___.

  a. 4 cm   **b.** 13 cm   **c.** 20 cm

 15. Use the Logo procedure TRI shown below with each set
of inputs. Record your results. Explain what the
procedure TRI does.

```
TO TRI :A :B :C
IF :C < :A + :B [PR IS, A, TRIANGLE] [PR NOT, A, TRIANGLE]
END
```

  a. TRI 3 4 5   **b.** TRI 7 8 9   **c.** TRI 1 2 3

Suppose m∠A = 90° in triangle *ABC* and
m∠A > m∠B > m∠C. What do you know about the
triangle?

SUMMING UP

Congruence

A geodesic dome is
constructed of many
congruent triangles.

▶ Two polygons are
congruent if they are the
same size and shape.
That is, two polygons are
congruent if their
corresponding sides and
angles are congruent.

If you trace △ABC and place it on top
of △LMN the sides and angles will
match. The sides and angles that match
are called **corresponding parts.**

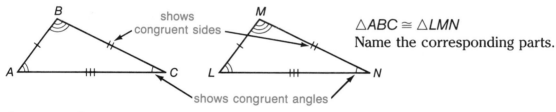

shows
congruent sides

shows congruent angles

$\triangle ABC \cong \triangle LMN$
Name the corresponding parts.

Congruent figures are named in the order of
their corresponding parts.

Vertices P, Q, and R correspond to vertices
S, T, and U, so

$\angle P \neq \angle S$, $\angle Q \cong \angle T$, and $\angle R \cong \angle U$. $\triangle PQR \cong \triangle STU.$

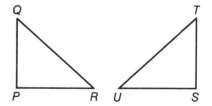

Check Your Understanding

Trace one of the figures in each pair. Place the tracing over
the other figure to see if the figures are congruent. Name
the corresponding parts.

1.

2.

Share Your Ideas   Draw $\triangle DEF \cong \triangle LMO$

Think visually. For each exercise, predict which figure is congruent to quadrilateral *ABCD*. Then trace *ABCD* and check your prediction. Name the corresponding parts.

3.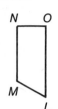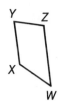

4.

The polygons in each exercise are congruent. Name the corresponding parts. Find the missing measures.

5.

6.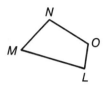

7.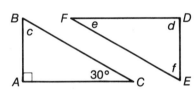

8.

9. A piece of glass measures 10 in. by 3 in. You need to cut it into two congruent pieces that together cover a region 15 in. by 2 in. How can you do this? Draw pictures and experiment.

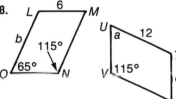

3 in.

10 in.

Quadrilateral *PQRS* ≅ quadrilateral *LMNO*. Draw the two quadrilaterals and identify the corresponding sides and angles.

---

1. 3.47×12.8

2. 61.7×0.85

3. $12.9 \div 0.3$

4. $3 \div 0.75$

5. $34.4 + 2.78 + 12.73$

6. $2.71 + 0.93 + 35.18$

7. $1.29 - 0.725$

8. $237.02 - 95.84$

9. $2\frac{3}{4} \times 1\frac{5}{8}$

10. $\frac{5}{12} \times 1\frac{1}{5}$

11. $2\frac{3}{5} \div \frac{3}{8}$

12. $\frac{3}{7} \div 4\frac{2}{3}$

13. $5\frac{1}{2} + 1\frac{3}{8}$

14. $1\frac{2}{3} + 5\frac{1}{2}$

15. $6\frac{3}{10} - 1\frac{5}{7}$

16. $3\frac{5}{32} - 1\frac{9}{16}$

Evaluate each expression.

17. $2n + 5$ for $n = 12$

18. $2(x - 3)$ for $x = 7$

19. $3q$ for $q = 7$

20. $2r + 7$ for $r = 5$

Midchapter Review

Find the missing measures. pages 116–117

1. 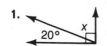 20° x

2.   y x 50° y

3. 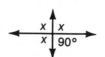 132° z

4. x x x 90°

Without measuring, find the measure of *a*, *b*, and *c*. pages 116–119

5.   x a b c y 60° x ∥ y

6. 45° a b c

Find each missing measure. pages 120–125

7.   3 3 a 3

8. 2 2 c 2 2 2 2

9. △ RST ≅ △ XYZ 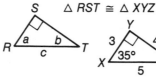 S R a b c T Y 3 35° 4 X 5 Z

10. △ DEF ≅ △ HIJ 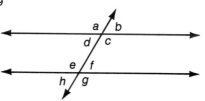 D 24 H c 10 140° E 15 F I a b J

Use the figure at the right to answer 11–13. pages 118–119

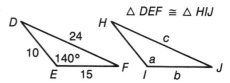

11. Name two sets of alternate interior angles.

12. Name two sets of alternate exterior angles.

13. Name four sets of vertical angles.

a b d c e f h g

Copy the puzzle. Fill in the correct answers.

Across

14. Two parallel lines intersected by a _____ form pairs of congruent angles.

17. A hexagon has _____ vertices.

18. ∠a and ∠b are _____ angles. a b

20. Two angles are _____ if the sum of their measures is 180°.

21. Two angles are _____ if the sum of their measures is 90°.

Draw each triangle if possible. Then classify it. If it cannot be drawn, explain why.
pages 122–123

22. ∠C = 90°, a = 3 cm, b = 4 cm

23. a = 6 cm, b = 8 cm, c = 14 cm

24. ∠A = 35°, ∠B = 65°, ∠C = 85°

25. ∠A = 80°, b = 5 cm, c = 5 cm

Down

15. Angles that have a common ray and vertex and interiors that do not overlap are called _____ angles.

16. A stop sign is an example of a(n) _____.

17. Two lines in different planes that do not intersect are _____.

19. Two lines in the same plane that do not intersect are _____.

Exploring Problem Solving

THINK
EXPLORE
SOLVE
LOOK BACK

Is It More Than Half?

While Amy and Fred were at a Mexican restaurant, they noticed a tiled wall that contained many geometrical patterns. "Look at the tiles that contain yellow and red triangles," said Amy.

Thinking Critically

Do you think that more than half of tile **A** is red? What fraction of tile **A** is red? Work in a group and make drawings to help you solve the problem.

Analyzing and Making Decisions

1. Look at **A**. How many of the largest red triangles could fit on **A**? What fraction of tile **A** is the large red triangle?

2. Look at **B**. Find the corner section of tile **B** that contains the red triangle labeled **1**. How many of these middle-sized red triangles would fit on this section? What fraction of this section is the red triangle? What fraction of tile **B** is the red triangle?

3. Look at **C**. Find the corner of tile **C** with the smallest red triangle labeled **2**. How many of these red triangles would fit in this section? What fraction of this section is the smallest red triangle? What fraction of tile **C** is the smallest triangle?

4. What fraction of tile **A** is red? Is it more than half? Explain.

Look Back How can you use a drawing to show whether more than half the tile is red?

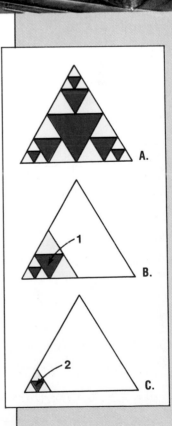

Problem Solving Strategies

Patterns

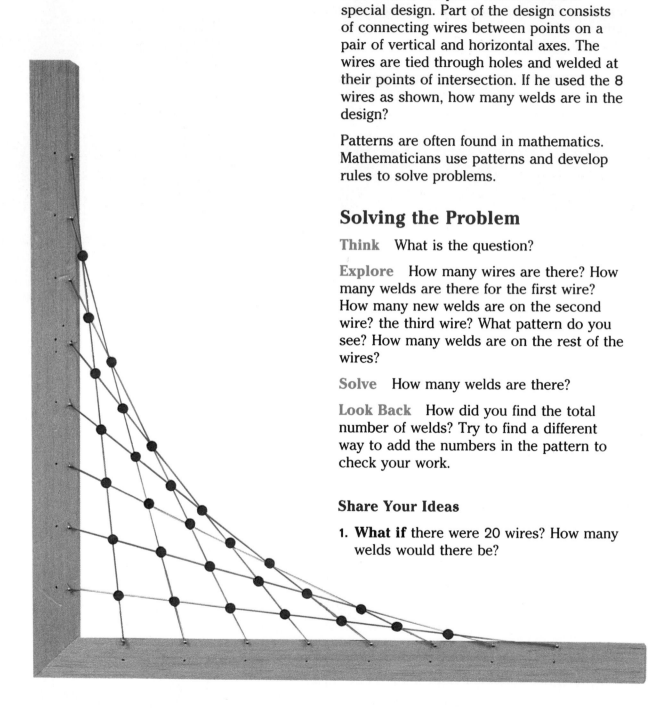

Jose built a sculpture that includes a special design. Part of the design consists of connecting wires between points on a pair of vertical and horizontal axes. The wires are tied through holes and welded at their points of intersection. If he used the 8 wires as shown, how many welds are in the design?

Patterns are often found in mathematics. Mathematicians use patterns and develop rules to solve problems.

Solving the Problem

Think   What is the question?

Explore   How many wires are there? How many welds are there for the first wire? How many new welds are on the second wire? the third wire? What pattern do you see? How many welds are on the rest of the wires?

Solve   How many welds are there?

Look Back   How did you find the total number of welds? Try to find a different way to add the numbers in the pattern to check your work.

Share Your Ideas

1. **What if** there were 20 wires? How many welds would there be?

Practice

THINK
EXPLORE
SOLVE
LOOK BACK

 Solve. Use a calculator where appropriate.

Study the patterns in **2** and **3**. What shapes come next?

2.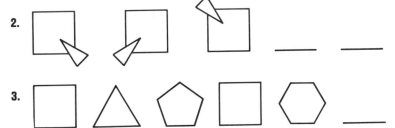

3.

4. Some art students created a sculpture that consists of layers of granite cubes, each weighing 1,500 pounds. The bottom layer of the sculpture contains 36 cubes. The second layer contains 25 cubes. The third layer contains 16 cubes, and so on. The topmost layer contains just one cube. What is the weight of the sculpture?

5. The staircase in front of the town hall is being rebuilt. Workers are using a series of marble blocks, each 1 foot × 1 foot × 10 feet. For a 1-foot-high staircase, they would use 1 block. If it were 2 feet high, they would use 3 blocks. If it were 3 feet high, they would use 6 blocks. How many blocks are needed to build the staircase if it is to be 8 feet high?

Mixed Strategy Review

6. The Washington Monument is 555 ft $5\frac{1}{8}$ in. high and 55 ft $1\frac{1}{2}$ in. square at its base. It has 8 small windows located near the top. How far are the windows from the top of the monument?

7. Eva is making a kite that requires sticks that are 92 cm and 45 cm long. The kite needs a tail that is 110 cm long. She has 96 meters of string and a stick that is 142 cm long. Is the stick long enough to make both sticks for the kite? Explain.

8. The face of the clock in the art museum is in the shape of a rectangle. The minute and hour hands on the clock are 25 feet long and 20 feet long, respectively. What is the angle formed by the hands of the clock at 4:10 P.M.?

9. What would the angle be at 4:20 P.M.?

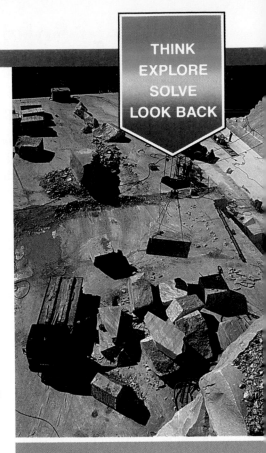

Create **Your Own**

Make up a pattern without numbers. Have someone try to continue your pattern and complete the next two parts of it.

Activity

Exploring Quadrilaterals

A quadrilateral is a four-sided polygon. A trapezoid, a parallelogram, a rhombus, a square, and a rectangle are quadrilaterals. What makes each special?

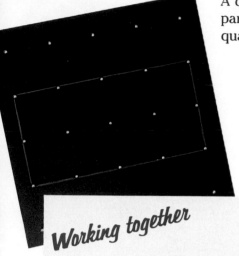

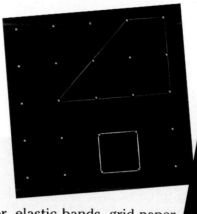

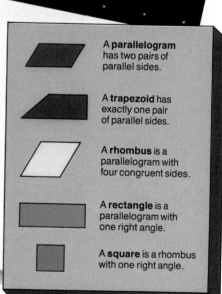

Working together

Materials: geoboard, ruler, protractor, elastic bands, grid paper

A. Show a parallelogram on the geoboard. Examine the figure and analyze its properties. Measure and record the length of each side. Do the same for each angle. Make note of the parallel parts and congruent parts.

B. Move one vertex of the parallelogram to create a trapezoid. Examine the figure and analyze its properties. Measure and record the length of each side and the measure of each angle. How many congruent parts does the trapezoid have? How many sides are parallel?

C. Beginning with a parallelogram each time, move vertices to form a rectangle and then a square. Examine and record the properties of these two quadrilaterals.

A **parallelogram** has two pairs of parallel sides.

A **trapezoid** has exactly one pair of parallel sides.

A **rhombus** is a parallelogram with four congruent sides.

A **rectangle** is a parallelogram with one right angle.

A **square** is a rhombus with one right angle.

Sharing Your Results

1. Which quadrilaterals were formed by moving one vertex of the parallelogram? by moving two vertices?

2. Is it possible to form a rhombus that is not a square on a geoboard? Explain.

3. Draw a parallelogram on grid paper. How many vertices should be moved to form a rhombus? Examine and record the properties of a rhombus.

Extending the Activity

Work on your own. Use the properties you discovered to find each missing measure. Identify each quadrilateral.

4.
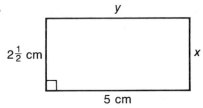

5.
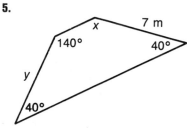

6.
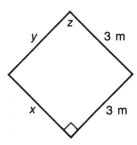

7.
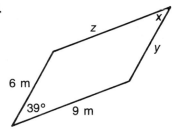

8.
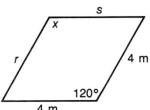

9.
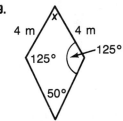

The tree diagram shows the relationship among the different classes of quadrilaterals. **Look back** at **4–9.** For each pair listed below, name the classification that includes both.

10. 4 and 7

11. 6 and 8

12. 4 and 6

13. 7 and 8

14. 4 and 5

15. 6 and 9

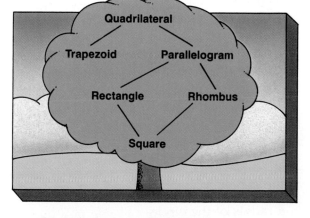

Draw and identify these quadrilaterals.

16. The vertices are *B, C, D, E.* $\overline{BC}$ is parallel to $\overline{DE}$ and $\overline{EB}$ is parallel to $\overline{CD}$. ∠*BCD* is a right angle. $\overline{BC}$ is not congruent to $\overline{EB}$.

17. The vertices are *P, R, S, T.* $\overline{PR}$ is parallel to $\overline{ST}$. $\overline{PT}$ is congruent to $\overline{RS}$, and $\overline{RS}$ is congruent to $\overline{PR}$. m∠*PRS* = 60°.

Summing Up

18. Make a list of the properties of quadrilaterals you have found. Identify those that belong to parallelograms, rectangles, rhombuses, and squares.

19. Can a polygon belong to more than one class of quadrilaterals? Explain your thinking.

131

Angles and Circles

This pizza cutter slices pizza into congruent pieces. Each section of the pizza includes a central angle.

What is the measure of ∠AOB? Suppose the cutter had 12 congruent sections. What would be the measure of one of the central angles?

► Each side of a **central angle** contains a radius.

► A central angle and its intercepted arc have the same degree measure.

m∠AOB = 45°. The intercepted arc, $\widehat{AB}$, also measures 45°.

An **inscribed angle** is an angle whose vertex is on the circle and whose sides contain chords of the circle.

► The measure of an inscribed angle is half the measure of its intercepted arc.

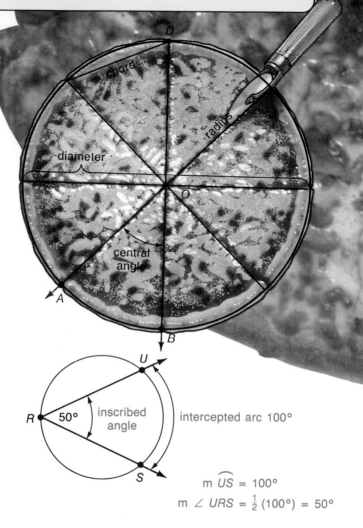

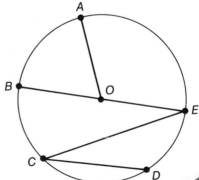

inscribed angle

intercepted arc 100°

m $\widehat{US}$ = 100°

m ∠ URS = $\frac{1}{2}$ (100°) = 50°

Check Your Understanding

Use the figure at the right. Name each.

1. the center of the circle

2. a radius of the circle

3. a chord of the circle

4. a central angle and its intercepted arc

5. an inscribed angle and its intercepted arc

6. m∠AOB if m $\widehat{AB}$ = 68°

7. m∠ECD if m $\widehat{DE}$ = 48°

Share Your Ideas Make a drawing to show a central angle and an inscribed angle that have the same intercepted arc. How are the measures of the angles related?

Practice

Which of the following are central angles? Which are
inscribed angles? Which are neither? Name the intercepted
arc if the angle is a central angle or an inscribed angle.

8. 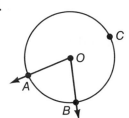   **9.** 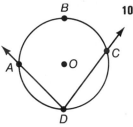   **10.** 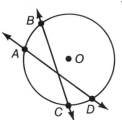   **11.**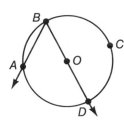

Find the missing measures.

12. 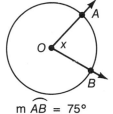   **13.** 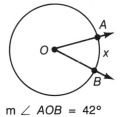   **14.** 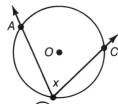   **15.**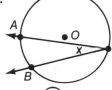

$m \widehat{AB} = 75°$ $m \angle AOB = 42°$ $m \widehat{AC} = 144°$ $m \widehat{AB} = 42°$

16. 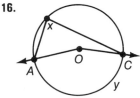   **17.**   **18.** 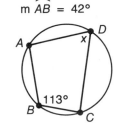   **19.**

$m \angle AOC = 160°$ ABCDE is a regular pentagon $\widehat{ABD}$ is a semicircle $m \angle ABC = 113°$

Think and Apply

20. Draw point P. Mark 8 points each 2 cm from P? **What if** you could mark all points 2 cm from P? What figure would you form?

21. Draw circle O with diameter AC and central angle AOB measuring 45°. What is the measure of $\angle BOC$?

22. Draw circle P with central angle LPN measuring 120°. Where can you place point M so that inscribed angle LMN measures 60°?

Visual Thinking

23. Which figure is the same as figure **A**?

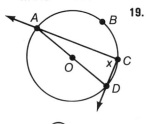

Make a drawing to show at least two inscribed angles with the same intercepted arc. What can you generalize about their measures?

SUMMING UP

133

Activity

Exploring Polyhedra

This spectrum of light is produced by a **prism**.
Prisms and **pyramids** are space figures called **polyhedra**.

A polyhedron is a space figure whose surfaces, called **faces,** are flat.

How are prisms and pyramids the same? How are they different?

Working together

Materials: scissors, tape, straightedge, Workmats 5, 27–31

A. Each member of the group makes one of the polyhedra shown.

B. Examine your polyhedron and record your observations. What polygons are represented? How many bases does the figure have? Make note of congruent or parallel parts.

C. Count the number of faces, edges, and vertices. Record your findings in a chart like the one below.

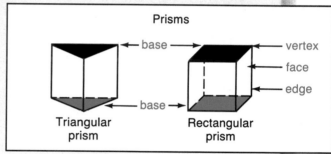

Prisms

Triangular prism • Rectangular prism

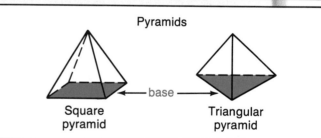

Pyramids

Square pyramid • Triangular pyramid

Polyhedron	Faces	Vertices	Edges
Triangular prism			
Rectangular prism			

Sharing Your Results

1. How are prisms and pyramids alike? How are they different?

2. There is a relationship among the number of faces, vertices, and edges for any polyhedron. Describe a way of finding the number of edges if you know the number of faces and vertices.

Extending the Activity

A prism is a polyhedron with two parallel faces called bases. The other faces, called lateral faces, are parallelograms.

A pyramid is a polyhedron with only one base. The base is a polygon. The other faces are congruent triangles.

3. Work in a group. Use the polygon at the right as a base. Construct a pyramid and a prism.

4. Make a copy of the pattern below. Fold and fasten edges to create a polyhedron called a dodecahedron. Is this polyhedron a prism, a pyramid, or neither? Explain.

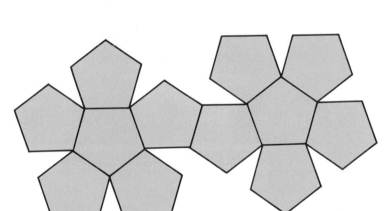

Summing Up

5. Write a formula to describe the relationship among the number of faces, vertices, and edges of any polyhedron. Use the relationship to complete this chart.

Polyhedron	Faces	Vertices	Edges
Hexagonal prism	8	12	
Hexagonal pyramid	7	7	
Pentagonal prism	7		15
Pentagonal pyramid		6	10

6. What type of polyhedra are used for packaging? Discuss the properties that make them suitable.

Activity

Exploring Cylinders, Cones, and Spheres

Cylinders, cones, and **spheres** are space figures. They are not polyhedra. They have surfaces that are curved, not flat.

What properties do cylinders, cones, and spheres share? What properties are unique to each?

Working together

Each person in your group makes one space figure.

Materials: scissors, tape, ruler, protractor, Workmats 6, 7

A. Identify your figure by matching it to one of the drawings below.

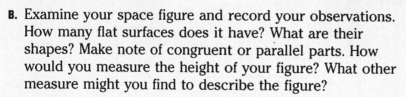

Cylinder → base

Cone → base

Sphere → great circle

B. Examine your space figure and record your observations. How many flat surfaces does it have? What are their shapes? Make note of congruent or parallel parts. How would you measure the height of your figure? What other measure might you find to describe the figure?

C. No pattern was given for a sphere. Use a ball or globe as a model. Try to make a pattern for a sphere. What difficulties do you encounter?

Sharing Your Results

1. How are cylinders and cones alike? How are they different?

2. How is a sphere different from both cylinders and cones?

3. If you tried to make a different cylinder or cone, what measure would you change?

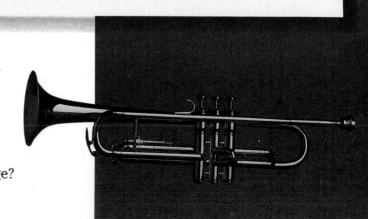

Extending the Activity

Work on your own.

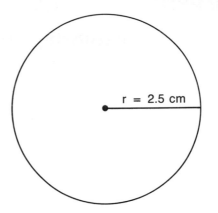

r = 2.5 cm

4. Using the circle at the right as a base, make a pattern for a cylinder. What shapes do you need to include in the pattern? What determines the size of each shape?

Name each figure and its parts.

5. figure: _____
   radius: _____
   height: _____

6. figure: _____
   radius: _____
   great circle: _____

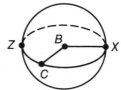

7. figure: _____
   radius: _____
   height: _____

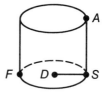

8. Roll a cylinder, a cone, and a sphere. Describe the paths they make. Describe how they differ from each other.

Summing Up

9. Compare the space figures you studied in this lesson with the polyhedra you have studied. Which polyhedron is most similar to a cylinder? Which is most like a cone? Describe the similarities and differences.

Activity

Exploring Different Perspectives

Does a figure's appearance change if it is viewed from different positions?

Working together

Materials: models of pyramids, prisms, cones, cylinders, and spheres; cardboard cutouts of a rectangle, triangle, and circle; light source; drawing paper

A. Place each solid in front of the light source so that you cast a shadow from a top view, a front view, and a side view. Record each shadow by tracing it.

B. Place each cardboard cutout in front of the light source. Rotate the figure. Record the shadow when the shape is perpendicular to the ray of light, at an angle to the ray of light, and parallel to the ray of light.

Sharing Your Results

1. Look at the shadows cast by the solid figures. Are any of the shadows the same shape?

2. Look at the shadows cast by the cutouts. Do the shadows always look like the figures that formed them? Give examples.

3. What is special about the shadows cast by the sphere?

Extending the Activity

Work on your own.

Match these shadows with the solid figures that cast them.
Then identify each shadow as a top, front, or side view.

4.

5.

6.

7.

a.

b.

c.

d.

e.

f.

g.

h.

Look at these perspective drawings. Then draw a top view,
a front view, and a side view.

8.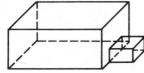

9.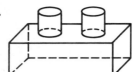

10.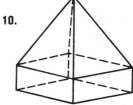

Summing Up

11. Describe how artists use different perspectives to make
    pictures seem realistic.

139

Using Problem Solving

Venn Diagrams

Look at the Venn diagram below. Each circle contains the names of the favorite sports of the members of one family. The region of intersection contains the names of the favorite sports common to both families.

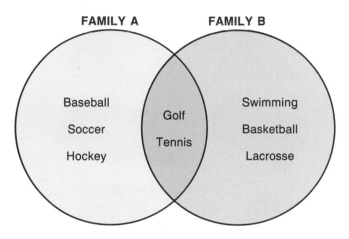

FAMILY A · FAMILY B

Baseball
Soccer
Hockey

Golf
Tennis

Swimming
Basketball
Lacrosse

Here are some features of baseball and basketball.

An indoor sport	A team sport
An outdoor sport	A ball is used.
A summer sport	A ball is hit.
A winter sport	A ball is thrown.

The players are constantly active.

Five players are on a side.

Nine players are on a side.

Make a Venn diagram to represent the features of basketball and baseball. Be sure to leave enough space to show the features of both games.

Sharing Your Ideas

1. Which features went only with basketball? only with baseball? with both games? Where did you write each feature?

2. Compare your diagrams. Did you disagree with the placement of any of the features? If so, why?

Practice

3. Venn diagrams can be used to compare properties of geometric figures. Make a Venn diagram to show the properties of equilateral triangles and right triangles. You may wish to start by listing the properties of each type. Here are a few.

- Has 3 angles

- Has angles that total 180 degrees

- Has angles that are each 60 degrees

- Has one angle that is 90 degrees

4. Make a Venn diagram that represents the properties of a rectangle and a square.

5. Choose the correct Venn diagram at the right for each group of terms. Label the diagram with the given terms.

a. prime
composite
two

b. factors of 10
multiples of 3
even numbers.

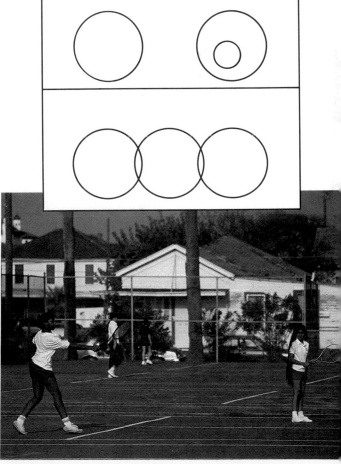

Summing Up

6. How many regions of intersection were in the Venn diagram for **3?** What did each such region represent?

7. Explain how the Venn diagram for **4** shows the properties of a rectangle and a square.

8. What does a Venn diagram help you do? When might someone want to make a Venn diagram?

141

Chapter Review

Without measuring, find the measure of *a*, *b*, *c*, and *d* in each figure. pages 116–123

1.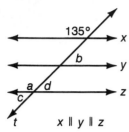

2.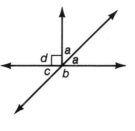

3.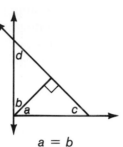

$a = b$

4.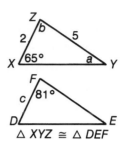

$\triangle XYZ \cong \triangle DEF$

Identify each figure. pages 116, 120, 122, 130

5.

6.

7.

8.

9.

Write *true* or *false* for each. pages 130–131

10. A rectangle is always a square.

11. A trapezoid has 2 pairs of parallel sides.

12. Every square is a rectangle.

13. A rhombus is always a parallelogram.

14. The number of degrees of each angle of a triangle is 90°.

15. The sum of the angles of any quadrilateral is 360°.

Match term with each phrase.

16. a rectangular solid whose faces are all squares

17. equal in measure to its intercepted arc

18. a polyhedron whose faces are rectangles

19. the vertex lies on the circle

20. a polygon with 2 pairs of parallel sides

  a. central angle

  b. rectangular prism

  c. inscribed angle

  d. trapezoid

  e. parallelogram

  f. cube

Use the figure at the right. pages 132–133

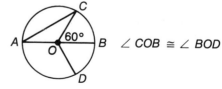

$\angle COB \cong \angle BOD$

21. m$\overset{\frown}{BC}$ = ____

22. m$\overset{\frown}{AD}$ = ____

23. m$\angle CAB$ = ____

24. m$\angle COD$ = ____

Solve. pages 128–129

25. Draw the next figure in the pattern.

   ____

Chapter Test

Without measuring, find the measure of *x*, *y*, and *z* in each figure.

1.
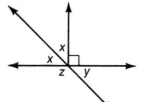

2.
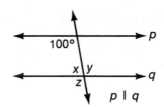
$p \parallel q$

3.
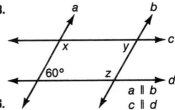
$a \parallel b$
$c \parallel d$

4.
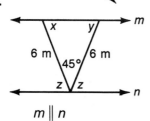
$m \parallel n$

5.
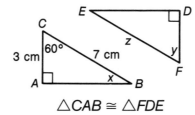
$\triangle CAB \cong \triangle FDE$

6.
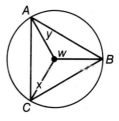
$\triangle ABC \cong \triangle DEF$

Identify each figure.

7.

8.
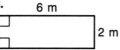

9.
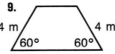

10.

Write *true* or *false*.

11. A parallelogram is a quadrilateral.

12. A square always has four right angles.

13. Every rectangle is a parallelogram.

14. Each angle of a regular hexagon measures 110°.

Use the figure at the right. $\overarc{AB} = \frac{1}{3}$ circumference.

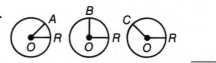

15. m$\overarc{AB}$ = _____

16. m$\angle w$ = _____

17. m$\angle x$ = _____

18. m$\angle y$ = _____

Draw the next figures for each pattern.

19.

20.

THINK Explain. Use an example.

Why can't an angle be both the complement and supplement of the same angle?

Regular Polygons and Stars

Regular polygons and stars can be drawn by connecting points equally spaced around a circle. A pair of numbers tells how such a figure is drawn. For example, the pair {5:2} means that there are 5 points around the circle, and each line segment cuts off 2 arcs.

arcs

Star {5 : 2}

AT THE COMPUTER

Figure {8:2} is shown at the right. Trace the circle and use it to draw {8:3}.

{8 : 2}

Some of the figures {P:A} are regular polygons and others are regular stars. P stands for the number of points, A for the number of arcs cut off. You can use the computer to figure out which pairs of numbers {P:A} make stars.

Materials: Logo

A. Define the POLY procedure. Enter POLY 5 4 to draw figure {5:4}. Describe the figure.

```
TO POLY :P :A
REPEAT :P [FD 50 RT :A*360 / :P]
END
```

B. Use POLY to draw the figures {8:1}, {8:2}, {8:3}, {8:4}, {8:5}, {8:6}, and {8:7}. Record your results.

Sharing Your Results

1. Which of the figures in **B** are stars? Which are regular polygons? Are any figures congruent?

2. Which polygons have eight sides? Which have fewer than eight sides?

Extending the Activity

3. Use POLY to draw the figures {10:1}, {10:2}, . . . , {10:9}. Record your results. Which figures are congruent? Which figures are 10-pointed stars?

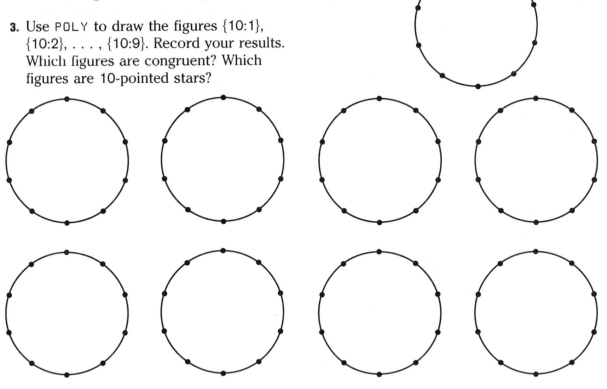

4. Use POLY to draw the figures {16:1}, {16:2}, . . . , {16:15}. Record your results. Which figures are congruent? Which figures are stars with 16 points?

Summing Up

5. Examine your results for 8, 10, and 16 points. For each number of points, some of the figures are congruent. Describe which ones. Which of the figures {30:1}, {30:2}, . . . , {30:29} would be congruent? You don't have to draw them all to decide.

6. Which figures are 8, 10, and 16-pointed stars? Can you predict which figures {30:1}, {30:2}, . . . , {30:29} will be 30-pointed stars without drawing them all on the computer? In general, what must be true about the numbers P and A for the figure {P:A} to be a star with P points? Why?

Hole In One

How good are your estimating skills? Estimate the distance to the cup on the green and the angle of the putt. Draw a line to show the path of your drive according to your estimates. If you miss, try again. Continue until you sink the ball. Can you get a hole in one?

Maintaining Skills

Choose the correct answer. Write A, B, C, or D.

1. What is the prime factorization of 120?

   A $2^2 \times 3^2 \times 5$ C $2^3 \times 3 \times 5$

   B $2^2 \times 3 \times 5$ D not given

2. What is 2.13 written as a fraction?

   A $2\frac{3}{10}$ C $\frac{13}{100}$

   B $2\frac{13}{100}$ D not given

3. What is $\frac{6}{24}$ in lowest terms?

   A $\frac{1}{4}$ C $\frac{1}{6}$

   B $\frac{1}{3}$ D not given

4. Evaluate. $(14 - 10) \div (26 - 22)$

   A 4   C 0

   B 1   D not given

5. Evaluate $4(x + y)$ for $x = 3$ and $y = 5$.

   A 35   C 32

   B 23   D not given

6. Which equation shows the sum of a number, b, and 3.4 is 10?

   A $10 + 3.4 = b$ C $b + 3.4 = 10$

   B $b - 3.4 = 10$ D not given

7. What is the inverse of add 17?

   A Multiply by 17.   C Subtract 17.

   B Divide by 17.   D not given

8. Solve for y. $18 + 3y = 27$

   A $y = 3$ C $y = 11\frac{2}{3}$

   B $y = 6$ D not given

9. Which are a pair of adjacent angles?

   A $\angle AOC$ and $\angle BOD$ C $\angle COD$ and $\angle AOB$

   B $\angle AOC$ and $\angle AOB$ D not given

10. $\overleftrightarrow{MN}$ and $\overleftrightarrow{XY}$ never intersect. What is their relationship?

   A $\overleftrightarrow{MN}$ intersects $\overleftrightarrow{XY}$.   C $\overleftrightarrow{MN} \parallel \overleftrightarrow{XY}$

   B $\overleftrightarrow{MN} \perp \overleftrightarrow{XY}$ D not given

11. What is the measure of $\angle x$?

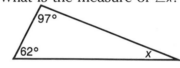

   A $21°$ C $83°$

   B $159°$ D not given

Solve.

12. Peggy, Alan, Christy, Jason, and Kim met at a party. If everyone shook hands, how many handshakes were there?

   A 5   C 10

   B 20   D not given

13. Beth has 3 different sweaters, 2 pairs of pants, and 3 scarves that all coordinate. How many different outfits can she make?

   A 8   C 18

   B 10   D not given

5 Pre-Algebra: Integers

Sharing What You Know

Undersea explorers discovered a fourteenth-century BC trading vessel that had sunk off the coast of Turkey. The vessel was filled with priceless artifacts. The first priority was to record the location on a map of the discovery site. Excavation plans require thousands of precise measurements and photographs. Discuss how you might set up a site plan so that the location of the vessel and its artifacts could be accurately recorded. What are other ways that mathematics would help these nautical archaeologists?

Using Language

Whether you are on land or water you can find and describe your location. That spot is the point where the lines of latitude and longitude intersect. In mathematics, we use an **ordered pair** of numbers to describe a point on a graph. How are lines of latitude and longitude like an **ordered pair**? How are they different?

Words to Know   integers, zero, opposite (additive inverse), quadrant, ordered pair, axes

Be a Problem Solver

The *Queen Victoria* left Liverpool for New York on a five-day crossing of the Atlantic. The first day she gained 12 nautical miles over her scheduled distance and the second day she gained 23 more. On the third day she lost 58 nautical miles and on the fourth day she lost 20. What must she do on her final day to arrive on schedule?

Write the latitude and longitude that best describes the location of your school. Then write a description of the location of the planet Earth in the solar system. Which location is described with greater precision? How do you know?

Activity

Exploring Addition and Subtraction of Integers

How is computation with integers the same as computation with whole numbers? How is it different?

Working together

A. Draw a number line. Mark the integers from ⁻20 to 20.

B. You can show addition of integers on the number line.

- Adding a positive integer is shown by moving to the right.

  Add ⁻5 + 2.

  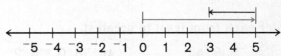

  ```
  ⁻5 ⁻4 ⁻3 ⁻2 ⁻1  0  1  2  3  4  5
  ```

  Start at 0. Move 5 units left.
  Move 2 units right.

  $$^-5 + 2 = {}^-3$$

- Adding a negative integer is shown by moving to the left.

  Add 5 + ⁻2.

  ```
  ⁻5 ⁻4 ⁻3 ⁻2 ⁻1  0  1  2  3  4  5
  ```

  Start at 0. Move 5 units right.
  Move 2 units left.

  $$5 + {}^-2 = 3$$

C. Use the number line to compute the following. Record your results.

   a. 9 + 4   **b.** 2 + ⁻6   **c.** ⁻6 + 2   **d.** ⁻4 + ⁻3   **e.** ⁻8 + 8   **f.** ⁻7 + 8

D. Look for patterns in the signs of the addends and the sums you recorded. Create other addition problems to compute and use them to verify the patterns you discover.

Sharing Your Results

1. Is the sum of two negative integers always negative? Is the sum of two positive integers always positive? Use the number line to explain your thinking.

2. When is the sum of a positive and a negative integer equal to a negative integer? When is the sum equal to a positive integer?

3. When you add a negative integer to any integer *x*, is the sum greater than or less than *x*?

4. **What if** you change the order of the addends? What conclusion can you draw?

5. What happens when you add an integer and its opposite?

Extending the Activity

You can use a calculator to explore addition and subtraction of integers. To enter a negative integer, press the key for the absolute value of that integer. Then press the change sign key. $\boxed{+/-}$

Enter $^-9 + {}^-5$. Press $\boxed{9}$ $\boxed{+/-}$ $\boxed{+}$ $\boxed{5}$ $\boxed{+/-}$ $\boxed{=}$ ⟶ $\boxed{-14}$

6. Use mental math to find each sum. Then use a calculator and compare your results.
   a. $15 + {}^-7$ b. $13 + {}^-3$ c. $17 + {}^-17$

7. Copy and complete the following.

	Add mentally.	Use a calculator.
a.	$3 + 4 = $ ____	$3 - {}^-4 = $ ____
b.	$16 + 9 = $ ____	$16 - {}^-9 = $ ____
c.	$23 + 6 = $ ____	$23 - {}^-6 = $ ____
d.	$^-8 + 2 = $ ____	$^-8 - {}^-2 = $ ____
e.	$^-4 + 10 = $ ____	$^-4 - {}^-10 = $ ____
f.	$^-10 + 4 = $ ____	$^-10 - {}^-4 = $ ____
g.	$^-15 + 12 = $ ____	$^-15 - {}^-12 = $ ____

Use the information in your table to answer these questions.

8. How are addition and subtraction related?

9. What happens when you subtract a negative integer from a positive integer x? Is the result greater or less than x? Is this always true? Explain.

10. What happens when you subtract a negative integer from a negative integer? Use $^-4 - {}^-9$ and $^-9 - {}^-4$ as examples and explain your thinking.

11. Does $^-4 - {}^-10 = {}^-10 - {}^-4$? Addition of integers is commutative. What can you conclude about subtraction?

Summing Up

12. Describe your method for adding two integers with unlike signs.

13. Compute each sum or difference and explain your results.
   a. $3 - 4$ b. $3 + {}^-4$ c. $^-4 + 3$ d. $^-4 - {}^-3$

Adding and Subtracting Integers

Ian and his friends are playing volleyball on the beach. One team hits the ball 5 m across the net. The other team hits it back 7 m. Where is the ball now?

Find $5 + {}^-7$.

You can use the number line to add.

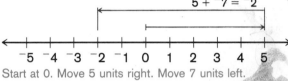

$$5 + {}^-7 = {}^-2$$

Start at 0. Move 5 units right. Move 7 units left.

You can also use absolute values.

▶ To add integers with unlike signs, subtract their absolute values. The answer has the same sign as the integer whose absolute value is greater.

Add $5 + {}^-7$. $|{}^-7| - |5| = 7 - 5 = 2$ $5 + {}^-7 = {}^-2$, since $|{}^-7| > |5|$.

The ball is 2 m *behind* its starting point.

▶ To subtract an integer, add its opposite, or **additive inverse.**

$4 - 7 = 4 + {}^-7 = {}^-3$ **Think** The opposite of 7 is ${}^-7$.

More Examples

a. $5 + {}^-2$
$|5| - |{}^-2| = 3$ The answer is positive,
$5 + {}^-2 = 3$ since $|5| > |{}^-2|$.

b. ${}^-6 + {}^-4$
${}^-6 + {}^-4 = {}^-10$ $(-) + (-) = (-)$

c. $4 - 17 = 4 + {}^-17 = {}^-13$
     ↑ opposites ↑

d. $5 - {}^-3 = 5 + 3 = 8$
     ↑opposites↑

Check Your Understanding

Find each sum or difference.

1. $7 + {}^-3$ **2.** $22 - 40$ **3.** $5 + {}^-4$ **4.** $31 - {}^-9$

5. $4 + {}^-5$ **6.** $3 + {}^-7$ **7.** ${}^-15 - 3$ **8.** ${}^-12 - {}^-6$

Share Your Ideas Look back at **7** and **8**. Explain how you computed each difference.

Rewrite each expression using the additive inverse.

9. $3 - 1$ **10.** $4 - {}^-7$ **11.** $7 - 4$ **12.** $7 - {}^-4$

13. $16 - 16$ **14.** $14 - {}^-12$ **15.** $8 - 0$ **16.** $0 - 8$

Find each sum or difference.

17. $8 - {}^-5$ **18.** $16 + {}^-13$ **19.** $19 - 27$ **20.** $31 + {}^-6$

21. ${}^-13 + {}^-6$ **22.** ${}^-21 - 4$ **23.** $33 - {}^-8$ **24.** ${}^-21 - {}^-4$

25. ${}^-14 + 81$ **26.** ${}^-61 + {}^-19$ **27.** $3 - 28$ **28.** $45 - 64$

29. $12 - 42$ **30.** ${}^-21 + 49$ **31.** $42 - 12$ **32.** ${}^-6 - 15$

33. $19 - {}^-4$ **34.** ${}^-15 - 6$ **35.** $4 - {}^-19$ **36.** ${}^-27 - {}^-15$

37. ${}^-65 + 8$ **38.** ${}^-15 - {}^-27$ **39.** $38 - {}^-19$ **40.** ${}^-51 - 3$

41. $3 - 25$ **42.** $5 - 16$ **43.** $17 + {}^-18$ **44.** ${}^-11 + 9$

45. $|16| - |{}^-4|$ **46.** $|2| + |{}^-9|$ **47.** $|2 + {}^-9|$ **48.** $|2 - {}^-9|$

Choose the correct operation to make each sentence true.

49. $6 \square {}^-7 = {}^-1$ **50.** $26 \square {}^-26 \square {}^-5 = {}^-5$

51. ${}^-11 \square {}^-4 \square 11 = 4$ **52.** $35 \square 21 \square {}^-5 \square {}^-19 = 0$

Think and Apply

53. The average water temperature along the Boston shoreline in the spring is 48° F. During the winter it is about 13° F lower. What is the average water temperature in the winter?

54. A share of stock in an underwater salvage company cost $26 per share. On Monday its price rose $2, on Tuesday it fell $3, and on Wednesday it fell $1. What was the cost of one share at the end of Wednesday?

55. Compare $({}^-3 + {}^-6) + 4$ and ${}^-3 + ({}^-6 + 4)$. Repeat for $({}^-11 + 8) + {}^-2$ and ${}^-11 + (8 + {}^-2)$. What can you conclude?

56. Find two integers whose sum is ${}^-16$ and whose difference is 12.

Create two expressions using both positive and negative integers to obtain a sum of 5.

SUMMING UP

What is the sign of the sum of 2 positive integers? of 3 positive integers? of 4 positive integers? Does a similar pattern exist for negative integers?

Multiplying Integers

A diver for an underwater salvage operation descends 14 ft each hour while working on a job. What is the total change in depth over a 3-hour period?

$$^-14 \cdot 3 = {^-14} + {^-14} + {^-14} = {^-42}$$

The total change is $^-42$ feet, a descent of 42 feet.

The sign of the product of two integers with unlike signs is always negative. Explain why.

Study these examples. What patterns can you find?

$$^-2 \cdot 3 = {^-6}$$
$$^-2 \cdot 2 = {^-4}$$
$$^-2 \cdot 1 = {^-2}$$
$$^-2 \cdot 0 = 0$$
$$^-2 \cdot {^-1} = 2$$
$$^-2 \cdot {^-2} = 4$$
$$^-2 \cdot {^-3} = 6$$

The sign of the product of two integers with like signs is positive.

Check Your Understanding

Tell whether each product will be positive or negative. Then compute.

1. $6 \cdot {^-14}$ **2.** $^-9 \cdot 11$ **3.** $^-12 \cdot {^-8}$ **4.** $^-3 \cdot 13$

5. $20 \cdot {^-5}$ **6.** $^-7 \cdot {^-8}$ **7.** $^-15 \cdot 4$ **8.** $^-10 \cdot {^-7}$

Share Your Ideas How is multiplying integers like multiplying whole numbers? How is it different?

Practice

Find each product.

9. $3 \cdot {}^-18$
10. ${}^-41 \cdot 2$
11. ${}^-5 \cdot {}^-17$
12. $7 \cdot {}^-11$
13. ${}^-1 \cdot 0$
14. $6 \cdot {}^-9$
15. $3 \cdot {}^-13$
16. ${}^-5 \cdot {}^-4$
17. ${}^-8 \cdot {}^-21$
18. $11 \cdot {}^-7$
19. ${}^-32 \cdot {}^-5$
20. $13 \cdot {}^-2$
21. $3 \cdot 18 \cdot {}^-1$
22. $5 \cdot {}^-4 \cdot 6$
23. ${}^-4 \cdot {}^-12 \cdot 2$
24. $5 \cdot {}^-2 \cdot {}^-8$
25. ${}^-5 \cdot 4 \cdot {}^-3$
26. ${}^-6 \cdot {}^-1 \cdot {}^-3$

Compute. Remember to use order of operations.

27. ${}^-1 + 2 \cdot 3$
28. ${}^-3 \cdot 4 + 5$
29. $10 \cdot 6 + {}^-7$
30. $7 \cdot ({}^-2 + {}^-4) \cdot 6$
31. ${}^-12 + {}^-8 \cdot (5^2)$
32. $(3^2 + {}^-6) \cdot {}^-1$

 Write the integer for each. Use paper and pencil, mental math, or a calculator.

33. $({}^-3)^3$
34. $({}^-7)^2$
35. $({}^-5)^4$
36. $({}^-2 - 7)^2$
37. $({}^-7 \cdot {}^-1)^2$
38. $(6 + {}^-2)^2$

Think and Apply

Solve. Use paper and pencil, mental math, or a calculator.

 39. Consult the financial section of a newspaper. Make up a portfolio of ten stocks and decide how many shares of each you own. How much was your profit or loss for that day?

40. An ocean liner company makes a profit of $150 per day for each reserved cabin and takes a loss of $45 per day for each empty cabin. If 110 cabins are reserved and 90 cabins are empty on an 8-day cruise, what is the company's profit or loss for that trip?

41. The outer edge of Cape Cod recedes at a rate of about 3 feet per year. About how much is the total change in the shoreline over a 6-year period?

What is the sign of the product of 3 negative integers? of 4? of 5? of 6? What can you conclude?

Write the prime factorization for each, using exponents.

1. 20
2. 27
3. 45
4. 96
5. 135

Find the GCF and LCM.

6. 8, 12
7. 6, 7
8. 48, 60
9. 27, 45
10. 44, 121

Evaluate.

11. $2 \times 4 + 3^2$
12. $8 \div 4 + (4 - 2)^3$
13. $(16 - 3 \times 2) \div 2$
14. $(12^2 - 10^2) \div 2$
15. $(6 \times 5)^2 - 5 \times 10^2$

Solve for n.

16. $n - 2.3 = 10.8$
17. $\frac{3}{8} + n = \frac{7}{10}$
18. $n \div \frac{1}{2} = 4$
19. $21n = 42$
20. $3n - 6 = 12$

SUMMING UP

Use integers to name four multiplication facts related to this division fact: $15 \div 5 = 3$.

Dividing Integers

John Pennekamp Coral Reef State Park in Florida was the first underwater park in the United States. Divers following the underwater trail descended 10 ft in 5 seconds. How did their position change each second?

Find $^-10 \div 5$

Think $5 \cdot {}^-2 = {}^-10$ So $^-10 \div 5 = {}^-2$.

They descended 2 feet each second. Multiplication and division are related. Look at the table below. What patterns do you see?

Multiplication fact		Division fact
$2 \cdot 4 = 8$	$\longrightarrow$	$8 \div 4 = 2$
$2 \cdot {}^-4 = {}^-8$	$\longrightarrow$	$^-8 \div {}^-4 = 2$
$^-2 \cdot 4 = {}^-8$	$\longrightarrow$	$^-8 \div 4 = {}^-2$
$^-2 \cdot {}^-4 = 8$	$\longrightarrow$	$8 \div {}^-4 = {}^-2$

▶ The quotient of two integers with like signs is positive.

▶ The quotient of two integers with unlike signs is negative.

More Examples

a. $^-16 \div 2 = {}^-8$
   Check $^-8 \cdot 2 = {}^-16$

b. $^-48 \div {}^-8 = 6$
   Check $6 \cdot {}^-8 = {}^-48$

Check Your Understanding

Divide. Check each answer, using multiplication.

1. $13 \div {}^-13$ 2. $14 \div {}^-7$ 3. $12 \div 3$ 4. $^-12 \div {}^-3$

5. $36 \div {}^-9$ 6. $^-36 \div 9$ 7. $0 \div {}^-5$ 8. $^-6 \div 2$

Share Your Ideas True or false? $6 \div {}^-3 = {}^-6 \div 3$. Explain.

Practice

Divide. Check each answer.

9. $72 \div {}^-6$ **10.** ${}^-72 \div {}^-6$ **11.** ${}^-72 \div 6$ **12.** $35 \div 5$

13. ${}^-35 \div {}^-5$ **14.** $81 \div {}^-3$ **15.** ${}^-81 \div 3$ **16.** ${}^-81 \div {}^-3$

Add, subtract, multiply, or divide. Choose paper and pencil, mental math, or a calculator.

17. ${}^-36 \div 12$ **18.** $36 \div {}^-3$ **19.** $6 \cdot {}^-6$ **20.** $13 + {}^-4$

21. $50 \div {}^-5$ **22.** ${}^-50 \div 10$ **23.** $24 - {}^-8$ **24.** ${}^-24 \div {}^-6$

25. ${}^-60 + 15$ **26.** ${}^-60 + {}^-15$ **27.** $60 \div 15$ **28.** $60 \div {}^-15$

29. ${}^-45 - 9 - 8$ **30.** ${}^-4 \cdot {}^-12 \div {}^-1$ **31.** $\dfrac{{}^-63 + {}^-7}{10}$ **32.** $7 + 65 \div {}^-5$

Compare. Write <, >, or = for each ⬤ .

33. $6 \cdot {}^-4$ ⬤ $4 \cdot {}^-6$ **34.** $\dfrac{10}{{}^-2}$ ⬤ $15 \div {}^-5$

35. ${}^-30 \div {}^-2$ ⬤ ${}^-30 \div 2$ **36.** $17 \cdot {}^-1$ ⬤ $17 \div {}^-1$

37. $11 + {}^-12$ ⬤ ${}^-11 - 12$ **38.** ${}^-7 - 6$ ⬤ $6 - 7$

39. ${}^-10 \div {}^-5 + 27$ ⬤ $({}^-5)^2$ **40.** $64 \div {}^-8$ ⬤ $({}^-2)^3$

Think and Apply

41. The product of two integers is ${}^-36$. Their quotient is ${}^-4$. What are the integers?

42. The temperature readings on four chilly January mornings were 2°F, ${}^-4$°F, ${}^-8$°F, and 2°F. What was the average temperature for the four mornings?

43. Emily's mom lost 4 pounds in February and in March, gained 2 pounds in April, and lost 3 pounds in May. What was her average weight change per month during this period?

44. A diver in the underwater park is swimming at 10 feet above the ocean floor. She swims up 3 feet to follow a fish and then down 10 feet to photograph a school of fish. If she then swims 16 feet up to the surface, how deep is the trail she was following?

Logical Thinking

45. In the third figure below, there is a number missing. By studying the first two figures, you should be able to find the missing number.

3 $\left({}^-13\right)$ 9 17 $\left({}^-11\right)$ 4 6 $\bigcirc$ 6

14 1 8

Find ${}^-128 \div {}^-2 \div {}^-2 \div {}^-2 \div {}^-2 \div {}^-2 \div {}^-2$.
Check your result on a calculator. Work carefully!

SUMMING UP

Midchapter Review

Write the integer for each. pages 150–151

1. positive four
2. 5°F below zero
3. 6 units to the left of 0
4. the inverse of $^+3$
5. negative ten
6. 3 units to the right of $^-2$

Compare. Use <, >, or = for each ⬤. pages 150–151

7. $^-3$ ⬤ 4
8. $^-6$ ⬤ $^-5$
9. 10 ⬤ $^-2$
10. $|^-6|$ ⬤ $|^-2|$

Write the integers in order from least to greatest. pages 150–151

11. $^-3$, 1, 0, $^-4$
12. $^-17$, $^-11$, 21, 3
13. 5, $^-5$, 6, 0

Add or subtract. pages 152–155

14. $6 - 3$
15. $^-2 - ^-2$
16. $^-3 + ^-1$
17. $^-6 + 2$

Multiply or divide. pages 156–159

18. $40 \div ^-8$
19. $^-3 \cdot ^-4$
20. $^-6 \cdot 2$
21. $^-6 \div ^-3$

Write *sometimes, always,* or *never* for each. pages 152–159

22. The sum of two positive integers is positive.
23. The sum of a positive and negative integer is positive.
24. The sum of two negative integers is positive.
25. The product of two positive integers is positive.
26. The product of two negative integers is positive.
27. The product of a negative and positive integer is positive.

Complete.

28. The numbers . . . $^-2$, $^-1$, 0, 1, 2, . . . are _____.
29. _____ is neither positive nor negative.
30. The sum of an integer and its _____ is zero.

Words to Know
zero
opposite
negative
absolute
integers
one

Solve.

31. A scuba diver dives to a depth of 17 feet, then swims up 15 feet to a coral reef. How far is the reef from the surface? Express the answer as an integer.

32. By June 30 the Gulf of Mexico often reaches a temperature of 87°F along the Florida coast. If the temperature is 15°F lower at the end of November, what is the temperature by November 30?

160

Exploring Problem Solving

THINK
EXPLORE
SOLVE
LOOK BACK

The Top Score

In surfing competition, each ride is judged on a scale of 1 to 10, with 10 being the highest. Different factors, such as making the wave and doing turns and cutbacks, are considered in scoring. Negative points may be awarded for interfering with someone else's ride. A score may be increased by up to half for surfing under difficult conditions. Only each competitor's 5 best rides are counted and the judges' scores are added together.

SCORES ON EACH RIDE

	1	2	3	4	5	6
Jane Kanekali						
1st Judge	8	8	9 + (⁻2)	7 + (⁻1)	9	7
2nd Judge	8	9	8 + (⁻1)	6	8	8 + (⁻1)
Laura Wallis						
1st Judge	7 + (⁻1)	9	8 + (⁻1)	9	9 + (⁻2)	9
2nd Judge	7	8	8	9	8 + (⁻1)	9

Thinking Critically

These two surfers have just competed. Who should win?

Analyzing and Making Decisions

1. In which rides were there penalties? What was each competitor's total score for each ride?

2. Which 5 rides should count for each competitor?

3. Who won the match? What was the score?

4. **What if** there had been difficult surf conditions on Ride 1 leading to a bonus of $\frac{1}{4}$ of the original score? (Penalty is taken after the bonus is added.) Who would win then?

Look Back   What if in addition to the bonus on the first ride there had been no penalties for either surfer on the third ride? Who would have won?

Problem Solving Strategies

Working Backwards

Scientists are trying to measure the age of a specific plant from a certain area in the ocean. They know that in this area these plants grow 3 feet more than double their previous height every year. They continue their growth until they reach their final height of 60 feet, when their growth stops. This year, one plant measured 45 feet. How old is the plant?

Sometimes you know the final result but need to find out what happened in the beginning. You can work backwards and reverse the operations to solve the problem.

Solving the Problem

Think What is the question?

Explore How can you find out how tall the plant was the year before? How tall is the plant this year? How tall was the plant last year? How tall was it the year before that? When should you stop finding out how tall the plant was the year before?

Solve How old is the plant?

Look Back To solve this problem, you had to find how tall the plant was at the end of each year. How did finding this help you determine how old the plant is?

Share Your Ideas

1. When will the plant reach its final 60-foot height?

Practice

 Solve. Use a calculator where appropriate.

2. During the first hour of a deep-sea fishing expedition, Humera caught $\frac{1}{4}$ of her catch for the day. During the next two hours she caught $\frac{1}{8}$ of the catch, and during the last two hours she caught 5 fish. How many fish in all did Humera catch in the 5 hours?

3. Jared went on an all-day deep-sea fishing expedition. During the morning, he caught $\frac{1}{2}$ of his total catch, but threw 4 small ones back. In the early afternoon he caught 8 fish, but threw 3 of them back, and during the rest of the expedition, he caught $\frac{1}{3}$ of his total catch, but threw 4 of them back. How many fish did he keep?

4. Mr. Acton runs a fishing supply store. He sells a fiberglass rod and reel in a case for $162. To determine that selling price, he added $10 for the case to the cost of the rod and reel. Then he doubled the total for his markup. Finally, he added on $12 sales tax. How much does the rod and reel cost Mr. Acton?

5. At the end of the week, Mr. Acton gives the leftover bait to his employees. He gave $\frac{1}{2}$ of the bait to Mr. Cruz. Then he gave $\frac{1}{3}$ of what was left to Mrs. Li. Mr. Stavros received $\frac{1}{4}$ of what was left after Mrs. Li took hers. The remaining 6 worms went to Mr. McSanto. How many worms did Mr. Acton give away?

Mixed Strategy Review

A fishing boat and a sailboat left the marina at 8:15 A.M. The fishing boat travelled 20 miles east, 16 miles southwest, and 14 miles back to the marina. The sailboat sailed 12 miles west, 12 miles northeast, and then 9 miles back to the marina. Both boats returned at 12:15 P.M.

6. Which boat travelled farther?

7. **What if** the sailboat had travelled at 6 mph? When would it have returned?

Create
Your Own

Write a problem where you know the final result and must work backwards to find out what happened in the beginning.

Evaluate $abc + ab + bc - b$ for $a = 2$, $b = 10$, $c = 3$.

Integer Expressions

A pelican flies over the harbor and spots a fish below. It dives down toward the water. How fast is it moving at the end of 2 seconds?

The expression ^-32t represents the velocity of the pelican in feet per second as it dives. The variable t represents time in seconds.

To find the velocity at the end of 2 seconds, let $t = 2$.

^-32t
$^-32(2) = ^-64$

Why is a negative sign used in this expression?

The pelican is moving at $^-64$ feet per second after 2 seconds.

More Examples

a. $2y + 7$ Let $y = ^-5$.   Remember to
$2(^-5) + 7 =$ use order of
$^-10 + 7 = ^-3$ operations.

b. $16 - ab \div 3$ Let $a = 4$ and $b = ^-9$.
$16 - (4)(^-9) \div 3 =$
$16 - ^-36 \div 3 =$
$16 - ^-12 =$
$16 + 12 = 28$

Evaluate each expression. Let $x = ^-2$, $y = 6$, and $z = ^-10$.

1. ^-4x
2. $3z - 2$
3. $x^2 + y^2$
4. xyz
5. $\dfrac{3x}{y}$
6. $20 \div (x + y)$
7. $\dfrac{z}{x} + y$
8. $3y + 5z$

Share Your Ideas   Compare the expressions d and d^2. For what integers is d^2 equal to d? When is d^2 greater than d? When is d^2 less than d?

Practice

Simplify. Remember to use order of operations.

9. $9 - 6 \cdot 7 + 5$

10. $(12 + {}^-8) \div ({}^-6 + 5)$

11. $56 \div ({}^-14 \div 2)$

12. $({}^-5)^2 + 16 \cdot 2$

13. $(56 \div {}^-14) \div 2$

14. ${}^-15 - 14 - 7$

Choose paper and pencil, mental math, or a calculator. Evaluate each expression. Let $a = {}^-1$, $b = {}^-6$, $c = 12$.

15. $4a + b$

16. $\dfrac{2c}{b}$

17. $3 - ab$

18. $17 + bc - a$

19. $1 - b \div a$

20. $b^2 + c$

Write an expression for each and then evaluate it.

21. the velocity in feet per second of a stone falling for 10 seconds

22. double a number x, added to ${}^-8$; Let $x = 9$.

23. the opposite of a number y, decreased by ${}^-12$; Let $y = 50$.

Use parentheses to make each sentence true.

24. ${}^-12 + 7 \cdot {}^-3 - 4 = {}^-37$

25. ${}^-13 \cdot 2 - 4 + {}^-20 = {}^-50$

26. $2 \cdot 3^2 + {}^-1 = 35$

27. ${}^-54 \div 9 \div {}^-3 \div 2 = 9$

28. $10 - 9 - 8 - 7 = 2$

29. ${}^-8 \div 10 \div 2 + 3 = {}^-1$

Think and Apply

30. The temperature reading at 6 PM was 57° F. Five hours earlier a newscaster forecast a drop in temperature of about 3 degrees per hour as a storm approached the shore. What was the expected reading for 1 PM?

31. Evaulate $({}^-1 \cdot 3)^2$ and ${}^-1 \cdot 3^2$. How do they compare? Explain, using order of operations.

32. If Chung throws a stone up in the air at a velocity of 40 feet per second, then the velocity of the stone after t seconds is $40 + {}^-32t$. How fast is the stone moving after 1 second? Is it falling or rising? Explain.

Evaluate $\dfrac{abc + abc}{abc}$ for $a = 4$, $b = {}^-5$, $c = {}^-7$.

Now evaluate it for $a = {}^-10$, $b = 6$, $c = 3$. Explain your results.

Mixed Review

1. $1,574 + 257.3 + 64$

2. $29 - 13.75$

3. $465 \cdot 7.1$

4. $114 \div 1.2$

5. $7\frac{1}{3} \cdot 3\frac{1}{2}$

6. $11\frac{1}{4} + 2\frac{1}{3} + 6\frac{1}{2}$

7. $8.7 + 4.34$

8. $67\overline{)\$15.41}$

9. $6\frac{1}{3} - 1\frac{1}{8}$

10. $2.07 \cdot 0.005$

Find the number of degrees in each angle of the regular polygons given.

11. triangle

12. square

13. hexagon

Find each angle measure.

14. a

15. b

16. c

17. d

18. e

19. f

20. g

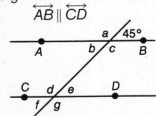

$\overleftrightarrow{AB} \parallel \overleftrightarrow{CD}$

Describe how you would solve this equation.
$7x + 15 = 50$

Solving Integer Equations

You can use the methods you learned with whole numbers to solve and check equations with integers.

$$^-2x + 9 = 41$$
$$^-2x + 9 - 9 = 41 - 9$$ First subtract 9 from both sides of the equation.

$$^-2x = 32$$

$$\frac{^-2x}{^-2} = \frac{32}{^-2}$$ Then divide both sides of the equation by $^-2$.

$$x = ^-16$$

Check $^-2(^-16) + 9 = 41$ Replace x with $^-16$ in the original equation.
$$41 = 41$$

More Examples

a.
$$3x - 14 = ^-2$$
$$3x - 14 + 14 = ^-2 + 14$$
$$3x = 12$$
$$\frac{3x}{3} = \frac{12}{3}$$
$$x = 4$$

Check $3(4) - 14 = ^-2$
$$^-2 = ^-2$$

b.
$$^-5x + ^-11 = 4$$
$$^-5x + ^-11 - ^-11 = 4 - ^-11$$
$$^-5x = 15$$
$$\frac{^-5x}{^-5} = \frac{15}{^-5}$$
$$x = ^-3$$

Check $^-5(^-3) + ^-11 = 4$
$$4 = 4$$

Check Your Understanding

Solve each equation and check.

1. $x + ^-45 = 12$

2. $^-9w = 63$

3. $12x - ^-7 = ^-5$

4. $^-6b + 5 = ^-10$

5. $10a - 7 = ^-57$

6. $15 + ^-2x = 19$

7. $^-2y - 12 = ^-90$

8. $9 - 4a = ^-7$

Share Your Ideas   How could you simplify $5x - ^-3$? Use this to solve $5x - ^-3 = ^-17$.

Solve each and check.

9. $y - 14 = {}^-5$

10. ${}^-3x = 54$

11. $t + {}^-16 = 1$

12. ${}^-6w = {}^-72$

13. $7n + 13 = {}^-36$

14. ${}^-8m + 19 = 3$

15. $9a - 20 = 7$

16. $15b - 23 = {}^-8$

17. $21x + 40 = {}^-2$

18. ${}^-y + 19 = 1$

19. $34 + 7x = {}^-1$

20. $3 = 2w - {}^-27$

21. ${}^-4x - 31 = 9$

22. $10b + {}^-11 = 29$

23. $15 + {}^-4t = {}^-17$

24. ${}^-9 + 41 = 5y - 8$

25. $7m + {}^-13 = 36$

26. ${}^-x + 2 = 9$

27. $31 = 3x + 52$

28. $91 = {}^-6n - 5$

29. $4n = 16 + {}^-20$

30. $5(8 + {}^-3) = 2y + {}^-11$

31. $3w + {}^-7 = {}^-15 + 11$

32. $5 - 9w = 10({}^-4)$

33. $12n + {}^-9 = 11(9)$

34. $7(2) = {}^-4x + 22$

35. $3n + 5 = 2({}^-16) - 11$

Write an equation for each sentence. Then solve and check.

36. 9 more than a number x is ${}^-13$.

37. Triple a number m, increased by 17, is 2.

38. The sum of a number p and ${}^-12$ equals the sum of ${}^-41$ and 15.

39. 22 decreased by the opposite of a number y is 30.

Follow the rule to find each missing number.

Rule: $y = 2x$

	x	y
40.	$^-7$	
41.	$^-5$	
42.	0	
43.	3	

Rule: $y = x + {}^-3$

	x	y
44.	$^-3$	
45.	$^-1$	
46.	0	
47.	5	

Rule: $y = 9 - x$

	x	y
48.	$^-3$	
49.	$^-1$	
50.	3	
51.	7	

52. Michael and Dan are planning a snorkeling trip. Is $100 enough to rent a boat, life vests, snorkels, and camera for 3 hours?

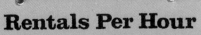

Rentals Per Hour

Boat - $20.00   Camera - $7.00

Life Vest - $1.00   Snorkel - $2.00

53. For what integer values of x does $\frac{14}{x}$ represent an integer?

54. For what integer values of x does $\frac{20 - x}{x}$ represent an integer?

Create your own problem using integers and write an equation to solve it.

SUMMING UP

If $^-3x + 4y = 15$ and $y = 0$, what is the value of x?

Graphing Ordered Pairs

To help scientists identify the location of artifacts taken from historic wrecks, plastic pipes are arranged to form a grid. The grid is used to record a location for each artifact.

Points on a **coordinate plane** can be located by using pairs of integers. The coordinate plane is determined by a horizontal number line called the **x-axis** and a vertical line called the **y-axis.** The axes intersect at a point called the **origin** and divide the plane into four regions called **quadrants.**

Each point on the plane corresponds to an **ordered pair** (**x, y**). The x-coordinate tells how many units to move left or right of the origin. The y-coordinate tells how many units to move up or down from the origin.

The coordinates of A are (2, 3).
The coordinates of B are ($^-2$, $^-4$).

What are the coordinates of C?

To graph an ordered pair (x, y), move x units horizontally and y units vertically from the origin.

To graph the point R ($^-3$, 2), count 3 units left and 2 units up from the origin. How would you graph P (3, $^-2$)?

Check Your Understanding

Write the coordinates of each point.

1. A
2. B
3. C
4. D
5. E
6. F
7. G
8. H

Draw the x-axis and the y-axis on graph paper and graph these points.

9. J($^-5$, 4)   10. K(3, 7)   11. L($^-7$, 0)   12. M($^-2$, $^-1$)

Share Your Ideas   Which quadrant contains each point?
A(2, $^-4$), B($^-2$, $^-4$), C(2, 4), D($^-2$, 4) Try to write a rule for naming the quadrant for any point (x, y).

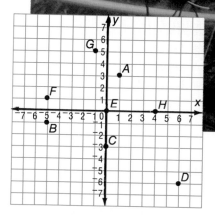

Using graph paper, draw the *x*-axis and the *y*-axis.
Then graph each point.

13. $A(^-1, 4)$ 14. $B(5, 6)$ 15. $C(3, ^-1)$

16. $D(0, 7)$ 17. $E(^-1, 0)$ 18. $F(^-4, ^-4)$

19. $G(^-6, ^-1)$ 20. $H(^-1, ^-6)$ 21. $I(0, ^-1)$

22. $J(5, 2)$ 23. $K(^-4, 3)$ 24. $L(1, ^-7)$

Name the point corresponding to each ordered pair.

25. $(1, 5)$ 26. $(0, ^-3)$ 27. $(^-2, ^-2)$

28. $(^-5, ^-4)$ 29. $(^-3, ^-2)$ 30. $(5, ^-1)$

31. $(0, 6)$ 32. $(5, ^-3)$ 33. $(^-3, 2)$

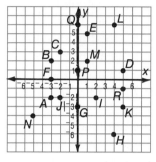

Use graph paper to draw the *x*-axis and the *y*-axis. Graph each group of points. Connect the points in order. Name the letter formed.

34. $(^-2, 3), (^-1, 0), (0, 2), (1, 0), (2, 3)$

35. $(^-1, 5), (^-1, 1), (2, 1)$

36. $(^-2, 5), (3, 5), (^-2, ^-1), (3, ^-1)$

37. $(^-1, ^-4), (^-1, 2), (2, 2), (2, ^-1), (^-1, ^-1), (2, ^-4)$

Think and Apply

38. Three vertices of a rectangle are $(1, 7), (1, ^-2),$ and $(^-3, ^-2)$. Graph the ordered pairs and give the coordinates of the fourth vertex.

39. Graph and connect ordered pairs $(5, 2)$ and $(^-3, ^-6)$. Give the coordinates of two other points on the same line.

40. Graph the ordered pairs $(^-4, 2)$ and $(6, 2)$. Connect the points to make a line segment. Find the coordinates of the midpoint of the segment. Find the length of the segment.

41. The grid to the left locates the chest, mast, and ship's hull of a historic wreck. How far apart are the mast and the chest? the chest and the sunken ship's hull?

1 unit = 1 meter

The ordered pair $(x, 0)$ describes any point on the *x*-axis. Write an ordered pair that describes a point 2 units from the *x*-axis; a point 2 units from the *y*-axis.

SUMMING UP

Using Problem Solving

Interview: Calculators at a Restaurant

Jamie Williams is a chef at Alda Louie's Seafood Restaurant. He uses a calculator to determine what prices to charge for their special dinners.

"Today, freshly caught mahi mahi costs us $4.15 a lb. Each serving is an 8-oz portion. Soup, salad, rice, and bread per entree costs us $1.50. My selling price must be 3.5 times what I pay for the food. Using a calculator, I divide $4.15 by 2 to find the cost of 8 oz of fish. To this $2.08, I add $1.50 for the soup, salad, rice, and bread. I get a sum of $3.58 as the cost of producing the meal. Then I multiply $3.58 by 3.5 to determine what I will charge my customer for the meal. I must charge at least $12.53 for a Mahi Mahi Dinner."

You are in charge of pricing the special dinners at Alda Louie's. Use the cost of the fish and find the selling prices of the specials for that day. Use a calculator as you solve the problem.

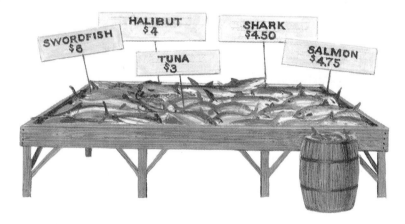

Sharing Your Ideas

1. **What if** you usually buy 20 lb of tuna for $3 per lb? Today the salesperson offers to sell you 40 lb at $\frac{1}{4}$ off the regular price. What would you do?

2. Cheryl decided that the restaurant charges customers $5.25 for the soup, salad, rice, and bread. She said that if you told her the price of a pound of fish, she could multiply it by one number and add it to $5.25 to find the price of the dinner. How did she calculate this?

Practice

3. Suppose you are operating a restaurant and you want to increase your business. Someone proposes that you have a child's portion. Children under 12 would receive soup, salad, rice, and bread, and a 4-oz piece of fish. The selling price of a child's dinner would be two times the cost.

Make a menu showing the selling price of a child's dinner. Use the prices of fish given on page 172.

4. Records were kept to see whether serving the children's portions was a good idea. During week 1, no children's portions were offered. During week 2, children's portions were offered.

Orders	Swordfish	Halibut	Tuna	Shark	Salmon
Week 1 Adults	35	24	30	10	46
Week 2 Adult Children	38 4	20 6	30 4	14 8	40 4

a. How much did the dinners cost the restaurant each week? Organize the costs on a table.

b. How much did the restaurant receive for the dinners in each week?

c. How much more did the restaurant take in than it spent for each dinner each week?

Summing Up

5. Would you continue the children's portion? Why or why not?

6. In deciding how much to charge for an adult dinner, what did Jamie Williams need to do? How did the calculator help him?

Chapter Review

Express a value for each statement. pages 150–151

1. the opposite of 2

2. the sum of $^-5$ and 3

3. the product of $^-8$ and $^-1$

Compare. Write <, >, or = for each ●. pages 150–151

4. 0 ● $^-3$

5. $^-8$ ● $^-6$

6. $^-4 \cdot 1$ ● $^-4 + 1$

7. $|^-8|$ ● $|0|$

Add or subtract. pages 152–155

8. $^-5 - 4$

9. $^-6 + 4$

10. $2 + {}^-5$

11. $^-6 + {}^-1$

Substitute the given values. Then simplify. $a = {}^-3, b = {}^-2,$
$c = 4$ pages 156–159, 164–167

12. $6a + bc$

13. $ac \div b$

14. $a + b + c$

15. abc

Solve. pages 168–169

16. $^-3 + n = {}^-2 \cdot 15$

17. $\frac{n}{^-2} + 4 = 8$

18. $^-4n + 8 = 12$

Write the ordered pair that locates each point. pages 170–171

19. A

20. B

21. C

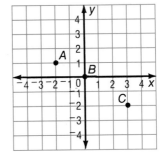

On graph paper, mark the x- and y-axes and graph these points. pages 170–171

22. $R(^-3, {}^-2)$

23. $S(0, 3)$

24. $T(2, 1)$

Complete.

25. The point $(^-2, 4)$ is in the ___ quadrant.

26. The location of any point on a coordinate plane is given by the ___ (x, y).

27. On a coordinate plane, points are located by using two perpendicular number lines, called the ___.

Words to Know	
first	quadrants
ordered pair	
x-and y-axes	
origin	second

Solve. pages 161–163

28. Bob walked along the beach each evening. On the fifth day he walked 12 miles. If he had increased his distance by 2 miles each day, how far did he walk the first day?

29. Luann started with a hole in the sand 4 inches deep. After each wave filled the hole with 2 inches of sand, she dug 4 inches deeper. How deep was the hole after the fourth wave came?

Chapter Test

Express a value for each statement.

1. the opposite of negative 15

2. the quotient when 100 is divided by ⁻5

3. the product of 3, ⁻9, and ⁻5

4. the difference when ⁻7 is subtracted from 3

Compare. Write <, >, or = for each .

5. 0 ⁻4

6. ⁻12 · ⁻4 12 · ⁻4

7. ⁻15 · 0 ⁻15 + 0

8. $\frac{36}{12}$ $\frac{-36}{-12}$

9. 12 − 7 7 − 12

10. |⁻16| |2|

Add or subtract.

11. ⁻3 − 8

12. ⁻9 − (⁻8)

13. ⁻4 + ⁻8

Substitute the given values. Then simplify. $x =$ ⁻5, $n = 7$, $y =$ ⁻3

14. $(x − y)n$

15. ⁻3n ÷ (xy + ⁻8)

Solve.

16. ⁻9 + n = ⁻3 · 5

17. ⁻3n − 6 = 12

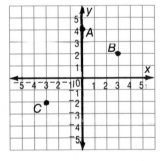

Write the ordered pair that locates each point.

18. *A*

19. *B*

20. *C*

On graph paper, mark the x- and y-axes and graph these points.

21. $P($⁻2, 4$)$

22. $Q(4,$ ⁻3$)$

23. $R($⁻5, 0$)$

Solve.

24. After a storm the tide rose to 6 ft above normal high tide. If the normal tide change is 5 ft, how far did the tide recede during ebb tide?

25. From 5 PM. to 10 PM. the temperature change on the beach was ⁻20 degrees. What was the average change in temperature per hour?

THINK   Evaluate.

⁻8(6 + ⁻2 − ⁻4) − ⁻49 ÷ ⁻7 + 2 · ⁻3

Graphing Pictures

A. Graph the following ordered pairs. Connect each pair to the one below it. Connect the pair at the end of column A to the first pair in column B.

A	B
(⁻4, ⁻1)	(1, 6)
(⁻2, ⁻4)	(6, 1)
(4, ⁻4)	(1, 1)
(6, ⁻1)	(1, ⁻1)
(1, ⁻1)	(⁻4, ⁻1)

What do you see?

B. You can make many pictures like this by graphing. Here is another one. Graph each ordered pair and connect them as described above. Connect the pair at the end of each column to the first pair at the top of the next one.

A	B	C
(⁻7, 5)	(5, 7)	(⁻1, 1)
(⁻7, 7)	(4, 8)	(⁻2, 2)
(⁻5, 8)	(1, 5)	(⁻2, 4)
(0, 5)	(2, 4)	(⁻1, 5)
(3, 10)	(2, 2)	(⁻6, 6)
(5, 9)	(1, 1)	(⁻7, 5)

Then connect each pair listed below.

a. (⁻1, 2), (⁻3, 3) **b.** (1, 2), (3, 3)

c. (⁻1, 2), (⁻3, 2) **d.** (1, 2), (3, 2)

e. (⁻1, 2), (⁻3, 1) **f.** (1, 2), (3, 1)

What do you see?

C. Create three pictures of your own. Write your graphing instructions and exchange with a classmate. See if you get the picture that your classmate designed.

Maintaining Skills

Choose the correct answer. Write A, B, C, or D.

1. What is the GCF of 16 and 48?

A 4   **C** 8

B 16   **D** not given

2. What is $\frac{4}{9}$ written as a decimal?

A 0.44   **C** 0.9

B 0.4   **D** not given

3. Which expression shows the quotient of a number, m, divided by 3?

A $\frac{3}{m}$ **C** $3m$

B $\frac{m}{3}$ **D** not given

4. Evaluate. $(3 + 3^2) \div 2^2$

A $2\frac{3}{4}$ **C** 3

B 13   **D** not given

5. Solve for z. $32 \div z = 8$

A $z = 4$ **C** $z = 24$

B $z = 3$ **D** not given

6. Solve for x. $2x + 4 = 14$

A $x = 5$ **C** $x = 10$

B $x = 4$ **D** not given

7. What is $m\angle x$?

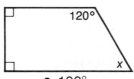

A 45°   **C** 100°

B 90°   **D** not given

8. What type of triangle has no angles congruent?

A equilateral   **C** scalene

B isosceles   **D** not given

9. What is $m\angle ACB$ if $m\overset{\frown}{AB} = 85°$?

A 160°   **C** 85°

B 170°   **D** not given

10. Compare. $^-4$ ⬭ $^-5$

A $<$ **C** $=$

B $>$ **D** not given

11. $14 + {}^-6$

A $^-18$ **C** 18

B 8   **D** not given

12. Evaluate $3x + 4$ for $x = {}^-2$.

A $^-2$ **C** 10

B $^-12$ **D** not given

What is the next term in each sequence?

13. 0, 4, 8, 12, _____

A 13   **C** 16

B 14   **D** not given

14. 1, 3, 9, 27, _____

A 81   **C** 45

B 36   **D** not given

15. 6.4, 5.9, 5.4, 4.9, _____

A 4.7   **C** 4.4

B 4.3   **D** not given

6 Rational Numbers

Sharing What You Know

What does the word *frontier* mean to you? Think about what it meant to the cave dweller, or to the early colonists on this continent. Today, space probes have extended our frontier into space. In what ways does mathematics contribute to space exploration?

Using Language

As our frontier extended into space, we have needed to use numbers to express both very large and very small measurements. While the cave dwellers may have ventured only about 20 miles from home, a space ship to the moon has traveled over 220,000 miles! To express such numbers, scientists devised a shorthand form called **scientific notation.** For example, the distance to our solar system's nearest star, Proxima Centaure, measures about 25 trillion miles, which in **scientific notation** is 2.5×10^{13}. What other measurements can you think of that would use scientific notation?

Words to Know   scientific notation, rational number, square root, hypotenuse

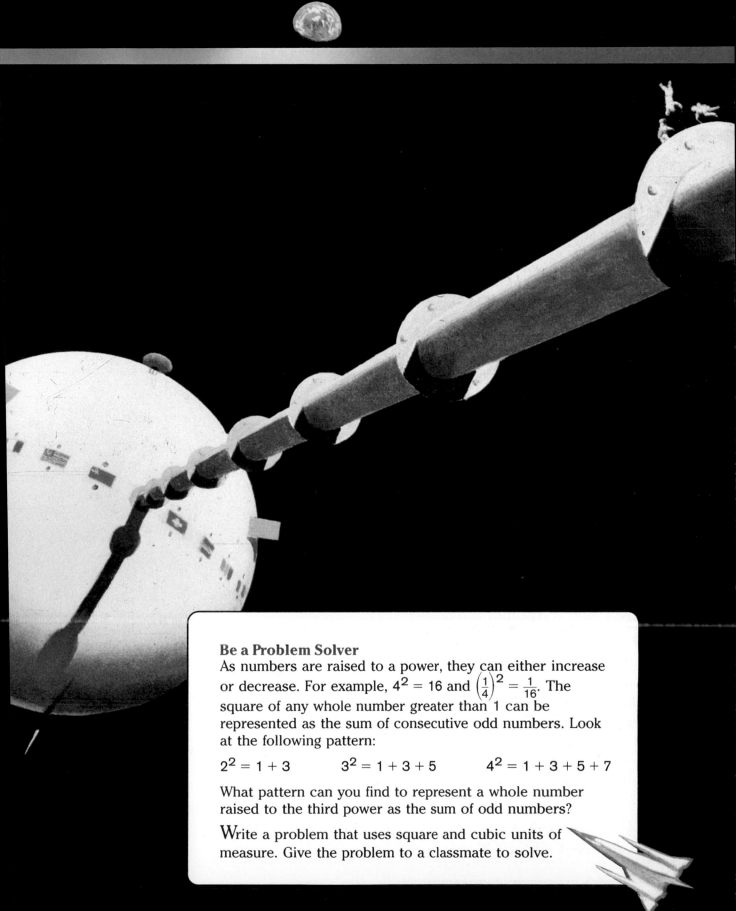

Be a Problem Solver

As numbers are raised to a power, they can either increase or decrease. For example, $4^2 = 16$ and $\left(\frac{1}{4}\right)^2 = \frac{1}{16}$. The square of any whole number greater than 1 can be represented as the sum of consecutive odd numbers. Look at the following pattern:

$$2^2 = 1 + 3 \qquad 3^2 = 1 + 3 + 5 \qquad 4^2 = 1 + 3 + 5 + 7$$

What pattern can you find to represent a whole number raised to the third power as the sum of odd numbers?

Write a problem that uses square and cubic units of measure. Give the problem to a classmate to solve.

GETTING STARTED

What numbers do A, B, and C represent? What is the opposite of B?

$A \quad -4 \quad 0 \quad C \quad 6 \quad B$

Understanding Rational Numbers

In the 1930s the explorer Dr. William Beebe used a bathysphere to study the ocean depths. Cables lowered $4\frac{1}{2}$-foot-wide chamber more than 3,000 feet deep. Its thick steel sides were able to withstand almost 100 atmopheres of water pressure. (1 atmosphere = 14.69 pounds per square inch)

$4\frac{1}{2}$, $^-3,000$, and 14.69 are rational numbers.

A **rational number** is any number that can be expressed as the quotient of two integers where the divisor is not 0.

$$4\frac{1}{2} = \frac{9}{2} \qquad ^-3,000 = \frac{^-3,000}{1}, \text{ or } \frac{3,000}{^-1} \qquad 14.69 = \frac{1,469}{100}$$

Rational numbers can be shown on a number line. What is the sum of a number and its opposite?

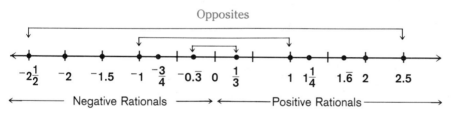

Opposites

$-2\frac{1}{2} \quad ^-2 \quad ^-1.5 \quad ^-1 \quad \frac{-3}{4} \quad ^-0.\overline{3} \quad 0 \quad \frac{1}{3} \qquad 1 \quad 1\frac{1}{4} \quad 1.\overline{6} \quad 2 \quad 2.5$

← Negative Rationals → ← Positive Rationals →

A rational number written as a quotient can also be expressed as an integer or a decimal number. Sometimes the decimal form is repeating and nonterminating.

$$\frac{27}{9} = 27 \div 9 = 3 \qquad \frac{^-3}{-24} = ^-3 \div ^-24 = 0.125 \qquad \frac{3}{7} = 3 \div 7 = 0.\overline{428571}$$

Check Your Understanding

Write each as the quotient of two integers in lowest terms.

1. $5\frac{1}{2}$　　　2. $^-3$　　　3. 0.6　　　4. $\frac{^-5}{80}$　　　5. $^-0.028$　　　6. 8

Write the opposite of each.

7. 5　　　8. $^-9$　　　9. $\frac{^-3}{5}$　　　10. $\frac{2}{7}$　　　11. $^-0.51$　　　12. 7

Share Your Ideas How many names can there be for any rational number? Explain.

Write each as the quotient of two integers in lowest terms.

13. $3\frac{1}{4}$ 14. $^{-}2\frac{3}{7}$ 15. 12 16. $^{-}5$ 17. 0.035

18. $^{-}0.14$ 19. $\frac{24}{9}$ 20. $-\frac{3}{81}$ 21. 0.802 22. $^{-}0.111$

Write the opposite of each.

23. 7 24. $^{-}3$ 25. 89 26. $^{-}18$ 27. $\frac{^{-}4}{9}$

28. $\frac{5}{8}$ 29. $\frac{^{-}7}{10}$ 30. $\frac{^{-}3}{^{-}11}$ 31. $\frac{^{-}19}{^{-}100}$ 32. $\frac{44}{^{-}100}$

CHOICES Express each as a whole number or a decimal number.
Use paper and pencil, mental math, or a calculator.

33. $\frac{2}{5}$ 34. $\frac{3}{8}$ 35. $\frac{^{-}20}{4}$ 36. $\frac{^{-}4}{20}$ 37. $\frac{8}{20}$

38. $\frac{^{-}15}{40}$ 39. $\frac{^{-}39}{^{-}13}$ 40. $-\frac{100}{25}$ 41. $\frac{^{-}36}{^{-}4}$ 42. $-\frac{11}{44}$

Write each in lowest terms.

43. $\frac{^{-}5}{50}$ 44. $\frac{7}{49}$ 45. $\frac{^{-}60}{3}$ 46. $\frac{0}{7}$ 47. $\frac{^{-}75}{^{-}25}$

Think and Apply

Rational numbers are **dense,** that is, between any two rational numbers, there is another rational number. 2.21 is between 2.2 and 2.3.

48. Name two other rational numbers between 2.2 and 2.3.

To find a rational number between $\frac{5}{12}$ and $\frac{6}{12}$, rewrite each number, using a greater denominator.

$$\frac{5}{12} = \frac{10}{24} \qquad\qquad \frac{6}{12} = \frac{12}{24}$$

$\frac{10}{24} < \frac{11}{24} < \frac{12}{24}$ So $\frac{11}{24}$ is between $\frac{5}{12}$ and $\frac{6}{12}$.

Find a rational number between each pair.

49. 6.6 and 7 50. $^{-}0.47$ and $^{-}0.52$

51. $\frac{3}{8}$ and $\frac{4}{8}$ 52. $\frac{4}{13}$ and $\frac{5}{13}$

Logical Thinking

53. If A and B are rational numbers, how many rational numbers are there between A and B? Explain.

Write *always, sometimes,* or *never true.* Explain. A rational number is an integer. A whole number is a rational number.

Use a number line to explain how to order 2 positive integers, 2 negative integers, and 2 integers with unlike signs.

British

Ordering Rational Numbers

In 1988 the *Daedalus,* a human-powered plane, was flown 74 miles across the Aegean Sea in $3\frac{1}{2}$ hours. In the same year a supersonic plane was flown from New York to London in just over $2\frac{11}{12}$ hours. Which flight took more time?

Rational numbers can be ordered by using the number line. Numbers increase in value from left to right along the line.

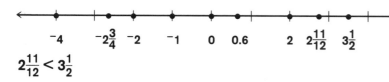

$$^-4 \qquad ^-2\frac{3}{4} \quad ^-2 \qquad ^-1 \qquad 0 \quad 0.6 \qquad 2 \quad 2\frac{11}{12} \quad 3\frac{1}{2}$$

$$2\frac{11}{12} < 3\frac{1}{2}$$

The *Daedalus* took more time.

▶ To compare unlike fractions, you can rewrite the fractions, using a common denominator. Then compare the numerators.

Compare $\frac{^-6}{7}$ and $\frac{^-5}{8}$. $\qquad \frac{^-6}{7} = \frac{^-48}{56} \qquad \frac{^-5}{8} = \frac{^-35}{56}$

$$^-48 < ^-35$$

$$\text{So } \frac{^-6}{7} < \frac{^-5}{8}.$$

▶ To compare fractions and decimals, you can rewrite the fraction as a decimal.

Compare $1\frac{5}{8}$ and 1.619. $\qquad 1\frac{5}{8} = \frac{13}{8} = 13 \div 8 = 1.625$

1.619 < 1.625 So **1.619 < $1\frac{5}{8}$.**

Check Your Understanding

Compare. Use <, >, or = for each ●.

1. $\frac{^-4}{9}$ ● $\frac{^-1}{3}$

2. $^-1\frac{1}{6}$ ● $^-1\frac{3}{5}$

3. $^-0.15$ ● $^-0.85$

4. 0.88 ● $\frac{7}{8}$

Write in order from least to greatest.

5. $\frac{^-3}{5}, \frac{^-5}{8}, \frac{3}{10}$

6. $^-0.58, \frac{9}{16}, ^-0.62$

7. $1\frac{5}{16}, 1.32, 1\frac{5}{14}$

Share Your Ideas When comparing fractions and decimals, we often change the fraction to a decimal form. How is this like using a common denominator to compare fractions?

Compare. Use <, >, or = for each ⬤.

8. $\frac{3}{8}$ ⬤ $\frac{-1}{4}$

9. $\frac{2}{9}$ ⬤ $\frac{1}{3}$

10. $\frac{-4}{7}$ ⬤ $\frac{1}{14}$

11. $^-0.5$ ⬤ $^-0.8$

12. $^-0.34$ ⬤ $^-0.3$

13. $\frac{4}{5}$ ⬤ $\frac{-9}{10}$

14. 1.375 ⬤ $1\frac{3}{8}$

15. $\frac{-6}{7}$ ⬤ $^-0.85$

16. $\frac{3}{7}$ ⬤ $\frac{11}{25}$

17. $\frac{10}{22}$ ⬤ $\frac{9}{20}$

18. $^-4\frac{1}{3}$ ⬤ $\frac{-14}{3}$

19. $^-6.74$ ⬤ $^-6.3$

Write a decimal and a fraction that name each point on the number line below.

20. A

21. B

22. C

23. D

24. E

Write in order from least to greatest.

25. $^-1.75, \frac{3}{8}, ^-2\frac{3}{5}$

26. $\frac{3}{8}, \frac{-5}{12}, \frac{4}{9}$

27. $\frac{-5}{16}, \frac{-1}{2}, \frac{-7}{12}$

28. $\frac{-6}{3}, 0.34, ^-1.38, \frac{9}{25}$

29. $^-0.62, \frac{4}{9}, ^-0.58, 0.44$

30. $\frac{7}{12}, \frac{5}{8}, 0.62, 0.48$

31. The pilot of the *Daedalus* was a cyclist. He pedaled for $2\frac{7}{8}$ hours one day and $2\frac{3}{4}$ hours the next day while training for the flight. Which day did he train longer?

Visual Thinking

32. Which fraction-coded shapes can be matched with identical decimal-coded shapes?

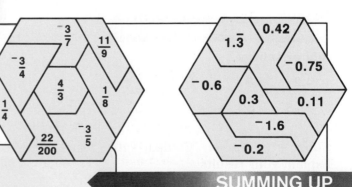

Explain how you would compare $\frac{-3}{8}$, 0.572, $^-1$, and $\frac{-7}{9}$.

SUMMING UP

Adding and Subtracting Rational Numbers

Antarctica, the coldest place on earth, has had temperature readings as low as $^-87.8°C$. Temperatures in the Arctic have dropped as low as $^-45.3°C$. How much colder is the reading from Antarctica?

Subtract to compare the readings.

$$^-87.8 - {}^-45.3$$

▶ To add or subtract rational numbers, use what you have learned about adding and subtracting integers.

Think To subtract a rational number, add its opposite.

$$^-87.8 - {}^-45.3 = {}^-87.8 + 45.3$$
$$= {}^-42.5$$

To add a positive and a negative rational number, find the difference between their absolute values. Subtract the lesser absolute value from the greater.
$$|{}^-87.8| - |45.3| = 42.5$$
Use the sign of the greater with the answer.

The reading in Antarctica is 42.5°C colder.

More Examples

a. $\frac{1}{5} + \frac{^-1}{2} = \frac{2}{10} + \frac{^-5}{10} = \frac{^-3}{10}$ **Think** $|\frac{^-5}{10}| - |\frac{2}{10}| = \frac{3}{10}$
Use the sign of the greater absolute value.

b. $3\frac{4}{5} - {}^-2\frac{2}{5} = 3\frac{4}{5} + 2\frac{2}{5} = 6\frac{1}{5}$ ← $(+) - (-) = (+) + (+) = (+)$

c. $^-5.83 - 2.96 = {}^-5.83 + {}^-2.96 = {}^-8.79$ ← $(-) - (+) = (-) + (-) = (-)$

Check Your Understanding

Add or subtract.

1. $4.2 - {}^-1.3$ **2.** $\frac{^-5}{8} + \frac{^-5}{6}$

3. $3.28 - 2.59$ **4.** $^-5\frac{2}{7} - {}^-3\frac{3}{10}$

Share Your Ideas Compare $10 - 5$ and $10 + {}^-5$. Explain your results.

Add or subtract. Choose pencil and paper, mental math, or a calculator for each.

5. $\frac{3}{7} - \frac{-2}{7}$

6. $\frac{-3}{8} - \frac{-7}{8}$

7. $\frac{-2}{3} + \frac{-1}{6}$

8. $^-12 - 5$

9. $8.56 - 9.23$

10. $^-10.45 + ^-6.88$

11. $\frac{-4}{9} + \frac{7}{12}$

12. $\frac{2}{5} + \frac{-3}{4}$

13. $^-19 - ^-14$

14. $^-50 - ^-88$

15. $\frac{-5}{12} - \frac{3}{8}$

16. $4\frac{2}{7} + ^-2\frac{1}{7}$

17. $\frac{-1}{3} - \frac{3}{5}$

18. $\frac{5}{6} + \frac{-7}{8}$

19. $^-3\frac{5}{8} - ^-2\frac{5}{24}$

20. $35 + ^-67$

21. $^-44 - ^-44$

22. $34 - ^-52$

23. $4.6 + ^-5.8$

24. $3.5 - ^-4.6$

25. $\frac{2}{3} + (\frac{-1}{5} - \frac{1}{6})$

26. $5.12 - (0.4 - ^-1.3)$

27. $^-1\frac{3}{8} + (2\frac{3}{4} - ^-1\frac{7}{8})$

Follow the rule, if given, to find each missing number.

Rule: Add $\frac{-2}{3}$.

	Input	Output
28.	$\frac{2}{3}$	
29.	$\frac{-2}{3}$	
30.	0	
31.	$\frac{1}{6}$	

Rule: Subtract 0.52.

	Input	Output
32.	1.5	
33.	$^-0.5$	
34.	4.32	
35.	0	

Find the rule.

	Input	Output
36.	0.4	0.375
	$\frac{3}{4}$	$\frac{1}{2}$
	$\frac{-1}{2}$	$\frac{-3}{4}$
	0.25	0

Think and Apply

37. At noon in Nome, Alaska, the temperature was $^-36°F$. By midnight the temperature had dropped 24 degrees. What was the temperature at midnight?

38. The stock of Polar Corporation was selling at $\$35\frac{1}{8}$. It dropped $\$2\frac{1}{2}$ by the end of the day. What was the closing price of the stock?

39. Colleen has $35.23 in her checking account. She needs to pay a $50.96 bill. How much must she deposit to have $10 left in her account after paying the bill?

Evaluate each sum or difference and explain your results.

$^-4.5 - ^-4.5 \qquad ^-4.5 + 4.5 \qquad 4.5 - 4.5 \qquad 4.5 + ^-4.5$

SUMMING UP

If $^-6 + a$ is negative, can a be negative? positive? If ^-6a is negative, can a be negative? positive? Explain.

Multiplying and Dividing Rational Numbers

At very high altitudes, the air is so thin that climbers cannot survive without extra oxygen. For each 1,000 feet that a climber ascends, the air pressure decreases by about 0.39 pound per square inch (psi). We can say the change is $^-0.39$ psi per 1,000 feet. If a climber goes up 3,500 feet, by how much does the air pressure change?

Multiply to find the change.

$^-0.39 \cdot 3.5$ **Think** How many 1,000's are in 3,500? $\dfrac{3,500}{1,000} = 3.5$

To multiply or divide rational numbers, use what you have learned about multiplying and dividing integers.

$$^-0.39 \cdot 3.5 = ^-1.365 \leftarrow (-) \cdot (+) = (-)$$

The pressure decreases by about 1.37 psi.

More Examples

a. $^-2.34 \div ^-0.39 = 6 \leftarrow (-) \div (-) = (+)$

b. $\dfrac{^-7}{8} \cdot \dfrac{^-4}{7} = \dfrac{1}{2} \leftarrow (-) \cdot (-) = (+)$

c. $4.32 \div ^-0.2 = ^-21.6 \leftarrow (+) \div (-) = (-)$

Check Your Understanding

Multiply or divide.

1. $4 \cdot ^-10$
2. $^-7 \cdot ^-8$
3. $\dfrac{^-2}{^-5} \cdot \dfrac{^-3}{4}$
4. $^-20 \div 5$

5. $^-72 \div ^-12$
6. $\dfrac{^-4}{9} \div \dfrac{^-5}{9}$
7. $\dfrac{^-2}{3} \cdot \dfrac{2}{7}$
8. $3.5 \cdot 2.6$

9. $6.4 \cdot ^-0.15$
10. $15.2 \div ^-3.8$
11. $\dfrac{^-3}{4} \cdot 0.4$
12. $4.2 \cdot \dfrac{^-8}{3}$

Share Your Ideas   Explain why multiplying a positive and a negative rational number always results in a negative product.

CHOICES **Add, subtract, multiply, or divide. Use mental math, paper and pencil, or a calculator.**

13. $^{-}32 \div ^{-}4$

14. $9 \cdot ^{-}6$

15. $^{-}12 \cdot ^{-}18$

16. $^{-}180 \div 15$

17. $\frac{-5}{7} \cdot \frac{-3}{4}$

18. $\frac{-1}{4} + \frac{-3}{8}$

19. $\frac{5}{12} \div \frac{-7}{12}$

20. $\frac{-6}{11} \cdot \frac{5}{7}$

21. $\frac{4}{9} - \frac{1}{3}$

22. $0.3 + ^{-}1.2$

23. $^{-}5.6 - ^{-}1.6$

24. $^{-}4.76 \cdot ^{-}1.5$

25. $\frac{-1}{2} \div 0.4$

26. $^{-}0.6 \cdot \frac{-5}{8}$

27. $^{-}1.86 \div \frac{-2}{3}$

28. $4\frac{3}{8} \cdot 0.2$

29. $^{-}17 \div 2\frac{1}{8}$

30. $^{-}16\frac{2}{3} + 4\frac{1}{9}$

31. $0.5(^{-}1.5 + 4.3)$

32. $(\frac{1}{2} \cdot \frac{2}{3}) \div (4\frac{5}{9} - 2\frac{1}{3})$

Evaluate each expression for $a = \frac{-1}{2}$ and $b = 0.4$.

33. $6a$

34. ab

35. $\frac{b}{a}$

36. $\frac{-2}{3}a \, (b + ^{-}1.5)$

37. $(^{-}3b - 0.6a) \div 3$

Think and Apply

38. The temperature drops 1.7°C for every 300 meters of altitude. How much will the temperature change if a climber ascends 660 meters?

39. If the temperature changes $^{-}6.8$°C, how has the altitude of a hiking party changed?

40. How can you show that $3 \cdot ^{-}1.5 = ^{-}4.5$? The statements below show that the product of a positive number and a negative number is negative. Use number facts and properties to explain each equation.

$$3 \cdot (1.5 + ^{-}1.5) = 0$$
$$(3 \cdot 1.5) + (3 \cdot ^{-}1.5) = 0$$
$$4.5 + (3 \cdot ^{-}1.5) = 0$$
$$3 \cdot ^{-}1.5 = ^{-}4.5$$

Create two problems, one for division and one for multiplication of rational numbers. Exchange with a friend to solve.

Mixed Review

1. $13.6 \cdot 21.5$

2. $25.4 \div 0.8$

3. $4.064 + 2.206$

4. $45.6 - 8.8$

5. $\frac{1}{2} - \frac{1}{6}$

6. $\frac{5}{20} - \frac{1}{4}$

7. $\frac{7}{10} \cdot \frac{1}{2}$

8. $\frac{3}{7} \div \frac{4}{5}$

9. $12\frac{1}{5} + 2\frac{3}{8}$

10. $11.31 + 9.09$

List all the factors.

11. 24

12. 140

13. 69

14. 121

15. 252

Solve.

16. $8x + 3 = 35$

17. $25 + 3x = 40$

18. $2y \div 3 = 4$

19. $r - 15 = ^{-}13$

20. $3.75t = 37.5$

SUMMING UP

Solving Equations

The force of gravity on the moon is about $\frac{1}{6}$ that of Earth's gravity. The weight of something on the moon would be about $\frac{1}{6}$ its weight on Earth. If an astronaut weighs 22 pounds on the moon, how much does she weigh on Earth?

Let w = weight on Earth.

$\frac{1}{6}w = 22$ What does $\frac{1}{6}w$ represent?

$\frac{1}{6}w \cdot 6 = 22 \cdot 6$ **Think**   What is the inverse of dividing by 6?
$w = 132$ Multiply *both* sides of the equation by 6.
                         Simplify to find the solution.

The astronaut weighs 132 pounds on Earth.   **Check** $\frac{1}{6}(132) = 22$
                                             $22 = 22$

Sometimes you need to use inverse operations more than once to solve an equation.

$2t + {}^-0.39 = 0.25$ What is the inverse of adding $^-0.39$?

$2t + {}^-0.39 - {}^-0.39 = 0.25 - {}^-0.39$ Subtract $^-0.39$ from *both*
               $2t = 0.25 - {}^-0.39$ sides and simplify.
               $2t = 0.25 + 0.39$
               $2t = 0.64$ What is the inverse of multiplying by 2?
               $\frac{2t}{2} = \frac{0.64}{2}$ Divide both sides by 2 and simplify.

               $t = 0.32$ **Check** $2(0.32) + {}^-0.39 = 0.25$
                               $0.64 + {}^-0.39 = 0.25$
                                     $0.25 = 0.25$

Check Your Understanding

Solve and check.

1. $3x - 10 = 14$ **2.** $8 + {}^-6x = 13$ **3.** $4y - {}^-13 = 38$

4. $\frac{x}{4} + \frac{1}{2} = \frac{5}{4}$ **5.** $\frac{{}^-5}{6} + \frac{y}{3} = \frac{{}^-1}{6}$ **6.** $\frac{x}{10} - \frac{{}^-3}{10} = \frac{3}{5}$

Share Your Ideas   Tell which operation you would use first to solve each. $x - 3 = 10$ $\frac{2x}{3} = 10$
Explain your thinking.

Solve and check.

7. $2.3x - 4.5 = 4.93$

8. $3.2 + {}^-4.3x = {}^-8.84$

9. $5.2y - {}^-8.9 = 42.18$

10. $\frac{x}{3} + 3.7 = 17.5$

11. $\frac{7}{10} + 2.5x = 10.7$

12. ${}^-6 + \frac{x}{8} = 1$

13. ${}^-4y + 10 = 54$

14. ${}^-9 + 8x = 47$

15. $6x + 13 = 85$

16. $6d + 15 = 66$

17. ${}^-11x - 18 = 202$

18. ${}^-15x - {}^-32 = 341$

19. $\frac{x}{9} + \frac{2}{9} = \frac{7}{9}$

20. $\frac{4}{11} + \frac{z}{11} = \frac{10}{11}$

21. $\frac{{}^-m}{12} - \frac{5}{6} = \frac{7}{12}$

22. $\frac{1}{3} + \frac{y}{4} = 1\frac{2}{3}$

23. $\frac{x}{5} + \frac{3}{2} = \frac{13}{4}$

24. $\frac{5}{9} + \frac{y}{6} = \frac{7}{9}$

Write and solve an equation for each.

25. A number t is multiplied by 6. Then 7 is subtracted from the product. The result is 49. What number is t?

26. A number p is multiplied by $\frac{2}{3}$. Then $\frac{1}{5}$ is subtracted from the product. The result is $\frac{1}{5}$. What number is p?

27. A number d is multiplied by $\frac{5}{6}$. Then $\frac{1}{4}$ is added to the product. The result is $\frac{7}{12}$. What number is d?

28. The sum of a number x divided by ${}^-12$ and 6 equals $\frac{1}{3}$ times $\frac{3}{4}$.

29. The product of 0.3, ${}^-1.2$, and a number r equals 1.8.

30. The sum of a number x divided by 6 and $\frac{1}{4}$ equals ${}^-5.25$.

31. Collect data about the gravitational attraction on other planets by consulting an encyclopedia. Use your data to calculate your weight on each planet you investigate. Combine the data your class collects to find the weight of a 100-lb student on each planet of the solar system.

32. Marge mowed three yards. Each person paid her the same amount. She was also paid $4.25 for trimming one yard. Marge earned $41.75. How much did she get paid for mowing each yard? Write an equation and solve it.

Create an equation to represent a situation. Exchange it with a friend to solve.

SUMMING UP

Divide 0.00001 by 1,000. How did you decide where the decimal point would go? Working with powers of 10 makes the problem easier.

Powers of 10

A proton is a particle that is part of an atom. The diameter of a proton is 274 quadrillionths of a centimeter. Written in standard form, that number is 0.000000000000274.

Powers of 10 may be used to write numbers less than 1 but greater than 0. Look at the patterns below. As the exponent decreases, how does the number change?

$10^4 = 10,000$
$10^3 = 1,000$
$10^2 = 100$
$10^1 = 10$
$10^0 = 1$
$10^{-1} = \frac{1}{10^1} = 0.1$
$10^{-2} = \frac{1}{10^2} = 0.01$
$10^{-3} = \frac{1}{10^3} = 0.001$

What does a positive exponent tell you about the number?

What does a negative exponent tell you about the number?

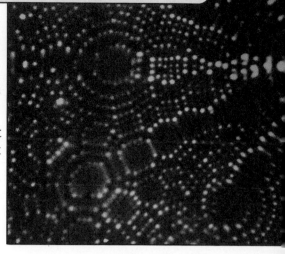

atoms on the point of a platinum needle magnified 2,000,000 times by a field ion microscope

▶ For any integer n, $\frac{1}{10^n} = 10^{-n}$

To multiply powers of 10, add the exponents.

a. $10^3 \cdot 10^2 = (10 \cdot 10 \cdot 10)(10 \cdot 10)$
$= 10^{(3+2)} = 10^5$

b. $10^{-5} \cdot 10^2 = 10^{(-5+2)} = 10^{-3}$

To divide powers of 10, subtract the exponents.

c. $10^4 \div 10^2 =$
$(10 \cdot 10 \cdot 10 \cdot 10) \div (10 \cdot 10) =$
$10^{(4-2)} = 10^2$

d. $10^{-3} \div 10^4 = 10^{(-3-4)} = 10^{-7}$

Check Your Understanding

Write each as a whole number or a decimal.

1. 10^4
2. 10^6
3. 10^{-4}
4. 10^{-6}
5. $\frac{1}{10^{10}}$

Write each as a power of 10.

6. 10,000
7. 1,000,000
8. 0.0001
9. 0.00001
10. 0.000000001
11. $10^3 \cdot 10^5$
12. $10^2 \div 10^{12}$
13. $10^{-3} \cdot 10^6$
14. $10^{-8} \cdot 10^7$
15. $10^{-7} \div 10^{-4}$

Share Your Ideas Rewrite $7^{-5} \cdot 7^4 = 7^{-1}$ without exponents to explain why multiplication can be done by adding exponents. Use a similar example to show how division is done by subtracting exponents.

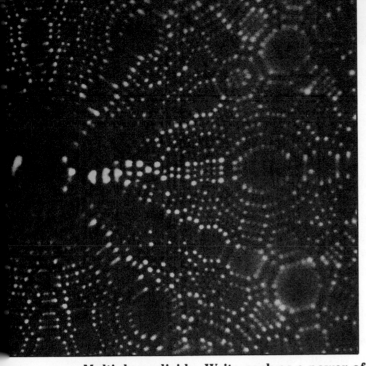

Write each as a whole number or a decimal.

16. 10^2 17. 10^{-3} 18. $\frac{1}{10^4}$

19. 10^2 20. 10^5 21. 10^{-8}

22. $\frac{1}{10^5}$ 23. 10^{-7} 24. 10^0

Write each as a power of 10.

25. 1,000   26. 10,000,000

27. 10   28. 1,000,000,000,000

29. 100,000   30. 0.0000001

31. 0.00001   32. 0.1

33. 0.01   34. 0.000000000001

Multiply or divide. Write each as a power of 10.

35. $10^2 \cdot 10^6$ 36. $10^8 \cdot 10^4$ 37. $10^{14} \cdot 10^4$ 38. $\frac{10^8}{10^{-5}}$

39. $10^{-5} \cdot 10^{-9}$ 40. $10^{-8} \div 10^{-3}$ 41. $\frac{10^{-7}}{10^7}$ 42. $10^{-9} \cdot 10^{10}$

43. $\frac{10^7}{10^3}$ 44. $\frac{10^9}{10^5}$ 45. $10^2 \cdot 10^8$ 46. $10^7 \div 10^{10}$

47. $10^7 \div 10^{-4}$ 48. $10^{-8} \div 10^5$ 49. $10^1 \div 10^{-9}$ 50. $10^{-8} \cdot 10^{-6}$

51. $\frac{10^3 \cdot 10^4}{10^{13}}$ 52. $\frac{10^{-3} \cdot 10^4 \cdot 10^{-3}}{10^2}$ 53. $\frac{10^5 \cdot 10^3}{10^3 \div 10^4}$

Think and Apply

The metric system is based on powers of 10. Write each answer as a standard number and as a power of 10. Use the table of values to help you.

54. How many grams are there in 100 kilograms?

55. How many metric tons are there in 10,000,000 kilograms?

56. One hectare is an area 100 meters square. A square meter is what part of a hectare?

57. The equator is 10^9 centimeters from the North Pole. How many meters is that? How many kilometers?

1 kg = 1,000 g
1 metric ton = 1,000 kg
1 m = 100 cm
1 km = 1,000 m

How does using powers of 10 make comparisons of numbers easier? Compare 0.0001 and 0.000000001. Which is greater? How many times as great?

SUMMING UP

1,000 can be written as 1×10^3. How could you write 1,500, using a power of 10 as a factor?

Scientific Notation

Venus revolves slowly in an almost perfectly circular orbit about 108,210,000 km from the sun. Since Venus is hidden by a dense layer of clouds, mapping its surface accurately has required the use of probes or radar. In 1989 the spacecraft *Magellan* was sent into space to make a radar mapping of Venus.

Large numbers are often written in **scientific notation,** using powers of 10.

▶ A number in scientific notation is written as the product of a number between 1 and 10 and a power of 10.

Write 108,210,000 in scientific notation.

$$108{,}210{,}000 = 108{,}210{,}000 \div 100{,}000{,}000 \times 100{,}000{,}000$$
$$= 1.0821 \times 100{,}000{,}000$$
$$= 1.0821 \times 10^8$$

How does dividing by 100,000,000 change the position of the decimal point? How does the exponent relate to this change?

To change a number in scientific notation to standard notation, multiply.

$$6.32 \times 10^3 = 6.32 \times 1{,}000 = 6{,}320$$

More Examples

a. Write 647,123.15 in scientific notation.
$$647{,}123.15 = 647{,}123.15 \div 100{,}000 \times 100{,}000 = 6.4712315 \times 10^5$$
5 places

b. Write 6.23×10^4 in standard form.
$$6.23 \times 10^4 = 6.23 \times 10{,}000 = 62{,}300$$
4 places

Check Your Understanding

Write each in scientific notation.

1. 637,210   2. 745,111,257   3. 153,772.2   4. 107 million

Write each in standard form.

5. 7.2×10^5 6. 1.235×10^4 7. 1.15×10^7 8. 9.876×10^{12}

Share Your Ideas   Explain how you would write 257,481.2 in scientific notation.

Write each missing exponent or factor.

9. $1{,}037{,}542 = 1.037542 \times 10^{\square}$ **10.** $7{,}450{,}000 = 7.45 \times 10^{\square}$ **11.** $123{,}000 = 1.23 \times 10^{\square}$

12. $\square \times 10^3 = 6{,}577$ **13.** $4{,}321{,}752 = \square \times 10^6$ **14.** $29{,}753 = \square \times 10^4$

Change each to scientific notation.

15. 3,750

16. 840,000

17. 7,890,000

18. 4,756,000,000

19. 9,070,000,000

20. 10,800,000

21. 6.5 billion

22. 104,321,175

23. 12.3 million

Write each in standard form.

24. 5.86×10^4

25. 7.92×10^9

26. 1.185×10^{11}

27. 6.78×10^5

28. 4.84×10^8

29. 9.108×10^{10}

30. 24.1×10^7

31. 673.1×10^5

32. 247.1×10^4

Change each number to scientific notation.

33. Jupiter, the largest planet, is 778,300,000 km from the sun.

34. Pluto, the outermost planet, is 5,900,000,000 km from the sun.

35. The sun has a diameter of 1,390,000 km.

36. Earth is 149,600,000 km from the sun.

Think and Apply

37. Many calculators use scientific notation and rounding if the result of a computation is larger than the display can show. The display shows 165,729,459 as it appears on a scientific calculator.

$$1.6573 \quad 08$$

Notice that 1.6573 is rounded to four decimal places. 08 is the exponent.

Write each number, using scientific notation.

a. $9.2838 \quad 13$

b. $6.3616 \quad 12$

c. $5.5625 \quad 08$

38. Karen bought three posters at the Air and Space Museum. She also bought a book for $10.95 and a T-shirt for $12.75. Her purchases totaled $47.55. How much was each poster?

Which operations are used to rewrite a number in standard or scientific notation? Explain how these operations are used.

SUMMING UP

Compare 3.4×10^4 and 3.4×10^7. Which is greater? How many times as great?

Scientific Notation: Numbers Less Than 1

The meter is defined as 1,650,763.73 wavelengths of light from the element Krypton 86. Wavelengths of light are very short. A wavelength of yellow light is about 0.0000589 cm.

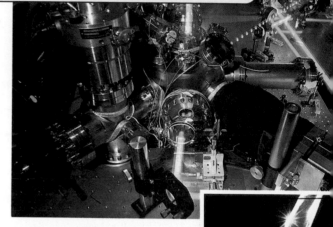

Lasers for communication
Bell Laboratories, Murray Hill, NJ

Write 0.0000589 in scientific notation.

Write the number as a product of two factors— a number between 1 and 10 and a power of 10.

$$0.0000589 = 0.0000589 \times 100,000 \div 100,000$$
$$= 5.89 \div 100,000$$
$$= 5.89 \times 10^{-5}$$

Think Dividing by 10^5 is the same as multiplying by 10^{-5}.

How does multiplying by 100,000 change the position of the decimal point? How does the exponent relate to this change?

To change a number in scientific notation to standard notation, multiply.

$$6.73 \times 10^{-4} = 6.73 \times 0.0001 = 0.000673$$
4 places

What does the negative exponent tell you about the number?

More Examples

a. Write 0.0043211 in scientific notation.
   $$0.0043211 = 0.0043211 \times 1,000 \div 1,000 = 4.3211 \times 10^{-3}$$

b. Write 6.766×10^{-5} in standard notation.
   $$6.766 \times 10^{-5} = 6.766 \times 0.00001 = 0.00006766$$

Check Your Understanding

Write each in scientific notation.

1. 0.0000064   2. 0.000000893   3. 0.00000001094   4. 0.0000000000348

Write each in standard notation.

5. 6.38×10^{-7} 6. 4.068×10^{-9} 7. 3.8×10^{-5} 8. 8.214×10^{-10}

Share Your Ideas Compare 3.4×10^{-4} and 3.4×10^{-5}. Which is greater? How much greater?

Find each missing exponent.

9. $0.0432 \times 10^{\square} = 4.32$

10. $0.0015 = 1.5 \times 10^{\square}$

11. $7.931 \times 10^{\square} = 0.0007931$

12. $6.17 \times 10^{\square} = 0.000617$

13. $5 \times 10^{\square} = 0.0005$

14. $0.0000017 = 1.7 \times 10^{\square}$

Find each missing factor.

15. $0.765 = \square \times 10^{-1}$

16. $\square \times 10^{-4} = 0.00073$

17. $0.004 = \square \times 10^{-3}$

18. $0.000012 = \square \times 10^{-5}$

19. $\square \times 10^{-7} = 0.0000005$

20. $\square \times 10^{-2} = 0.014$

Write each in scientific notation.

21. 0.00093

22. 0.000006

23. 0.000000472

24. $756,170,000$

25. $34,171,151.2$

26. 3.4 million

27. 92 ten-thousandths

28. 21 millionths

29. 5.7 billion

Write each in standard form.

30. 8.7×10^{-5}

31. 7.92×10^{-8}

32. 2.03×10^{-10}

33. 3.005×10^{-9}

34. 4.5×10^{-6}

35. 6.32×10^{8}

36. 1.08×10^{-7}

37. 7.15081×10^{4}

38. 2.79×10^{-14}

39. 1.753×10^{13}

40. 1.0078×10^{-12}

41. 9.32×10^{12}

Think and Apply

42. Small numbers often occur in scientific work. Change each wavelength to scientific notation.

a. red 0.00006867 cm

b. blue 0.00004861 cm

43. The mass of an electron is 9×10^{-28} grams. How many zeroes are needed to write that number in standard notation?

44. A proton weighs 1,836 times as much as an electron. Express its weight in scientific notation.

Which is greater, 9.211×10^{-8} or 1.293×10^{-6}? Which factor is more important in comparing numbers in scientific notation? Explain.

SUMMING UP

Midchapter Review

Express each as a quotient of two integers in lowest terms. pages 180–181

1. $4\frac{2}{3}$ 2. $^-3\frac{4}{5}$ 3. 9   4. $^-1.3$ 5. 0.095

Compare. Write <, >, or = for each ●. pages 182–183

6. $^-5$ ● $^-1$ 7. $\frac{7}{9}$ ● $\frac{2}{3}$ 8. $\frac{^-5}{6}$ ● $\frac{5}{12}$ 9. $^-3$ ● 5.1   10. 0.6 ● 0.4

Add, subtract, multiply, or divide. pages 184–187

11. $7.23 - 9.79$ 12. $\frac{^-5}{8} \div \frac{^-7}{8}$ 13. $\frac{^-4}{9} \cdot \frac{^-1}{3}$ 14. $^-18 - ^-21.15$

15. $\frac{1}{5} \div \frac{^-2}{5}$ 16. $^-6.36 + ^-8.35$ 17. $14 \cdot ^-3.2$ 18. $5 + \frac{^-5}{6}$

19. $\frac{1}{4} \cdot ^-3$ 20. $^-2.25 + 3.28$ 21. $\frac{^-3}{4} + ^-5$ 22. $^-3 - ^-4.5$

23. $7 + ^-2.4$ 24. $\frac{^-2}{5} \cdot \frac{^-5}{6}$ 25. $^-9.9 + 2$ 26. $\frac{3}{9} - \frac{^-5}{9}$

Solve each equation. pages 188–189

27. $\frac{1}{4} + \frac{y}{5} = \frac{3}{5}$ 28. $\frac{^-x}{6} + \frac{^-3}{8} = \frac{13}{8}$ 29. $\frac{4}{6} - \frac{^-y}{6} = \frac{9}{4}$

30. $6.2x + 8.3 = 23.8$ 31. $4.4t - 7.43 = 2.91$ 32. $6.4w - ^-8.32 = 49.6$

Write each as a whole number or a decimal. pages 190–191

33. 10^3 34. 10^{-4} 35. 10^5 36. 10^{-5} 37. 10^{-6}

Write each as a power of 10. pages 190–191

38. 0.0001   39. 1,000   40. 0.000001   41. 10,000,000   42. 10,000,000,000

Write each in scientific notation. pages 192–195

43. 8,420,000   44. 0.00093   45. 4,170,000,000   46. 0.0000000857

Write each in standard notation. pages 192–195

47. 7.3×10^6 48. 6.31×10^{-8} 49. 9.44×10^7 50. 3.28×10^{-6}

Complete each statement.

51. 3.57×10^8 is written in ___ notation.

52. A number that can be written as a quotient of 2 integers is a ___ number.

Words to Know
standard
scientific
rational

Solve.

53. A number d is multiplied by $\frac{1}{2}$. Then 12 is added to the product. The result is 17 What number is d?

54. The gravitational attraction on Mercury is 0.36 that of Earth. If an astronaut weighs 110 pounds on Earth, how much would she weigh on Mercury?

Exploring Problem Solving

Is It Possible?

You are on a polar expedition, 700 miles from the Pole. Your snowmobile can travel 100 miles on a tank of fuel. Your snowmobile can also carry a removable barrel that holds 5 tankfuls of fuel.

Thinking Critically

How could a single snowmobile make the trip to the Pole and return to the base camp? Make diagrams or tables to help you or use Workmat 8.

Analyzing and Making Decisions

1. Can your snowmobile reach the Pole without refueling?

2. **What if** you store fuel along the way? How far from the base camp would you store your first barrel of fuel? Explain.

3. On the second trip from base camp, should you store the next barrel with the first or take it farther? If so, how much farther? Explain. Will you need to store more fuel? Explain. What is the best method of recording what you are doing? Try a few methods before deciding.

4. How could a single snowmobile make the trip to the Pole and return to the base camp? Make drawings and keep records explaining what you did. Compare your total distance travelled with that of other groups.

Look Back To protect the environment, expeditions should not leave abandoned fuel behind unnecessarily. Try to plan a trip so that you leave behind as little fuel as possible.

Problem Solving Strategies

Guess and Test

Explorers who visited a fishing village found they could trade for food. One fish hook and one spear were worth 20 fish. One knife and one spear were worth 25 fish. One knife and one fish hook were worth 13 fish. How many fish was each item worth?

Sometimes the best way to find an answer is to make a guess, test it, and use the results to help make the next guess, until you find the answer.

Solving the Problem

Think   What is the question?

Explore   How many fish are a hook and a spear worth? a knife and a spear? a knife and a hook? Guess how many fish a hook and a spear are each worth. Use that guess to see how many fish a knife is worth. How can you check to see if your guess was correct? What should you do if your guesses are not correct?

Solve   How many fish is each item worth?

Look Back   What if you had guessed that the hook was worth 8 fish and the spear was worth 12 fish? How would you know that is not correct?

Share Your Ideas

1. **What if** you had guessed that the fish hook was worth 12 fish and the spear was worth 8 fish? How would you know that is not correct?

Practice

 Solve. Use a calculator where appropriate.

2. The Alaskan research team is planning to explore part of the frozen tundra. Ten members of the team each have a dog team. There are 56 huskies all together. If there are only 7- and 5-dog teams, how many of each will there be?

3. The research team collected 40 samples of whale bones and walrus bones. They sent $\frac{1}{2}$ of the walrus bones and $\frac{1}{3}$ of the whale bones back to the main base. The other 25 samples were stored for the next trip. How many of each kind of bone did they send back?

4. At the end of a dig, the archaeologists entered the results in their journal. They had gathered a total of 108 samples. They had 3 times as many fossils as arrowheads. They had $\frac{1}{7}$ as many pieces of pottery as arrowheads, and $\frac{1}{3}$ as many tools as fossils. How many of each type of relic did they find?

5. The combined weight of the fossils and arrowheads was 9 pounds. The fossils were 2 times as heavy as the arrowheads. What was the weight of each?

Mixed Strategy Review

6. The astronauts will be doing a total of 135 experiments during their 5 days in space. They will run the same number of tests on days 2, 3, and 4. If they run 35 tests on day 1, how many tests will they do on day 5?

7. The research team awoke to find that the temperature was −11 degrees Fahrenheit. Later the temperature warmed up to 15 degrees Fahrenheit. That night the temperature decreased by 23 degrees Fahrenheit. What was the low temperature that night?

Create Your Own

Look at **7.** Write a problem that involves working with temperatures below 0 degrees Fahrenheit.

Activity

Exploring Square Roots

What dimensions would you choose to make a square with an area of 2,500 square units?

When a number s is multiplied by itself, the product, s^2, is the square of the number.

$$5 \cdot 5 = 5^2 = 25 \qquad 8 \cdot 8 = 8^2 = 64$$

The **square root** of a number n, written $\sqrt{n}$, is a number whose square is n.

$$\sqrt{25} = 5 \qquad \sqrt{64} = 8$$

When s is a whole number, s^2 is a **perfect square.**

25 and 64 are perfect squares.

Working together

Materials: grid paper, calculator

A. Use grid paper to draw six squares. Use a chart to record the area of each square and the length of each side.

B. Find out whether 256 is a perfect square. Could you use grid paper? Could you use a calculator without a square root key? Explain. Use your method to tell whether 300 is a perfect square.

Sharing Your Results

1. Compare your method with those of other groups.

2. Use your chart to write all the squares and their square roots that you found.

3. Explain how you would test whether a number is a perfect square.

4. What is the square root of 2,500?

Extending the Activity

5. Look at the pattern of squares in the design at the right. Record how many squares of each design appear.

a. How many ?

b. How many ?

c. How many ?

d. How many ?

e. How many ?

f. How many ?

6. Find a pattern in this table of sums.
- How does the table represent the pattern of squares above? Extend the pattern for three more rows.
- What numbers are being added?
- How is the sum related to the number of addends?

$$1 = 1 = 1^2$$
$$1 + 3 = 4 = 2^2$$
$$1 + 3 + 5 = 9 = 3^2$$
$$1 + 3 + 5 + 7 = 16 = 4^2$$
$$1 + 3 + 5 + 7 + 9 = 25 = 5^2$$

7. Use the pattern you found to write the sum of the first 20 odd numbers.

8. How many addends are in this sum?
$1 + 3 + 5 + \ldots + 49$ Use the number of addends to help you find the sum.

9. Make up other sums like this and exchange with another group to solve.

Summing Up

10. Explain why squaring a number and finding the square root are inverse operations.

11. How many perfect squares are there? Think about pairing each square with the positive integer that is its square root. What can you conclude?

12. $5^2 = 25$ What is $(^-5)^2$? How many square roots does 25 have? $^-\sqrt{25}$ means the negative square root of 25. Find the negative square root of each number.

a. $^-\sqrt{36}$ **b.** $^-\sqrt{64}$ **c.** $^-\sqrt{100}$

Activity

Understanding and Estimating Square Roots

The area of a square is 72 square units. What is the length of each side of the square?

Working together

Materials: grid paper, calculator

A. Can you draw a square on grid paper whose area is close to but less than 72 square units? Record the length of the side and the area.

B. Draw a second square whose area is close to but greater than 72 square units. Record the length of the side and the area.

C. Which square has an area closer to 72 square units? Use the dimensions of each square to estimate the length of a side of a square whose area is 72 square units.

Sharing Your Results

1. What was the length of the side of the smaller square? the larger square?

2. What length did you estimate for the side of a square whose area is 72 square units?

3. Use a calculator to check your results. Revise your estimate if necessary.

4. **What if** your calculator does not have a square root key? How can you use it to check your results?

5. How would you estimate $\sqrt{32}$? Explain your method and compare your results.

202

Extending the Activity

The graph below relates the numbers from 0 to 100 and their positive square roots.

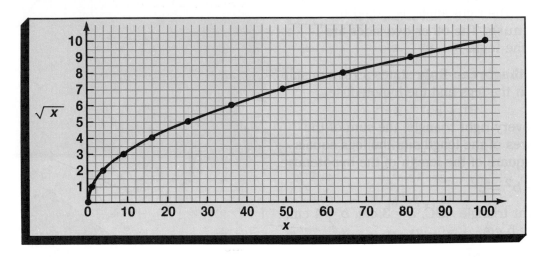

6. Use the graph to name each square root.

   a. $\sqrt{25}$ **b.** $\sqrt{49}$ **c.** $\sqrt{81}$ **d.** $\sqrt{100}$

7. Use the graph to estimate each square root.

   a. $\sqrt{40}$ **b.** $\sqrt{89}$ **c.** $\sqrt{32}$ **d.** $\sqrt{67}$ **e.** $\sqrt{53}$

8. Use a calculator or the square root tables on page 535 to check your results in exercise **7.**

9. A diagonal of a square is $\sqrt{2}$ times the length of one side. How long is the diagonal of a square 68 cm on a side?

10. The height of an equilateral triangle is $\frac{\sqrt{3}}{2}$ times the length of one side. What is the height of an equilateral triangle whose side equals 28 cm?

Summing Up

11. If s is the square root of n, then $s^2 = n$. What equation can you write if c is the cube root of n?

12. Estimate the cube root of 50. Guess and use a calculator to check.

Missing Sides of Right Triangles

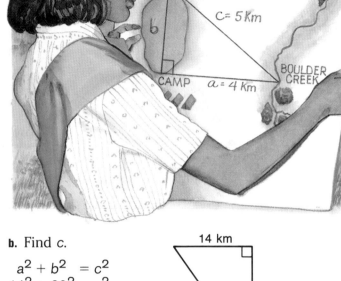

An explorer scout wants to find the distance from the meadow to the camp across the lake. She knows the distances from the creek to the camp and from the creek to the meadow. Use the Pythagorean Rule and the triangle she has drawn to find the distance b.

$$a^2 + b^2 = c^2$$
$$4^2 + b^2 = 5^2$$
$$16 + b^2 = 25$$
$$b^2 = 25 - 16$$
$$b^2 = 9$$
$$\sqrt{b^2} = \sqrt{9}$$
$$b = 3$$

The distance is 3 kilometers.

More Examples

a. Find a.

$$a^2 + b^2 = c^2$$
$$a^2 + 7^2 = 25^2$$
$$a^2 + 49 = 625$$
$$a^2 = 625 - 49$$
$$a^2 = 576$$
$$a = \sqrt{576}$$
$$a = 24 \text{ m}$$

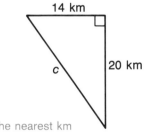

b. Find c.

$$a^2 + b^2 = c^2$$
$$14^2 + 20^2 = c^2$$
$$196 + 400 = c^2$$
$$596 = c^2$$
$$\sqrt{596} = c$$
$$24 \text{ km} = c \leftarrow \text{to the nearest km}$$

Check Your Understanding

For each right triangle, find the missing measure, to the nearest unit.

1.

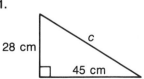

2.

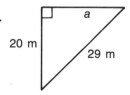

3.

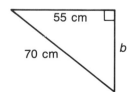

Share Your Ideas   Describe a situation where using the Pythagorean Rule would help you find a measure.

Find each missing measure, to the nearest unit.

4.
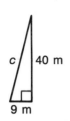
c / 40 m / 9 m

5.
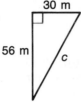
30 m / 56 m / c

6.
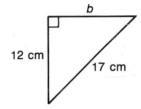
b / 12 cm / 17 cm

7.
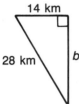
14 km / 28 km / b

8.
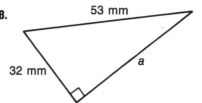
53 mm / 32 mm / a

9.
a / a / 32 m

For each right triangle, find the missing measure, to the nearest unit.

10. $a = 10$ m
   $b =$ _____
   $c = 19$ m

11. $a =$ _____
   $b = 11$ cm
   $c = 41$ cm

12. $a = 10$ m
   $b = 17$ m
   $c =$ _____

13. $a =$ _____
   $b = 72$ mm
   $c = 105$ mm

14. $a =$ _____
   $b = 200$ km
   $c = 400$ km

15. $a = 120$ cm
   $b =$ _____
   $c = 300$ cm

16. $a = 1$ m
   $b =$ _____
   $c = \sqrt{2}$ m

17. $a = 20.5$ mm
   $b = 10.5$ mm
   $c =$ _____

18. $a = \sqrt{3}$ cm
   $b = \sqrt{13}$ cm
   $c =$ _____

Think and Apply

19. A pole holding up the tent in camp has a rope tied to a peg 2 meters away. The rope is 3 meters long from the top of the pole to the peg. How high is the pole, to the nearest meter?

20. The scouts hiked from the creek to the foot of the hills. What is the shortest distance they might have hiked?

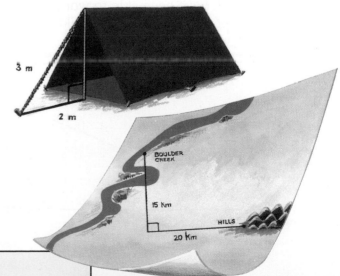

Write a problem that uses the Pythagorean Rule. Exchange it with a friend to solve.

SUMMING UP

Using Problem Solving

What Is the Quickest Route?

Charles was studying the map. "If I take the route from Aberdine straight south to Benton and then straight west to Chadwick, I can go 30 miles an hour. If I go straight across country from Aberdine to Chadwick, I can go only 15 miles an hour."

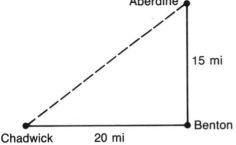

Aberdine

15 mi

Benton

Chadwick 20 mi

Use a calculator to help you solve these problems.

A. Which is the quickest route for Charles to travel from Aberdine to Chadwick?

B. About how much faster would Charles have to travel so the slower route would become the faster route?

Sharing Your Ideas

1. How were you able to find the distance of the missing route?

2. Would you have been able to work the problem if the map had looked like this? Why or why not?

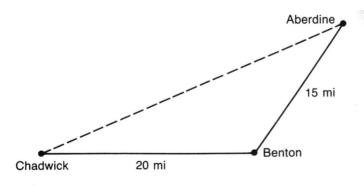

Aberdine

15 mi

Benton

Chadwick 20 mi

Practice

 Use your calculator when appropriate.

3. About how far is it from town A to town C?

4. The distance from town E to F is the same as from town F to G. About how far is it?

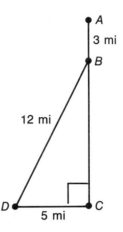

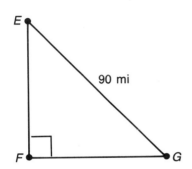

5. Mindy is trying to catch her rope in a bracket about 30 ft up in a tree. She needs about 20 ft of extra rope so she can throw easily. She is going to stand about 30 ft from the tree. What is the least amount of rope that she can use?

6. A cat corners a mouse atop the sail of a sailboat. The mouse slides down the sail at 10 ft per second. The cat runs from one end of the sail to the other at 5 ft per second. Do you think the mouse will get away? Explain.

7. A 35-ft telephone pole needs a support wire attached at the top of the pole to a point in the ground 20 ft away from the pole. About how long should the wire be?

8. A firetruck with a 45-ft ladder responds to a fire. The fire fighters need to rescue someone who is at a window 40 ft high. The ladder is on the truck 7 ft off the ground. If the ladder is 20 ft from the building, can they rescue the person? Explain.

Summing Up

9. Write a problem about using a ladder to clean out the gutters of a house.

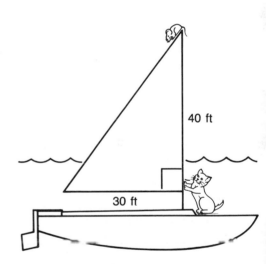

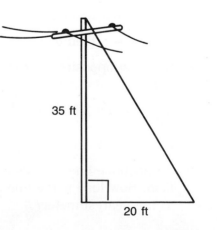

Chapter Review

Express each as a quotient of two integers in lowest terms. pages 180–181

1. $^-3$

2. $^-2.15$

3. 0.5

4. $\dfrac{^-24}{^-6}$

5. $9\dfrac{1}{3}$

Compare. Write <, >, or = for each ⬤. pages 182–183

6. $\dfrac{^-5}{6}$ ⬤ $\dfrac{^-2}{3}$

7. $\dfrac{1}{8}$ ⬤ $\dfrac{1}{4}$

8. $^-3.1$ ⬤ 4.5

9. 5.8 ⬤ $^-16$

10. $^-7$ ⬤ 5

Add, subtract, multiply, or divide. pages 184–187

11. $4.21 - 6.85$

12. $\dfrac{^-3}{10} - \dfrac{^-6}{10}$

13. $15 \cdot {}^-3.5$

14. $\dfrac{5}{6} \cdot \dfrac{^-3}{4}$

15. $\dfrac{1}{8} \div \dfrac{^-5}{8}$

16. $^-12.92 + {}^-1.35$

17. $\dfrac{^-3}{4} + \dfrac{^-1}{2}$

18. $^-19 - {}^-27$

19. $\dfrac{1}{4} \div \dfrac{^-2}{3}$

20. $0.8 - {}^-2.4$

21. $^-1.2 - {}^-5.8$

22. $7.14 \div {}^-3$

Solve. pages 188–189

23. $\dfrac{1}{6} + \dfrac{y}{6} = \dfrac{5}{6}$

24. $\dfrac{^-x}{2} + \dfrac{3}{4} = \dfrac{12}{5}$

25. $8.6t - 9.44 = 31.84$

Write each as a power of 10. pages 190–191

26. 0.001

27. $10{,}000$

28. 0.000001

29. $100{,}000{,}000$

30. 0.00000001

Write each in scientific notation. pages 192–195

31. $71{,}600{,}000$

32. 0.000037

33. $3{,}580{,}000{,}000$

34. 0.0000000047

Find each square root. pages 200–203

35. $\sqrt{144}$

36. $\sqrt{81}$

37. $\sqrt{64}$

38. $\sqrt{400}$

39. $^-\sqrt{225}$

Find each missing side. pages 204–207

40. hypotenuse = 25 cm   leg = 20 cm

41. leg = 9 m   leg = 12 m

Complete each statement.

42. If $q \times q = r$, then q is the ___ of r.

43. The side opposite the right angle of a right triangle is the ___.

44. The number 3.58×10^{-4} is written in ___ notation.

Words to Know

scientific
square root
hypotenuse
leg

Solve. pages 197–199

45. A telephone line crosses a field. How long is the line to the nearest meter?

200 m   x
400 m

46. The sum of two rational numbers is 11. The greater number is 4 times the other number. What are the numbers?

Chapter Test

Express each as the quotient of two integers in lowest terms.

1. $6\frac{1}{8}$

2. $^-5.38$

Compare. Write <, >, or = for each ●.

3. $\frac{^-5}{8}$ ● $\frac{^-3}{4}$

4. $^-0.8$ ● $^-0.9$

5. $1\frac{3}{5}$ ● $^-1\frac{1}{2}$

Add, subtract, multiply, or divide.

6. $7.72 - 9.46$

7. $\frac{^-5}{6} + \frac{2}{3}$

8. $\frac{^-2}{3} \cdot \frac{3}{10}$

9. $^-9.8 \div 2.8$

10. $1.4 \cdot {^-4.7}$

11. $\frac{^-4}{9} \div \frac{7}{9}$

Solve.

12. $\frac{1}{2} + \frac{y}{3} = \frac{2}{3}$

13. $\frac{^-x}{6} + \frac{^-3}{2} = \frac{9}{4}$

14. $2.8t - 6.16 = 8.12$

Write each as a single power of 10.

15. $100{,}000$

16. $10^{-6} \cdot 10^{-9}$

17. 0.001

Write each in scientific notation.

18. 0.000017

19. $6{,}590{,}000{,}000$

Find each square root.

20. $\sqrt{169}$

21. $\sqrt{49}$

Find each missing side.

22.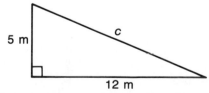

23.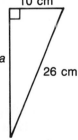

Solve.

24. The distance from the top of a 30-m building to the outermost edge of its shadow is 50 m. How long is the shadow?

25. The product of 2 rational numbers x and $x + 1.1$ is 6.2. What are the numbers?

THINK   A number x is divided by 8. Then 10 is subtracted from the quotient. The result is 4. What is x?

EXTENSION

Triangles and the Pythagorean Rule

Materials: straws, scissors, cm ruler

The Pythagorean Rule states that a triangle that satisfies the condition $a^2 + b^2 = c^2$, where c is the longest side, is a right triangle.

What about the triangles that do not satisfy the rule? Is there some way that the Pythagorean Rule can be used to classify them?

Use a calculator to complete the first two blank columns of this chart.

	Lengths of Sides in centimeters			$a^2 + b^2$	c^2	Type of Triangle
	a	b	c			
1.	3	4	5.5			
2.	3	4	4.5			
3.	11	12	13			
4.	12	13	18.2			
5.	8	10	14			
6.	10	14	20			
7.	8	10	11			
8.	5	8	10			
9.	6	9	9			

Cut straws into the given lengths and construct each triangle in the chart. Classify your constructions as acute or obtuse triangles. Record your findings in the chart.

Examine the relationship between c^2 and $a^2 + b^2$ and the triangle's classification.

10. What general rule can you make that will allow you to classify a triangle if you know the lengths of its sides?

11. Choose 3 lengths that will form an acute triangle. (Remember, in any triangle the sum of the lengths of two sides must exceed the third.)

12. Choose 3 lengths that will form an obtuse triangle.

Chapters 4 through 6 of this book presented topics in geometry, algebra, and rational numbers.

Watch Your Step!

One way that algebra is different from arithmetic is in the numbers that are used. Arithmetic uses only positive numbers. In algebra, negative numbers and positive numbers are used.

Play the following game with your family. The object of the game is to climb the ladder.

1. Write the following numbers on index cards or on slips of paper.

0 1, ⁻1, 2, ⁻2, 3, ⁻3, 4, ⁻4

You should have 9 cards in all.

2. Turn the cards facedown on the table. Each player draws one card and moves up or down the ladder the number of steps shown on the card. The beginning position is on the zero step. Return the card and reshuffle each time.

3. There are two ways you can win the game.

   a. The first player to go above the top of the ladder (12) wins.

   b. The last player remaining in the game wins.

   If a player falls off the ladder, by going below ⁻12, he or she is out of the game.

4. Each player keeps track of his or her position on the ladder by making a chart like the one shown below.

Notice that your End number becomes your Begin number in the next round of drawing.

Joe	Position		
Round	Begin	Card Drawn	End
1	0 +	⁻1	= ⁻1
2	⁻1 +	3	= 2
3	2 +	4	= 6

Ladder

12	12	
11	11	
10	10	
9	9	
8	8	
7	7	POSITIVE
6	6	
5	5	
4	4	
3	3	
2	2	
1	1	
0	ZERO	0
⁻1	⁻1	
⁻2	⁻2	
⁻3	⁻3	
⁻4	⁻4	
⁻5	⁻5	
⁻6	⁻6	
⁻7	⁻7	NEGATIVE
⁻8	⁻8	
⁻9	⁻9	
⁻10	⁻10	
⁻11	⁻11	
⁻12	⁻12	

After the game is over, discuss how positive and negative numbers are used in real life. Is football a good example? How many different examples can you name?

7 Statistics

Sharing What You Know

Which peanut butter tastes best? Do you buy cassettes, CD's, or records? What dog food do you feed your dog? These are some of the questions a company doing market research might ask. Businesses want to find out what products people like and don't like. They have people try different brands and pick the one they like best. Companies then use this information to create new products or improve old ones. How might market researchers use mathematics?

Using Language

When you buy one product rather than another, you are making a choice. The market researcher who records your decision is gathering facts or data. **Statistics** is the science of collecting, organizing, and analyzing data. How could **statistics** be used to determine the top ten albums? What other information could **statistics** describe?

Words to Know line plot, mode, range, median, stem and leaf plot, box and whisker plot, mean, scattergram, correlation, frequency table, histogram

Be a Problem Solver

One person in 10 preferred product A while one person in 5 preferred product B. Which product had more sales?

Write a story about the person who preferred product A. What data did he or she use to make the choice?

Activity

Exploring Sampling

The eighth-grade social committee is planning a dance for February 14. All students from the sixth-, seventh-, and eighth-grade classes will be invited. Since all 1,000 students cannot be polled, how can the committee find out student preferences for music, refreshments, and decorations?

Working together

Select a random sample of students and use a questionnaire to poll their preferences.

A. Prepare a questionnaire on student preferences for the dance. Each question should include a first, second, and third choice.

B. Discuss several ways to select a random sample of students in your class.

C. Select 5 students according to the method you think is most likely to be random.

D. Present your questionnaire to the sample of students you have chosen and then to the entire class.

E. Record your results for the 5 students you selected and also for the whole class.

Sharing Your Results

1. Describe your method for selecting a random sample. Explain why you believe it is valid.

2. Present the results of your questionnaire. How did your sample group respond? How did this response compare with that of the entire class?

3. How confident are you that your results are representative of the class preferences? Would you change your method of sampling? Why or why not?

Extending the Activity

A question may be asked in a way that suggests an expected or correct response. Such a question is a **biased** question. If a question does not suggest what the answer should be, the question is **unbiased,** or neutral.

4. The committee for the dance included this question in its survey: Which do you prefer, a lively, professional local band or an amateur DJ with recordings made at a dance studio? Is this a biased or neutral question? If biased, how could you rewrite it to make it neutral?

5. Study the magazine advertisement. Is it biased? Why or why not? Does the ad make any claims or promises?

6. Write your own advertisement for a product that suggests what the product will do without actually making a promise. Is your ad biased? Why or why not?

7. List three situations in which biased questions might be asked. Explain why such questions might be asked. Then choose one situation and write two questions, one biased and one neutral. Which question was easier to write? Explain.

8. Find examples of biased questions in newspapers and magazines. For each example, try to give a reason why the question was written in a biased form.

Summing Up

9. The school cafeteria asked the following question in a random survey. Most students chose **b.** Should the cafeteria conclude that this is the students' favorite food? Explain.

   Which of these foods do you like best?
   a. green beans **b.** pizza **c.** creamed corn

10. An advertisement reads, "63% of all dentists surveyed recommend Scrubola Toothpaste." What questions should you ask about that statement?

DO YOU WANT CLEANER, WHITER TEETH? THEN USE SCRUBOLA TOOTHPASTE.

Midchapter Review

Make a line plot and a stem and leaf plot for each set of data. Then find the mode, median, and range for each. pages 220–223

1. 28, 31, 25, 42, 22, 24, 25, 29, 32, 31, 31, 33, 35, 33, 33, 40, 39, 33

2. 3, 4, 6, 6, 8, 10, 8, 10, 2, 6, 7, 9, 9, 6, 6, 5, 4, 6, 2, 9, 7

Make a box and whisker plot for each set of data, using a single number line. pages 224–225

3. Weekly income for after-school jobs
   Jane: $18, 14, 14, 13, 10, 15, 16
   Mei Hua: $17, 16, 18, 12, 13, 10, 16

4. Closing price per share of stock
   PLAY Toys: $38, 35, 37, 35, 34
   READ Books: $39, 32, 31, 35, 39

Complete. Use the line plot for 5–8.

5. The scores have a _____ of 30.

6. 85 is the _____.

7. 87 is the _____.

8. The _____, or average, of the scores is 87.6.

9. "Why did everyone do so poorly?" is a _____ question.

10. A box and whisker plot divides the data into _____.

11. Two sets of quiz grades could be presented in a back-to-back _____.

12. _____ is the study of organized data.

13. The mode, mean, and median are _____.

Words to Know
quartiles
mode
median
measures of central tendency
biased
range
mean
statistics
stem and leaf plot

Solve.

14. Make a back-to-back stem and leaf plot. Which team do you think had the better season? Use measures of central tendency to explain.

	POINTS PER GAME
Ferrets	120, 110, 108, 110, 115, 121, 132, 106, 116, 100, 98, 115, 118
Ocelots	118, 117, 108, 116, 116, 116, 117, 106, 104, 99, 115, 114, 116

15. Colleen scored the following points in each of 5 games. What score should she make in the sixth game for an average of 105 points per game? 92, 105, 116, 99, 120

Exploring Problem Solving

Vacation Spots

The chart below uses $100 worth of goods or services in
New York City as an index base for comparing costs. A
hotel room that would cost $100 in New York would cost
the following amount in each of these cities. The chart also
shows the normal high temperatures for June.

City	Cost Index (NY = $100)	Normal June High Temp. Degrees F	City	Cost Index (NY = $100)	Normal June High Temp. Degrees F
Amsterdam	$ 77	66	Madrid	$ 94	84
Athens	65	88	Mexico City	59	75
Bangkok	49	91	Nairobi	61	70
Brussels	83	70	Oslo	134	66
Cairo	58	95	Paris	87	72
Copenhagen	115	70	Seoul	90	81
Dublin	92	64	Singapore	86	88
Geneva	112	73	Stockholm	122	66
Hong Kong	72	84	Sydney	92	61
Lisbon	63	93	Tokyo	196	77
London	94	68	Vienna	90	75

Thinking Critically

Which cities are the least expensive to visit? Which ones
are coolest in June? Is there a relationship between the
cost of a vacation and the normal high temperature?

Analyzing and Making Decisions

1. Which are the most expensive cities? the least
   expensive?

2. Which cities are the warmest? the coolest?

3. Make a graph. Let the horizontal axis be the Cost Index.
   Let the vertical axis be the June High Temperature. What
   range of values should you use for each axis? What are
   the indexes for the least and most expensive cities? What
   are the temperatures for the warmest and coolest cities?
   Plot and label each city.

4. Is there a relationship between the temperature and
   cost? Are there any exceptions to the patterns you see?

Look Back   Is there a relationship between latitude and
temperature? Look up the latitudes and decide.

Problem Solving Strategies

Divide and Conquer

The 10 members of the Great Rink Skating Club wanted to buy classy satin jackets and silk shirts. Jackets cost either $24.50 or $37.90 each. Shirts were $12.90 or $17.70 each. They could not decide which kind to buy. They decided to have a flea market and then buy the most expensive combination they could afford. They raised $540. Which jackets and shirts will they buy?

If a problem offers a choice or if it has several parts in its solution, a good plan is to solve each part separately. Then compare the results to find the solution.

Solving the Problem

 Use a calculator where appropriate.

Think   What is the question?

Explore   How much does each jacket cost? How much does each shirt cost? How much does each combination of a jacket and a shirt cost? What is the cost of 10 jackets and shirts of each type? How much money was raised?

Solve   What jackets and shirts should they buy?

Look Back   Could they have bought other combinations? Explain.

Share Your Ideas

1. One of the members suggested that each member contribute $1.60 before they bought their jackets. Why, do you think, this was suggested?

Practice

 Solve.   Use a calculator where appropriate.

Less Dollars Car Rental
$39 per day
$189 per week

Less By Day Car Rental
$30 per day
$210 per week

2. Mr. Andrews will be renting a car for 12 days. Which car rental company will charge him less for the car? Explain.

3. What if Mr. Andrews wants to rent a car for 14 days? Which company should he rent it from? Explain.

4. Ms. Johnson wants to hire a lawn service for May through September. She thinks she will need to have the yard cut 5 times a month. Which service should she choose? Explain.

5. What if Ms. Johnson thinks she can get by with only 4 cuts a month? Which service should she choose?

CREATIVE SCAPES
MONTHLY FEE $67.00
UP TO 5 CUTS A MONTH

OAKLEAF COMPANY
$15.00 PER LAWN CUTTING

Mixed Strategy Review

Use this information to solve 6–7.

Rhonda must choose between two summer jobs. As a lifeguard she could earn $3.75 an hour and work 5 days a week from 2:00 P.M. to 10:00 P.M. As a camp counselor she would work 5 days a week from 8:00 A.M. to 3:30 P.M. and earn $4 per hour.

6. Which job pays more? Explain.

7. Which job has longer hours? Explain.

Use this information to solve 8–9.

Penn has to board his two dogs for a week. The Harvest Home Kennel charges $13 per day for dogs over 100 lb and $10 a day for other dogs. The Dog House Kennel charges $12 a day for dogs over 80 lb and $11 a day for other dogs.

8. A friend of Penn's paid $65 to board one dog at one of the two kennels. Which kennel did he use? Explain.

9. Where should Penn board his dogs?

Create
Your Own

Write a problem where the person who solves it must make a choice.

How could the principal estimate the number of eighth graders in next year's class? Think of several ways.

Drawing Inferences

The table and the graph both display U.S. Census population figures. How can you estimate the population for 1975?

Read the value on the graph at the point representing 1975. About 210 million people were included in the U.S. population in 1975.

Estimating values between two known values is called **interpolation.**

To estimate the population after 1980, extend the graph along the line determined by the last few points on the graph.

What is the expected population for the year 2010?

Estimating values beyond known values is called **extrapolation.**

You can also extrapolate values by calculating the difference between values in the table. Look for a pattern.

What is the change in population between 1960 and 1970? between 1970 and 1980? What increase in population might you expect between 1980 and 1990?

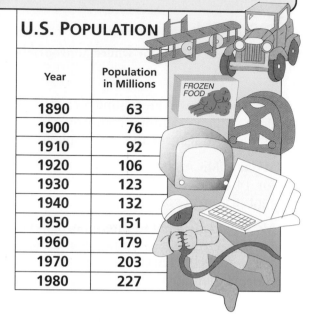

U.S. POPULATION

Year	Population in Millions
1890	63
1900	76
1910	92
1920	106
1930	123
1940	132
1950	151
1960	179
1970	203
1980	227

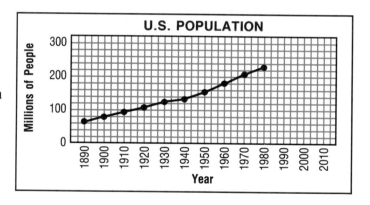

U.S. POPULATION

Check Your Understanding

Graph the data in the table. Use the graph to estimate the number of eighth graders enrolled each year.

1. 1977   **2.** 1990   **3.** 1995   **4.** 2000

Use data patterns in the table to estimate the number of eighth graders enrolled each year.

5. 1990   **6.** 1995   **7.** 2000

Share Your Ideas Which method, extending graphs or finding differences, is more accurate? Why do you think so?

EIGHTH-GRADE ENROLLMENT	
1960	249
1965	261
1970	294
1975	329
1980	361
1985	402

Use the table and graph on bacteria for 8–10.

8. Estimate the number of bacteria in the culture after $3\frac{1}{2}$ h and after $5\frac{1}{2}$ h.

9. Look for a pattern. How many bacteria do you expect to find in the culture after 10 hours?

10. Use a calculator to estimate the number of bacteria in the culture after 20 hours.

Use the table and graph on the mile run for 11–14.

11. What does the graph show about changes in the world record for the mile?

12. Estimate what the world record might have been in 1929.

13. What might the record be in 2100?

14. If a 3-minute mile is humanly possible, when might it happen?

Think and Apply

15. Copy the graph below and sketch what you think the graph will look like for August through December.

16. Can you extrapolate a reasonable reading for August from the graph at the right? for November? Why or why not?

17. Can you use calculated differences to find a reasonable temperature for August through December? If so, how?

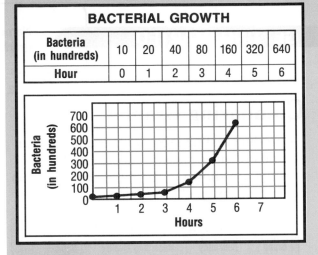

BACTERIAL GROWTH

Bacteria (in hundreds)	10	20	40	80	160	320	640
Hour	0	1	2	3	4	5	6

WORLD RECORDS FOR THE MILE

Year	Time	Year	Time
1868	4:29	1944	4:01.6
1882	4:19.2	1954	3:58
1913	4:14.6	1967	3:51.1
1923	4:10.4	1979	3:49
1934	4:06.8	1985	3:46.32

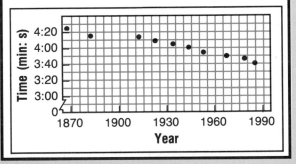

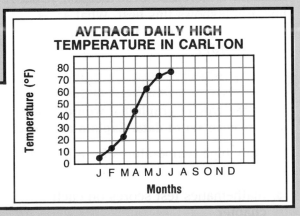

AVERAGE DAILY HIGH TEMPERATURE IN CARLTON

Month	Temp	Month	Temp
January	5°F	May	62°F
February	12°F	June	73°F
March	22°F	July	79°F
April	45°F		

How reliable can a prediction be that is based on data about past trends? What factors could influence a trend in population growth?

Activity

Exploring Scattergrams

What is the relationship between a student's age and grade level? How can you show that relationship?

Working together

Materials: grid paper

A **scattergram** is a graph made by plotting points on a coordinate plane.

A. Make a scattergram by plotting points representing the grade levels and corresponding ages of 30 students listed in the table. Plot grade level on the horizontal axis and age on the vertical axis.

B. Draw a line through the cluster of points on your graph so that the line passes close to as many points as possible.

C. Find the median and range of ages for each grade level. Label the point for the median age for each grade on the graph.

Grade Level	Age (months)
3	97
8	157
5	126
4	111
6	129
6	114
7	149
4	105
6	138
6	133
8	164
3	102
5	138
7	162
4	114
8	178
3	90
7	128
4	102
8	138
5	112
4	106
5	120
6	133
3	100
3	92
5	116
8	163
7	147
7	150

Sharing Your Results

The graph shows that age and grade level are **correlated**, or related.

1. If you know a student is in the sixth grade, what can you say about the student's age?

2. If you know a student is 125 months old, what can you say about the student's grade level?

3. The closer the points are to the line drawn through them, the better or more reliable the correlation. How close does the line come to the median points?

4. Does the line slant up or down as you move from left to right? Does a student's age increase or decrease as the grade level increases?

Extending the Activity

When the variables in a correlation both increase or both decrease at the same time, the correlation is **positive.** When one variable decreases as the other increases, the correlation is **negative.**

5. **Look back** at the correlation between student age and grade level. Is that correlation positive or negative? Explain.

6. Make a scattergram showing the correlation between temperature and ticket sales. Draw a line through the points as you did before. What type of correlation do you see?

7. How does the slant of the line you drew on each scattergram indicate whether the correlation is positive or negative?

In 1989 a study was conducted on the possible correlation between population density and highway safety. Data from the study are listed in the table.

8. Make a scattergram of the data and identify the correlation it shows. Try to give a reason for such a correlation.

9. Sometimes there is no correlation between two sets of data. How do you think a graph might show this?

TEMPERATURE AND LIFT TICKET SALES	
Temp.(°F)	Sales
45	97
40	239
35	417
32	885
30	1,079
25	1,152
20	1,277
15	1,385

POPULATION DENSITY AND HIGHWAY SAFETY

State	A*	B**	State	A*	B**	State	A*	B**
AL	77	32	LA	95	29	OH	263	21
AK	1	20	ME	36	21	OK	44	19
AZ	24	39	MD	429	23	OR	27	27
AR	44	35	MA	733	17	PA	264	25
CA	151	24	MI	163	22	RI	898	18
CO	28	23	MN	51	16	SC	103	40
CT	638	18	MS	53	40	SD	9	22
DE	308	25	MO	71	25	TN	112	32
FL	180	32	MT	5	31	TX	54	23
GA	94	27	NB	21	24	UT	18	24
HI	150	19	NV	7	30	VT	55	24
ID	12	33	NH	102	21	VA	135	19
IL	205	22	NJ	986	19	WA	62	19
IN	153	26	NM	11	41	WV	81	36
IA	52	23	NY	370	24	WI	87	21
KS	29	25	NC	120	30	WY	5	25
KY	92	29	ND	9	17			

*Column A: Persons per square mile
**Column B: Auto fatalities per billion vehicle miles

Summing Up

10. Give an example of a positive correlation and explain how the variables are related.

11. Give an example of a negative correlation and explain how the variables are related.

Describe the mode and range of a set of data. Use 2, 5, 7, 6, 6 as an example.

Frequency Tables and Histograms

Taking a survey of 1,000 people creates a very large set of data. How can so much data be organized and displayed?

Large quantities of data can be organized in a **frequency table** and displayed in a **histogram.**

Study the frequency table and its histogram. Notice that 9 equal intervals were chosen to group the data. The frequency tells how many items occurred within each interval.

How many people reported an annual income between $15,000 and $19,999? Which interval represents almost $\frac{1}{4}$ of the wage earners surveyed?

To calculate the range and mode of data displayed in a frequency table, use the midpoint of each interval to represent the value of each item within the interval.

The **range** is the difference between the midpoint of the highest interval and the midpoint of the lowest interval.

The **mode** is the midpoint of the interval containing the greatest number of items. What is the mode?

frequency table

ANNUAL INCOME SURVEY OF 1,000 WAGE EARNERS	
Income	Frequency
$ 5,000–9,999	6
$10,000–14,999	43
$15,000–19,999	153
$20,000–24,999	167
$25,000–29,999	241
$30,000–34,999	176
$35,000–39,999	162
$40,000–44,999	49
$45,000–49,999	3

histogram

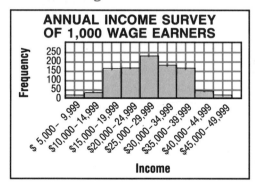

┌midpoint of highest interval

$47,500 − 7,500 = $40,000 ← range

↑
midpoint of lowest interval

1. Make a frequency table and a histogram for the state math test scores. Use intervals of 10–19, 20–29, . . .

2. Compute the range and the mode.

STATE MATH TEST SCORES																		
42	45	33	39	37	42	15	23	41	39	26	21	14	20	24	29	46	41	12	36
28	34	23	48	48	10	12	47	32	49	17	27	33	30	19	36	36	38	44	27

Share Your Ideas What are the advantages of grouping data in a frequency table? the disadvantages?

Use the data in the table at the right to answer 3–6.

3. Make a frequency table and a histogram. Use intervals of 20–29, 30–39, . . .

4. Use the frequency table to compute the range and the mode.

5. How many drivers in the study drive 50 or more miles per day?

6. How many drivers drive less than 40 miles per day?

Think and Apply

7. Make a histogram of the data on gasoline mileage.

8. Compute the range and the mode of the data on gasoline mileage.

9. How many cars get more than 35 miles per gallon?

10. How many cars get less than 16 miles per gallon?

11. The average miles per gallon of all cars in 1986 was 18.3. How many cars in this study exceeded this mileage? How many got poorer fuel economy?

12. Why are your answers to **11** approximate? What data would you need to get exact answers to these questions?

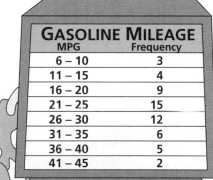

AUTOMOBILE MILEAGE STUDY: DAILY MILEAGE for 54 Drivers

25	37	35	79	39	67
53	58	89	37	71	55
51	80	68	67	42	84
42	78	50	33	37	42
29	54	85	32	67	65
41	56	58	71	36	52
73	35	34	22	38	82
54	29	32	86	55	43
35	43	64	87	67	31

GASOLINE MILEAGE

MPG	Frequency
6 – 10	3
11 – 15	4
16 – 20	9
21 – 25	15
26 – 30	12
31 – 35	6
36 – 40	5
41 – 45	2

Visual Thinking

13. Look at each line plot. Try to find the median without counting. How can you check your results?

```
                                              x
                        x    x x x        x
  x              x      x    x x x    x    x
  x x x    x      x x   x    x x x    x    x x
 ←┼─┼─┼─┼─┼─┼─┼─┼─┼─┼─┼─→   ←┼─┼─┼─┼─┼─┼─┼─┼─┼─┼─┼─→
  1 2 3 4 5 6 7 8 9 1011     1 2 3 4 5 6 7 8 9 1011
```

Are the mode and range calculated from a frequency table the same measures you would find using the original data? Explain.

SUMMING UP

Using Problem Solving

Who Is Top Dog?

There are 25 breeds of terriers in the dog show and two rings for judging them. Groups of dogs will be judged on an hourly basis. Judging should take no more than 7–8 hours in all. About 2 to 3 minutes are allotted per dog.

Breed	Entrants	Breed	Entrants	Breed	Entrants
A. Airedale Terriers	11	J. Fox Terriers (smooth)	15	S. Scottish Terriers	12
B. American Staffordshire	18	K. Fox Terriers (wire)	16	T. Sealyham Terriers	8
C. Australian Terriers	11	L. Irish Terriers	20	U. Skye Terriers	13
D. Bedlington Terriers	9	M. Kerry Blue Terriers	15	V. Soft-coated Wheaten	13
E. Border Terriers	13	N. Lakeland Terriers	15	W. Staffordshire Bull Terriers	1
F. Bull Terriers (white)	4	O. Manchester Terriers	3	X. Welsh Terriers	6
G. Bull Terriers (Other)	9	P. Miniature Schnauzers	14	Y. West Highland White Terriers	21
H. Cairn Terriers	26	Q. Norfolk Terriers	14		
I. Dandie Dinmont Terriers	12	R. Norwich Terriers	21		

Working together

Organize the information in a chart to help you make a schedule for the judges.

A. How many dogs are there altogether? How many judging rings are there? How many groups of dogs are there?

B. There are two rings and a judge in each ring. If about 2 min is allotted for each dog, how long will the judging take? If about 3 min is allotted for each dog, how long will the judging take?

C. Do you think you will need to combine some groups of dogs? Why or why not?

Sharing Your Ideas

1. How long would you spend judging each dog? Explain.

2. What is the mean, the median, and the mode for the number of entrants in the groups of dogs? What is the range? How might this help you in scheduling?

3. Organize the groups with a stem and leaf plot. How might that help you in scheduling?

Extending Your Thinking

4. Write a schedule for the judging of the dog show. It should start at 9:00 A.M. and must end by 5:00 P.M. with an hour for lunch.

5. **What if** you only had 5 hours to judge the exhibit? Write a schedule for judging the dog show. It should start at 9:00 A.M. and end by 2:30 P.M. with a half an hour for lunch.

Summing Up

Answer 6 and 7 for both the five and one half and the eight-hour dog shows.

6. What is the greatest number of dogs that you would have judged at one time? What is the fewest number of dogs that you would have judged at one time? What is the average judging time per dog in each group?

7. How many breeds were judged by themselves? How many times did you combine two breeds? Did you ever combine 3 or more breeds?

8. Was it easier to schedule the judging for $5\frac{1}{2}$ hours or for 8 hours? Explain.

Chapter Review

Plot each set of data. Use the plots indicated. Find the mode, median, and range. pages 220–225

1. 35, 38, 28, 29, 35, 38, 42, 18, 16, 18, 19, 20, 28, 28, 31, 35
(line plot; stem and leaf plot)

2. 125, 128, 125, 129, 132, 142, 152, 108, 110, 111, 118, 125, 148, 127
(stem and leaf plot; box and whisker plot)

Use the graph at the right for 3–5. pages 232–235, 238–239

3. How many earmuffs were sold when the temperature dropped to 10°F?

4. Estimate the number of earmuffs sold when the temperature was 20°F.

5. Does there appear to be a correlation between temperature and sales? If so, what kind?

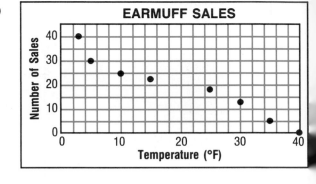

Use the graph at the right for 6–9. pages 226–227, 240–241

6. How many days had temperatures over 60°F?

7. What temperature represents the mode?

8. What was the range of temperatures?

9. More than half the days had temperatures over 50°F. Was the mode or median used to make this statement?

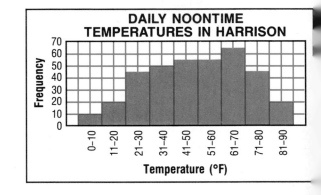

Match each phrase with the word that it describes.

10. estimating between known values

11. estimating beyond known values

12. graph made by plotting points on a coordinate plane

13. relationship between 2 sets of data

a. interpolation

b. correlation

c. scattergram

d. extrapolation

Solve. pages 229–231

14. Describe two ways a bar graph can be changed to affect the interpretation of the data.

15. On a Thursday and Friday, 35 and 50 pizzas were sold. On the same two nights the next week, 37 and 62 pizzas were sold. How much greater is the average number of pizzas sold on Friday than on Thursday?

Chapter Test

Make a line plot and a stem and leaf plot for each. Find the mode, median, and range of data in 1 and 2.

1. 5, 18, 18, 17, 2, 3, 5, 5, 5

2. 21, 21, 32, 41, 40, 32, 21, 26, 33

3. 150, 163, 151, 152, 171, 172, 150

4. 1,000; 1,100; 1,200; 1,010; 1,115; 1,222; 1,225

Use Graph A for 5–10, Graph B for 11–14, and Graph C for 15–18.

5. How could you alter the graph to suggest that the number of viewers was about the same each day?

6. How many viewers watch TV on Tuesday?

7. What is the average number of daily viewers?

8. Find the median.

9. Find the range of the number of viewers.

10. Which day had the least number of viewers?

11. Which type of recording had the greatest increase in shipments?

12. What was the dollar increase in cassette shipments from 1986 to 1987?

13. What was the dollar decrease in record shipments from 1986 to 1987?

14. Why was a double bar graph used for this set of data?

15. How many people scored above 60?

16. What was the range of scores?

17. Find the mode.

18. Draw a conclusion about the data.

Solve.

19. **Look back** at Graph **B**. About how many more dollars worth of cassettes than of CDs were shipped in 1987?

20. Use nine numbers. Create a set of data with a range of 16, a mode of 10, and a median of 18. What is the mean?

THINK   Complete the graph for 1990 and 1994.

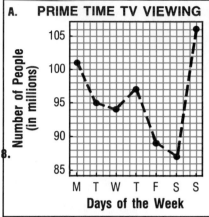

A. **PRIME TIME TV VIEWING**

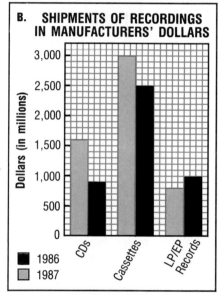

B. **SHIPMENTS OF RECORDINGS IN MANUFACTURERS' DOLLARS**

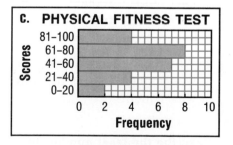

C. **PHYSICAL FITNESS TEST**

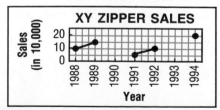

XY ZIPPER SALES

Binary Search

Mandy is working on her go-cart. She needs to tighten a bolt but is not sure of its size because of its location. Her socket set has 14 sockets as pictured. How can she find the correct socket?

1. **What if** Mandy starts with the smallest socket in her set and tries each in turn until she finds one that fits? How many trials would she have to make if the bolt was 1 inch?

Mandy thought of another way. Her first choice would be the $\frac{9}{16}$-inch socket. If it didn't fit, it would be either too small or too large. Next she would choose the middle socket in the appropriate half of the set.

Each choice reduces the number of sockets left to try by half. This method is called a **binary search.**

2. What is the least number of trials she would make by this method if the bolt was 1 inch?

Describe the least number of sockets that could be tried to find a match for each bolt, using a binary search.

3. $\frac{3}{16}$ inch

4. $\frac{7}{8}$ inch

5. $\frac{11}{16}$ inch

6. $\frac{3}{8}$ inch

7. $\frac{1}{4}$ inch

8. $\frac{3}{4}$ inch

Maintaining Skills

Choose the correct answer. Write A, B, C, or D.

1. $\angle ABD$ and $\angle CBE$ are _____ angles.

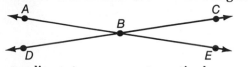

   A adjacent   C vertical

   B perpendicular   D not given

2. Two lines that do not intersect and that lie in different planes are _____ lines.

   A vertical   C congruent

   B skew   D not given

3. $^-8 + 6$

   A $^-14$ C 14

   B $^-2$ D not given

4. $^-8 \cdot {}^-20$

   A 160   C $^-160$

   B $^-180$ D not given

5. $^-81 \div {}^-3$

   A 27   C 29

   B $^-27$ D not given

6. Evaluate $\frac{x}{4} + 7$ for $x = {}^-12$.

   A 3   C 4

   B $^-4$ D not given

7. What is the opposite of $\frac{^-14}{15}$?

   A $\frac{^-14}{15}$ C $\frac{14}{15}$

   B $-\frac{14}{15}$ D not given

8. $^-3.7 + {}^-2.1$

   A $^-5.9$ C 5.9

   B 5.8   D not given

9. $1\frac{2}{3} \div 2\frac{1}{2}$

   A $\frac{2}{3}$ C $^-4\frac{1}{6}$

   B $-\frac{2}{3}$ D not given

10. What is 0.0001 written as a power of 10?

    A 10^4 C 10^3

    B 10^{-3} D not given

11. What is 42,300,000 written in scientific notation?

    A 423×10^5 C 4.23×10^7

    B 4.23×10^8 D not given

12. What is the mean of 8, 3, 7, 3, 6, 1, 1, 4, and 3?

    A 4   C 3

    B 7   D not given

13. What is the mode of 4.1, 3.2, 6.2, 4.1, 3.2, and 4.1?

    A 4.15   C 3

    B 4.1   D not given

Use guess and test to solve 14 and 15.

14. The area of a corral is 2,016 ft^2, and the perimeter is 180 ft. What are the dimensions of the corral?

    A 45 ft by 45 ft   C 40 ft by 50 ft

    B 42 ft by 48 ft   D not given

15. Find the number. The tens digit is 3 times greater than the ones digit. The hundreds digit is 1 more than the ones digit. The sum of the digits is 16.

    A 493   C 463

    B 862   D not given

8 Ratio and Proportion

Sharing What You Know

Have you ever heard older people tell about what it was like when they were your age? For example, the cost of a loaf of bread was so much less, or they had to walk so much farther to school. Certainly one change from those days is the number of cars on the roads. In 1960 there were only about 125,000,000 registered cars and trucks on the roads. Today there are more than 500,000,000, or half a billion! How have such changes affected our world? How can mathematics describe those changes?

Using Language

Not only has the number of cars increased, but also the speed at which they can travel. Most highways post speed limits in terms of a **ratio** between distance and time, or miles per hour. What does a speed limit of 55 mph mean? Discuss other ways that you use ratios.

Words to Know   distance, ratio, proportion, scale drawing, unit price, rate, precision of measurement

Be a Problem Solver

John cycles 2 miles to school each morning. He knows that he must average 10 miles per hour in order to get to school on time. One morning he averaged only 5 miles per hour for the first mile. How fast would he have to ride for the second mile in order to get to school on time?

Write explanations that John could use when he arrived late at school. Select the one that you think is best.

Yesterday you were younger than you are today. Today you are older than you were yesterday. How are these comparisons the same? How are they different?

Ratios and Equal Ratios

The largest animals that ever lived on Earth were the dinosaurs. *Tyrannosaurus rex* was about 540 cm high. The height of an average man is about 180 cm. How can you compare the height of the dinosaur with the height of a man?

▶ A **ratio** is a comparison between two quantities.

A ratio can be expressed in different ways.

540 : 180   540 ⟵ first term
            180 ⟵ second term

Read each ratio as 540 to 180.

The order in which the terms are expressed is important. 540 : 180 and 180 : 540 are different ratios.

How would the ratio change if you compared the height of a man with that of the dinosaur?

▶ You can multiply or divide to find equal ratios.

$$\frac{540}{180} = \frac{540 \div 180}{180 \div 180} = \frac{3}{1}$$

▶ You can use cross products to test whether two ratios are equal. If cross products are equal, the ratios are equal.

a.  ⟵ cross
                        ⟵ products

$4 \cdot 2 = 8 \cdot 1$

so $\frac{4}{8} = \frac{1}{2}$

b.

$1 \cdot 9 \neq 3 \cdot 6$

so $\frac{1}{3} \neq \frac{6}{9}$

Check Your Understanding

Write a ratio for each. Then write two equal ratios.

1. 5¢ sales tax per dollar

2. 6 pages out of 16

3. 2 min on; 3 s off

Write = or ≠ for each ⬤ .

4. $ .06 for $1 ⬤ $.07 for $2

5. $\frac{4}{30}$ ⬤ $\frac{7}{50}$

6. $\frac{12}{3}$ ⬤ $\frac{4}{1}$

Share Your Ideas How could you use division to test whether $\frac{9}{21}$ and $\frac{3}{7}$ are equal ratios?

Write a ratio in fraction form for each.

7. 6 shoes out of 10

8. 3 dogs out of 11 pets

9. 4 to 2

10. 10 days out of 13

11. 5 m to 24 mm

12. 14:35

13. 5 cars out of 500

14. 6 out of 11 people

15. 12 to 1

Write two equal ratios for each.

16. $\frac{1}{2}$

17. $\frac{6}{5}$

18. $\frac{16}{28}$

19. $\frac{110}{20}$

20. $\frac{1.5}{7}$

21. $\frac{100}{13}$

22. $\frac{1\frac{1}{4}}{3}$

23. $\frac{a}{b}$

Use the figure at the right to write a comparison for each ratio.

24. 3 to 6

25. 6 out of 9

26. 9 to 3

27. 1:9

Write = or ≠ for each ●.

28. 3:5 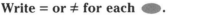 6:9   **29.** 1 to 2 ● 17 to 34   **30.** $\frac{2}{7}$ ● $\frac{6}{21}$

31. $\frac{3}{4}$ ● $\frac{75}{100}$ **32.** $\frac{1.5}{3}$ ● $\frac{2}{1}$ **33.** 1.5:3 ● 1:2

34. $\frac{1\frac{1}{2}}{3}$ ● $\frac{5}{10}$ **35.** $\frac{2\frac{1}{3}}{12}$ ● $\frac{3\frac{1}{3}}{36}$ **36.** x to y ● $2x$ to $2y$

37. $x:y$  $\frac{x}{2}:\frac{y}{2}$ **38.** $\frac{x}{y}$ ● $\frac{x+1}{y+1}$ **39.** $\frac{x}{y}$ ● $\frac{x-1}{y-1}$

40. Utah's Dinosaur National Monument was visited by 25 students on Monday. Fifty students were admitted Tuesday. Write two different ratios using these numbers and describe the comparisons they represent.

Test Taker

Analogies sometimes appear on tests. Notice how the first two words are related.

Addition is to subtraction as multiplication is to _____
The answer is *division*.
Complete each analogy below.

41. Rectangle:perimeter::circle: _____

42. Three:triangle::five: _____
43. Two:polygon::three: _____

Create a situation that can be described by the ratio $\frac{2}{5}$.

Sometimes buying a greater quantity gives you a better buy. How can you be sure? Which is the better buy, a pound for $3.00 or an ounce for $.20?

Rates

In the 1930s your great-grandfather might have paid $1 to have his lawn mowed 4 times. Today a student doing yardwork in the summer might charge $10 to mow one lawn.

A ratio can be used to compare the charge with the number of lawns mowed.

$1 for 4 lawns $\quad \dfrac{1}{4} \begin{array}{l}\longleftarrow \text{dollars} \\ \longleftarrow \text{lawns}\end{array}$ $10 for 1 lawn $\quad \dfrac{10}{1}$

▶ Ratios that compare quantities of different units are called **rates.**

What was the cost of mowing one lawn in the 1930s? Finding the cost of one lawn is finding the **unit price,** or unit rate.

$\dfrac{\$1}{4} = \dfrac{\$1 \div 4}{4 \div 4} = \dfrac{\$.25}{1}$ $\qquad$ The unit price was $.25.

Another Example

Find the price per pound if one quarter of a pound is $2.89.

$\begin{array}{l}\text{price} \longrightarrow \\ \text{pounds} \longrightarrow\end{array} \dfrac{\$2.89}{\frac{1}{4}} = \dfrac{\$2.89 \times 4}{\frac{1}{4} \times 4} = \dfrac{\$11.56}{1}$

One pound costs $11.56.

Write a ratio for each and find the unit rate.

1. 3 shirts for $45

2. $2.50 for 10 stamps

3. 4 beats in 2 notes

4. 2 teachers for 28 students

5. 165 miles in 3 hours

6. $\dfrac{1}{2}$ box for $1.65

Share Your Ideas $\dfrac{1}{4}$ bag for $2; 3 bags for $24. Find each unit price and explain your method.

Write three equal rates for each.

7. four cassettes for $10

8. 2 feet for $10.98

9. 2 doz for $9.98

10. $\frac{1}{2}$ lb for $2.39

11. 420 beats per hour

12. 3.5 mi in 28 min

Find the unit rate for each. Round to the nearest cent where appropriate. Use mental math, paper and pencil, or a calculator.

CHOICES

13. A racing car travels 180 miles in 1.5 hours.

14. In the 1960s a 5-lb bag of sugar cost $.29.

15. 1.5 pounds of cheese cost $3.98.

16. 25 people entered in half an hour.

17. 530 pages are $\frac{1}{3}$ of the book.

18. 32 books given to 16 students

19. 24 boards were used to replace 3 sections of the wall.

20. 10 ounces of milk were needed for 4 servings.

21. A 2-foot-long sandwich costs $10.98.

22. Muffins cost $2.79 per dozen.

Think and Apply

Which is a better buy, 6 for $.70 or 8 for $1?

Estimation can help you choose.   **Think** 6 for $.70 is less than $.12 each.
8 at $.12 each is $.96
So 6 for $.70 is the better buy.

Choose the better buy for each.

23. a. 12 oz for $1.68
    b. 18 oz for $2.70

24. a. 12 for $2.49
    b. 20 for $3.90

25. a. 1 lb 8 oz for $1.50
    b. 2 lb for $2.40

26. a. a box of 20 for $7.90
    b. a box of 25 for $9.00

27. a. 6 cans for $.89
    b. 8 cans for $1.50

28. a. 7 pads for $6
    b. 4 pads for $2.90

55 mph is a rate. What units does it compare? Explain what this rate means.

SUMMING UP

253

Analogies are based on comparisons. Complete this analogy. *Inside* is to *outside* as *upstairs* is to _____.

Proportions

Before the middle of the nineteenth century, wooden sailing ships were used to transport passengers and cargo all over the world. Commercial ships today are made of steel and powered by steam. A passenger ship crossing the Atlantic may burn 320 tons of fuel oil in 8 hours. How much does it use in 24 hours?

Use equal ratios to find the amount of fuel used.

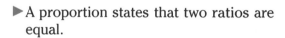

$$\begin{array}{c} \text{fuel} \rightarrow \\ \text{time} \rightarrow \end{array} \quad \overset{\times 3}{\underset{\times 3}{\frac{320}{8} = \frac{x}{24}}}$$

Think $24 = 8 \cdot 3$, so $x = 320 \cdot 3$, or 960. 960 tons of fuel are burned in 24 hours.

▶A proportion states that two ratios are equal.

$\begin{array}{c} \text{fuel} \rightarrow \\ \text{time} \rightarrow \end{array} \dfrac{\mathbf{320}}{\mathbf{8}} = \dfrac{\mathbf{960}}{\mathbf{24}}$ How can you find the rate of fuel burned in 1 hour?

You can use cross products to test whether a proportion is true.

a. $\dfrac{2.5}{5} \, \bullet \, \dfrac{3}{6}$

$2.5 \cdot 6 = 5 \cdot 3$

so $\dfrac{2.5}{5} = \dfrac{3}{6}$

b. $\dfrac{3}{42} \, \bullet \, \dfrac{1\frac{1}{2}}{20}$

$3 \cdot 20 \neq 42 \cdot 1\frac{1}{2}$

so $\dfrac{3}{42} \neq \dfrac{1\frac{1}{2}}{20}$

Check Your Understanding

Write = or ≠ for each ● .

1. $\dfrac{1}{4} \, \bullet \, \dfrac{5}{20}$

2. $\dfrac{3}{5} \, \bullet \, \dfrac{6}{5}$

3. $\dfrac{1.2}{12} \, \bullet \, \dfrac{4.5}{45}$

4. $\dfrac{2\frac{1}{2}}{6} \, \bullet \, \dfrac{5}{12}$

Share Your Ideas Describe two ways to tell whether this proportion is true. $\dfrac{25}{30} = \dfrac{5}{6}$

254

Practice

Write = or ≠ for each ⬭ .

5. $\frac{2}{5}$ ⬭ $\frac{4}{8}$ **6.** $\frac{1}{7}$ ⬭ $\frac{2}{14}$ **7.** $\frac{3}{9}$ ⬭ $\frac{4}{5}$ **8.** $\frac{9}{10}$ ⬭ $\frac{4}{5}$

9. $\frac{8}{7}$ ⬭ $\frac{3}{4}$ **10.** $\frac{6}{5}$ ⬭ $\frac{6}{7}$ **11.** $\frac{64}{1,000}$ ⬭ $\frac{16}{300}$ **12.** $\frac{60}{25}$ ⬭ $\frac{120}{50}$

13. $\frac{1.2}{16}$ ⬭ $\frac{2.4}{32}$ **14.** $\frac{5\frac{1}{3}}{100}$ ⬭ $\frac{16}{300}$ **15.** $\frac{4\frac{1}{4}}{13}$ ⬭ $\frac{12\frac{3}{4}}{39}$ **16.** $\frac{7.25}{5.75}$ ⬭ $\frac{21.75}{16.5}$

CHOICES

Write a proportion for each. Then solve. Use mental math or paper and pencil. Check each answer.

17. 12 out of 34
48 out of how many?

18. 1 in 6
10 in how many?

19. 5 for $.25
How many for $2?

20. 11 for $1.21
1 for how much?

21. 25 in 100
75 in how many?

22. 20 out of 80
How many out of 100?

23. 15 out of 45
How many out of 3?

24. 3 yd for $9
10 yd for how much?

25. 8 oz for $.70
1 lb for how much?

Use equal ratios to solve. Check each answer.

26. $\frac{24}{400} = \frac{x}{100}$ **27.** $\frac{x}{15} = \frac{12}{45}$ **28.** $\frac{11}{x} = \frac{330}{60}$ **29.** $\frac{16}{40} = \frac{4}{x}$

30. $\frac{1.5}{4} = \frac{3}{x}$ **31.** $\frac{x}{200} = \frac{30}{50}$ **32.** $\frac{3\frac{1}{3}}{x} = \frac{10}{6}$ **33.** $\frac{x}{5} = \frac{16}{y} = \frac{4}{10}$

Think and Apply

34. Huge shipyards are needed to construct the giant tankers that carry cargo around the world today. A shipyard in Sweden can produce 6 ships every year. How many are produced in 2 years? in 6 months?

35. In 1884 the clipper ship *Champion of the Seas* traveled 532 miles in 24 hours, the farthest distance ever traveled under sail in one day. How many miles did it travel in 6 hours? About how many miles did it travel in 1 hour?

2 oz cost $.10 and 8 oz cost $.40. Is one a better buy than the other? How can using a proportion help you decide?

SUMMING UP

Which of these ratios can form a proportion? $\frac{1}{3}$ $\frac{2}{7}$ $\frac{3}{9}$ $\frac{0.5}{1.5}$

Solving Proportions

One of the first bicycles was built in 1870 by James Starley in Coventry, England. The most popular cycling road race today is the Tour de France, in which more than 100 cyclists race through Europe. The race may last 24 days and covers about 2,500 miles. How far might a cyclist travel in 5 days of the race?

Write a proportion to compare time and distance.

$\frac{24}{2,500} = \frac{5}{x}$ Estimate first. **Think** 5 is about $\frac{1}{5}$ of 24.

So x is about $\frac{1}{5}$ of 2,500, or 500.

▶ You can use cross products to find a missing term in a proportion.

$\frac{24}{2,500} = \frac{5}{x}$ $24 \cdot x = 2,500 \cdot 5$

$24x = 12,500$

$x = 521$, to the nearest mile

A cyclist might travel 521 miles in 5 days.

More Examples

a. $\frac{4}{0.6} = \frac{x}{3}$

$4 \cdot 3 = 0.6x$

$12 = 0.6x$

$20 = x$

b. $\frac{9}{x} = \frac{4\frac{1}{2}}{8}$

$9 \cdot 8 = 4\frac{1}{2}x$

$72 = 4\frac{1}{2}x$

$16 = x$

Find each missing term.

1. 3 for $1.29
   7 for how much?

2. 12 mi in 10 min
   How far in $\frac{1}{2}$ h?

3. $\frac{2}{\$4.50} = \frac{x}{\$22.50}$

4. $\frac{25}{29} = \frac{5}{x}$

Share Your Ideas Look back at example **b** above. What other method could you use to find the missing term?

Practice

Find each missing term. Use paper and pencil, mental math, or a calculator.

5. $\dfrac{6}{x} = \dfrac{\$1.50}{\$2.50}$

6. $\dfrac{11}{100} = \dfrac{33}{x}$

7. $\dfrac{12}{1} = \dfrac{y}{1\frac{1}{3}}$

8. $\dfrac{y}{66} = \dfrac{5}{11}$

9. $\dfrac{7}{10} = \dfrac{x}{8}$

10. $\dfrac{p}{1.6} = \dfrac{9}{4}$

11. $\dfrac{4}{1.7} = \dfrac{12}{x}$

12. $\dfrac{64}{y} = \dfrac{1.2}{3.6}$

13. $\dfrac{58}{p} = \dfrac{6}{1.2}$

14. $\dfrac{14}{3\frac{1}{2}} = \dfrac{y}{\frac{2}{7}}$

15. $\dfrac{n}{\frac{3}{2}} = \dfrac{40}{6}$

16. $\dfrac{\frac{1}{4}}{\frac{7}{8}} = \dfrac{x}{49}$

Write a proportion for each. Then solve.

17. 4 pages in 7 minutes
How long for 38 pages?

18. 10 people out of 30
45 people out of
how many?

19. 4 in 13
12.4 in how many?

20. one dozen for $1.92
One costs how much?

21. $1\frac{1}{2}$ lb for 8
How many ounces for 10?

22. $1\frac{1}{3}$ for 16
1.2 for how many?

Estimate to choose the correct answer.

23. $\dfrac{5}{12} = \dfrac{x}{34}$

  a. $x = 30.2$ **b.** $x = 14.1\overline{6}$
  c. $x = 1.4$ **d.** $x = 20.3$

24. $\dfrac{x}{4.2} = \dfrac{1.5}{9}$

  a. $x = 0.7$ **b.** $x = 3$
  c. $x = 1.7$ **d.** $x = 0.3$

Think and Apply

The legend on a map indicates that $\frac{1}{4}$ in. represents 75 mi. Use this information to answer the questions below.

25. If the distance from Dallas, Texas, to Kansas City, Missouri, is about 450 mi, how far apart are these cities on the map?

26. If the distance on the map from one city to another is $1\frac{1}{4}$ in., how many miles apart are the cities?

$\dfrac{3}{4} = \dfrac{6}{x}$ Describe two different ways to find the missing term. Which do you prefer? Why?

Mixed Review

1. $146.51 + 2.04 + 8.351$

2. $21.62 - 10.2$

3. $6\frac{1}{2} + 2\frac{1}{4} + 1\frac{5}{6}$

4. $28\frac{1}{8} - 16\frac{1}{2}$

5. $16 + {}^-2$

6. ${}^-12 + 3$

7. $8 + {}^-5$

8. ${}^-2 + {}^-3$

9. $3 \cdot {}^-4$

10. ${}^-8 \cdot {}^-5$

11. ${}^-\frac{1}{2} + \dfrac{{}^-5}{8}$

12. $\dfrac{{}^-3}{7} + \dfrac{1}{9}$

13. $6.025 \cdot 10^2$

14. $638.19 \cdot 10^{-4}$

15. $10^2 \div 10^4$

Solve for n.

16. $4n + {}^-3 = 9$

17. $n - 5 = \frac{2}{3} \cdot {}^-9$

18. $\dfrac{n}{8} - {}^-8 = 16$

19. $\dfrac{3n}{2} = 6$

20. ${}^-16n + 2 = 34$

SUMMING UP

Illustrations in books often show objects reduced in size to show the entire object on a single page. What can you think of that might be shown enlarged?

Scale Drawing

Building and racing electric remote controlled cars is a popular hobby worldwide. A scale of 1:24 is used for many of the model cars. If a model is 192 mm long, how long is the actual car from which it was modeled?

You can use a proportion to find the missing measure in a comparison of measurement.

scaled measurement $\rightarrow \dfrac{1}{24} = \dfrac{192}{x}$ $\leftarrow$ scaled measurement
actual measurement $\rightarrow$ $\leftarrow$ actual measurement

$$x = 24 \cdot 192$$

$$x = 4{,}608$$

The actual car is 4,608 mm, or 4.608 meters long.
What if the scale were 24:1? What would this mean?

More Examples

a. Scale 1 cm:6 km
distance on map   4 mm
How great is the actual distance?

$\dfrac{1 \text{ cm}}{6 \text{ km}} = \dfrac{0.4 \text{ cm}}{x}$

$x = 2.4$ km

Think   4 mm = 0.4 cm

b. Scale 500 mm:1 mm
length of actual object   0.1 mm
How long is the magnified object?

$\dfrac{500 \text{ mm}}{1 \text{ mm}} = \dfrac{x}{0.1}$

$x = 50$ mm

Check Your Understanding

Find each missing measure, using a scale of 1 cm to 2 m.

1. scaled ____
   actual 3 m

2. scaled ____
   actual 6 m

3. scaled 5 mm
   actual ____

Share Your Ideas   True or false? When a scale drawing is a reduction, each measurement on the drawing must be less than the corresponding actual measurement. Explain.

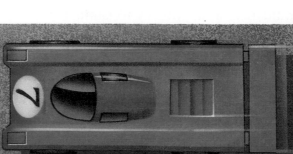

Using the scale 1 cm: 12 m, find each missing measure.

4. scaled 0.75 cm
actual ___

5. scaled ___
actual 576 m

6. scaled 14 cm
actual ___

7. scaled 3 cm
actual ___

8. scaled ___
actual 60 km

9. scaled 50 mm
actual ___

Use the picture to answer each question.

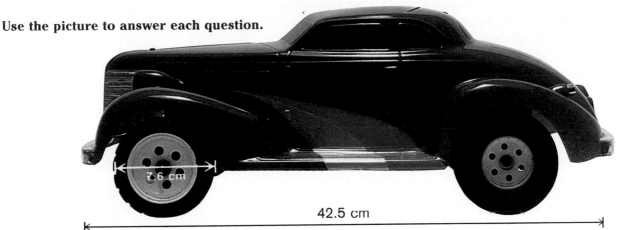

7.6 cm

42.5 cm

Scale 1:10

10. Find the actual length of the car, to the nearest meter.

11. Find the actual diameter of the wheel, to the nearest centimeter.

12. About how many times as large as the drawing is the actual car?

13. A 170-cm driver would be how tall drawn to the same scale?

Make a scale drawing of each, using a compass and ruler.

14. a rectangle 4.5 m by 10 m   scale 1 cm: 1 m

15. a kite with crosspieces 2 m and 3 m long
scale 4 cm:10 m

16. a circle with a diameter of 0.3 cm   scale 3 cm: 1 mm

Think and Apply

17. Make a scale drawing of a room in your home. Find the length and width of the room and use this data to choose an appropriate scale. Be sure the scale you choose allows the entire room to be shown on your paper.

Would a length of 2 cm be represented by a length longer or shorter than 2 cm in a drawing done to a scale of 300 cm to 1 cm? Explain.

SUMMING UP

What information do you need to determine the amount of time it takes to travel from one city to another?

Distance, Rate, and Time

In 1919, John Alcock and Arthur Brown were the first to fly an aircraft nonstop across the Atlantic. Today supersonic aircraft can cross the Atlantic in 3 hours, flying at a speed of 2,000 km per hour. What is the air distance across the Atlantic?

You can use a proportion to find the distance.

$$\frac{2,000}{1} = \frac{d}{3} \quad \begin{array}{l}\leftarrow \text{ distance} \\ \leftarrow \text{ time}\end{array} \qquad \begin{array}{l} d = 2,000 \cdot 3 \\ d = 6,000 \end{array}$$

You can also use a formula.

distance = rate × time
$$d = 2,000 \cdot 3$$
$$d = 6,000$$

The distance is 6,000 km.
How does the formula relate to the proportion?

More Examples

a. How long would it take a supersonic plane to travel 100 km?

$$\text{distance} = \text{rate} \times \text{time}$$
$$100 = \frac{2,000}{1}\, t$$
$$\frac{100}{2,000} = t$$
$$\frac{1}{20} = t$$

The time is $\frac{1}{20}$ h, or 3 min.

b. What if a plane travels 600 km in 2 h? How far can it travel in 3 h?

$$\text{distance} = \text{rate} \times \text{time}$$
$$= \frac{600}{2} \cdot 3$$
$$= 300 \cdot 3$$
$$= 900$$

The plane can travel 900 km in 3 h.

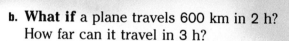

Check Your Understanding

Find each missing measure.

1. 60 m in 2 h
   d m in 1 h

2. 4 km in t h
   10 km in 8 h

3. d m in 5 s
   12 m in 20 s

Share Your Ideas A rate is a comparison. What is meant by a rate of speed? How is rate expressed in example **b** above?

Write a proportion for each.

4. 2 km in 3 min
6 km in 9 min

5. 4.5 m in 13 s
9 m in 26 s

6. 1 km in 5 h
2.5 km in 12.5 h

7. 12 cm in $4\frac{1}{2}$ s
18 cm in $6\frac{3}{4}$ s

8. 3.5 m in 1 s
7 m in 2 s

9. 625 m in 3 h
125 m in 0.6 h

 Complete. Use paper and pencil, mental math, or a calculator.

10. 23 km in 2 h
___ km in 6 h

11. 1.2 m in 2 min
12 m in ___ min

12. ___ m in 5.4 s
10 m in 1.8 s

13. 4.2 m in 12 s
___ m in 2 s

14. 625 km in $\frac{1}{2}$ h
300 km in ___ h

15. 121 m in ___ s
11 m in 1.4 s

16. 139 cm in 15 s
___ cm in 4.5 s

17. 2,500 m in 16 min
3,000 m in ___ min

18. 320 m in 2 s
400 m in ___ s

19. 100 cm in 10 s
___ cm in 1 min

20. 3,200 m in 5 h
1 km in ___ h

21. 250 m in 45 min
1,500 m in ___ h

Use estimation to choose the missing measure for each.

22. 12 m in 6 h
___ m in $\frac{1}{2}$ h

 a. 1   **b.** 0.1   **c.** 100

23. 16 m in ___ s
100 m in 4 s

 a. 64   **b.** 6.4   **c.** 0.64

24. 4 km in 2 h
64 km in ___ h

 a. 3.2   **b.** 32   **c.** 320

Think and Apply

25. In 1908, Wilbur Wright flew about 98 km in 1.5 h. Estimate the average speed per hour of Wright's aircraft.

26. Ellen went to an air show 50 km from her home. She left at 8 A.M. and returned home at 4:45 P.M. If she drove about 80 km per hour, about how long did she spend at the show?

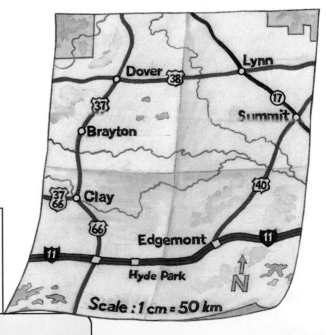

Visual Thinking

27. Write clear directions for using Route 38 to drive from Lynn to Hyde Park. Include the approximate distances traveled on each road.

As distance increases, does rate increase or decrease if the amount of time stays the same? Explain.

SUMMING UP

Midchapter Review

Write a ratio for each and find the unit rate. pages 250–253

1. 3 pairs for $15.00
2. 4 teachers for 40 students
3. 16 beats in 8 notes

Write = or ≠ for each ●. pages 250–251, 254–255

4. 6:8 ● 3:4
5. $\frac{2}{7}$ ● $\frac{3}{8}$
6. $\frac{1\frac{2}{3}}{4}$ ● $\frac{5}{12}$
7. $\frac{11}{12}$ ● $\frac{7}{9}$

Choose the better buy. pages 252–253

8. **a.** 10 oz for $1.00
   b. 4 oz for 30¢
9. **a.** 3 for $2.00
   b. 6 for $3.98
10. **a.** 5 lb for $22.00
    b. 2 lb for $11.00

Write a proportion for each. Then solve. pages 254–255

11. 13 out of 26
    8 out of how many?
12. 2 in 12
    How many in 36?
13. 24 for $12.00
    8 for how much?

Find each missing term. pages 254–257

14. $\frac{5}{x} = \frac{12}{120}$
15. $\frac{10}{4} = \frac{y}{\frac{1}{5}}$
16. $\frac{n}{33} = \frac{6}{11}$
17. $\frac{32}{24} = \frac{8}{c}$

Use a scale of 1 in. = 1 ft. pages 258–259

18. Draw a rectangle 3 ft by 4 ft.
19. Draw a circle with a radius of 2 ft.

Complete. Then find the word in the grid at the right.

20. Rate multiplied by time equals ____.

21. five : ten = six : ____.

22. A ____ compares quantities of different units.

23. A scale ____ uses a ratio to reproduce an actual object.

24. The ____ is the cost of one item.

25. A ____ states that two ratios are equal.

26. To compare two ratios, use cross ____.

27. A ____ compares two quantities.

U	A	R	B	C	X	Y	Z	E	E
N	N	A	X	R	A	P	E	I	L
I	N	T	I	O	L	A	R	G	E
T	E	I	L	M	O	R	E	H	V
P	R	O	P	O	R	T	I	O	N
R	I	C	R	A	B	C	X	A	Z
I	L	M	O	K	R	R	D	B	E
C	O	E	D	R	A	W	I	N	G
E	C	E	U	E	T	E	S	E	R
N	I	L	C	N	E	N	T	R	A
G	A	M	T	M	I	X	A	B	L
R	S	O	S	B	L	O	N	C	D
E	S	N	E	W	T	O	C	F	G
L	T	T	W	E	L	V	E	J	H

Solve.

28. How far can Robert ride in 3 hours if he travels 16 miles in 2 hours?

29. Helen drove 110 miles to colonial Williamsburg. She left at 10 A.M. and returned at 6:30 P.M. If she drove 55 mph, how much time did she spend there?

Exploring Problem Solving

What Is the Average Speed?

Sally and Howie were bicycling. They traveled 6 miles in the first hour. During the second hour they were in the country, and they bicycled 12 miles in one hour.

Thinking Critically

They disagreed as to what their average speed was. Help them decide what it was.

Analyzing and Making Decisions

1. Sally computed the average speed this way. They bicycled 18 miles in 2 hours.
$\frac{18 \text{ miles}}{2 \text{ hours}} =$ _____ mph

   What did she think the average speed was?

2. Howie computed the average speed in this way: For $\frac{1}{3}$ of their trip they went 6 miles per hour and for $\frac{2}{3}$ of their trip they went 12 miles per hour.
$\frac{1}{3} \times 6 \text{ mph} + \frac{2}{3} \times 12 \text{ mph} =$ _____ mph.

   What did he think the average speed was?

3. Here is another way to look at what they did: Sally looked at the speedometer every 10 minutes and Howie looked at the speedometer every mile. What readings did each see? How many readings did each person have? How many miles per hour did each person have for an average?

4. Sally's method is called an average over time. Howie's method is called an average over distance. In what kind of situation might you want to use an average over distance? Explain.

Look Back **What if** they had biked 5 miles in the first hour and 15 miles in the second hour? What would have been the average speed over time? over distance? When would the average speed over distance and the average speed over time be the same?

Problem Solving Strategies

Solving a Simpler Problem

When the first automobiles came to Allenville, the streets
were so narrow that they were all one way. Mr. Appleton
lives at point *A* and drives to point *H*. How many ways can
he drive from point *A* to point *H*?

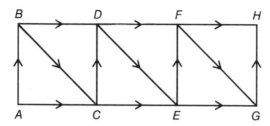

Many problems deal with a large number of cases. Often you
can solve a simpler part of the problem to find the solution.

Solving the Problem

Make a copy of the drawing on a piece of paper.

Think What is the question?

Explore How many ways are there to get from *G* to *H*?
from *F* to *H*?
From *E*, how many ways can you get to *F*? to *G*?
Since you know the total number of routes from *G* and *F* to
H, how many routes are there from *E* to *H*?
Continue to use this simpler problem until you get to *A*.

Solve How many routes are there from *A* to *H*?

Look Back What pattern do you see?

Share Your Ideas

1. Why might solving a simpler problem be
a good strategy for this problem? What
could happen if you started at *A* and
tried to find all the routes?

Practice

 Solve. Use a calculator where appropriate.

2. Paul likes to climb the stairs in his old house. He climbs by taking 1 or 2 steps at a time. How many different ways can he climb the 10 stairs?

3. Paul found a small set of 6 stairs. He climbs either 1, 2, or 3 steps at a time. How many different ways can he climb them?

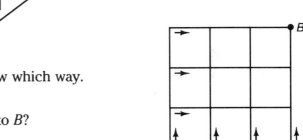

All these streets are one way. The arrows show which way. Use this information to solve **4–5.**

4. How many different ways are there from *A* to *B*?

5. Which way is the shortest?

Mixed Strategy Review

6. Mrs. Lotta mixes 2 batches of cinnamon raisin bread at one time. She rolls the dough and cuts it into 8 equal pieces. From each of these 8 pieces she makes 4 loaves of bread. How many batches of dough does she need to make 80 loaves of bread?

7. Ms. Palmer is a calligrapher. She is numbering pages in a manuscript beginning with page 1. She is paid $.01 per digit. If she earned $4.89, how many pages did she number?

8. Look at **7. What if** Ms. Palmer charges $.02 for each digit 8 and $.01 for the other digits? How much would she charge for numbering a book from page 1 to page 222?

9. Luis's rectangular garden required 80 feet of fencing. When he fertilized it, he covered 375 square feet. What were the lengths of each side?

Create Your Own

Write a problem for which someone needs to solve a simpler part of the problem in order to solve the whole problem.

265

Explain the difference between congruent and similar polygons.

Drawing Similar Polygons

In 1860 an eight-sided house was built overlooking the Hudson River. The shape formed by the exterior walls of the house was similar to the shape formed by the porch surrounding the house. Both shapes were similar octagons.

Two polygons are **similar** if they have the same shape.

Polygons that are similar can be drawn by using different-sized grids.

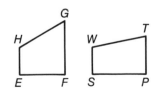

$RXYZ \sim STWV$

↑ is similar to

Similar polygons are named in the order of their corresponding parts.

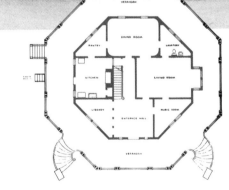

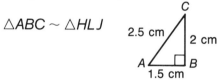

What is the unit measure of ZR? of VS?

You can also draw similar polygons by using a ruler and protractor.

 $\triangle ABC \sim \triangle HLJ$

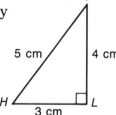

2.5 cm   2 cm

A   1.5 cm   B

5 cm   4 cm

H   3 cm   L

J

C

▶ Corresponding angles have equal measures. $\angle A \cong \angle H$ $\angle B \cong \angle L$ $\angle C \cong \angle J$

▶ Corresponding sides are proportional. $\frac{AC}{HJ} = \frac{AB}{HL} = \frac{CB}{JL} = \frac{1}{2}$

Check Your Understanding

1. Which polygons are similar?

2. Draw a polygon half as large as *ABCD*.

3. Use a larger grid to draw a polygon twice as large as *ABCD*.

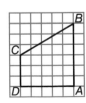

Share Your Ideas   Trace $\triangle HJL$ above.
Draw $\triangle VZY$ similar to $\triangle HJL$ and describe your method.

4. Name the polygons that are similar.

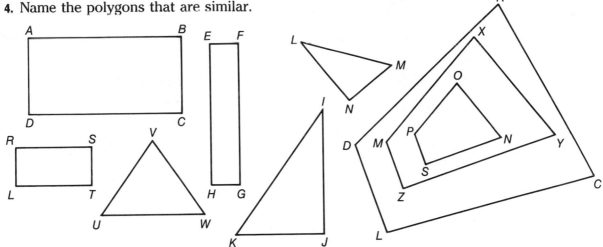

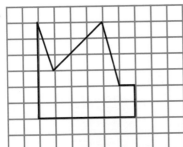

5. Identify corresponding parts and congruent angles for the similar figures in **4.**

Use larger or smaller grid paper to draw a similar figure for each.

6.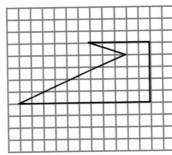

7.

8.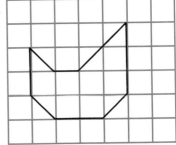

Look back at 7. Use a ruler and protractor to draw each polygon.

9. $\frac{1}{4}$ as large as **7**

10. 3 times as large as **7**

11. $\frac{5}{4}$ as large as **7**

Write *sometimes*, *always*, or *never*. Explain your thinking.

12. Similar polygons are congruent.

13. Congruent polygons are similar.

14. If the ratio of corresponding sides of two similar polygons is 3 to 1, the ratio of their angle measures is also 3 to 1.

15. If two polygons have proportional sides, their angles are congruent.

True or false? Every square is similar to every other square. Every rectangle is similar to every other rectangle. Explain.

SUMMING UP

$\triangle ABC \sim \triangle DEF$. What information does this tell you?

Similar Triangles

Ancient sundials recorded the passage of time as early as 2000 B.C. Jody and her mother admired the sundial in the garden of the arboretum. Each person cast a shadow as she stood in the garden. Jody is 5 ft tall and cast a 3-ft shadow. Her mother's shadow is 3.3 ft long. How tall is her mother?

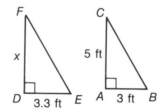

$\triangle ABC \sim \triangle DEF$

$$\frac{AC}{AB} = \frac{DF}{DE}$$

▶ Similar triangles have congruent corresponding angles. Corresponding sides are proportional.

You can use a proportion to find a missing measure.

height $\longrightarrow$ **5** $=$ ***x*** $\longleftarrow$ height
shadow $\longrightarrow$ **3** $=$ **3.3** $\longleftarrow$ shadow

$$3x = 5 \cdot 3.3$$
$$\frac{3x}{3} = \frac{5 \cdot 3.3}{3}$$
$$x = 5.5$$

Jody's mother is 5.5 ft tall.

Check Your Understanding

For each pair of similar triangles, find the unknown measure.

1.

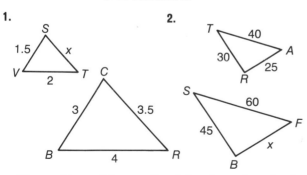

2.

Share Your Ideas Look back at the shadow problem. Write two other proportions that could be used to find *x*.

For each pair of similar triangles, find the unknown measures.

3.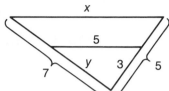

4.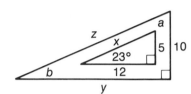

5.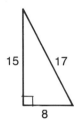

6.

Use these similar triangles to answer 7–9.

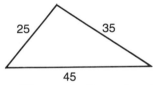

7. These similar triangles are

   a. isosceles   **b.** equilateral   **c.** scalene

8. n is

   a. less than 45   **b.** more than 90   **c.** between 50 and 60

9. Which proportion could not be used to find n?

   a. $\frac{35}{45} = \frac{42}{n}$ **b.** $\frac{25}{30} = \frac{45}{n}$ **c.** $\frac{35}{42} = \frac{n}{45}$

Think and Apply

10. A surveyor needs to measure AB. She uses similar triangles as shown. Find AB.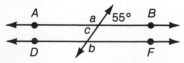

11. Draw two similar triangles whose corresponding sides have a ratio of 2:1.

Create a rule for finding a missing measure, given two similar triangles. What measures do you need?

Mixed Review

Evaluate.

1. $3 \cdot 4 \div 2^2 + 5 \cdot 2$

2. $3^3 + 2^2 \cdot (5 + 7)$

3. $3^3 + 2^2 \cdot 5 + 7$

4. $5 + (3 + 4)^2 \div 10$

5. $41.2 - 4.2 \cdot {}^-9$

6. $(16 \div 2 \cdot 5)^2$

7. $6n + n^2$, when $n = 5$

8. $8a + \frac{b}{c}$, when $a = 2$, $b = 6$, $c = {}^-3$

State the property illustrated.

9. $4 + (6 + 5) =$ $(4 + 6) + 5$

10. $23 \cdot 1 = 23$

11. $a(b + c) = ab + ac$

12. $a + 0 = a$

13. $a + b - b = a$

Find each angle measure.

14. $a =$

15. $b =$

16. $c =$

$(\overleftrightarrow{AB} \parallel \overleftrightarrow{DF})$

SUMMING UP

269

How long is this piece of chalk? What unit did you use to measure it?

Precision and Greatest Possible Error

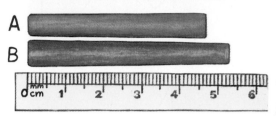

Each piece of chalk measures 5 cm, to the nearest centimeter. What is the measure of A, to the nearest millimeter? the measure of B, to the nearest millimeter?

All measurements are approximate. The difference between the actual measure and the approximate measurement is called the **error of measurement**. The **greatest possible error (GPE)** is half the unit of measurement.

Measurement	Precision (Unit of Measurement)	GPE	Actual measurement is between
5 cm	1 cm	0.5 cm	4.5 cm and 5.5 cm
31.0 mm	0.1 mm	0.05 mm	30.95 mm and 31.05 mm
14.25 km	0.01 km	0.005 km	14.245 km and 14.255 km
570 m	10 m	5 m	565 m and 575 m

Measurements made with smaller units are more **precise**. **Look back** at the chart. Which measurement is most precise?

► When you add or subtract measurements, the answer cannot be more precise than the **least precise** unit of measurement.

a. Add. 3.42 m + 7.8 m

   3.42 m ← precise to 0.01 m
 + 7.8　m ← precise to 0.1 m
  11.22 m = 11.2, to the nearest 0.1 m

b. Subtract. 38 cm − 141 mm

Think Subtract like units.
   38 cm = 380 mm

   380 mm ← precise to 10 mm
 − 141 mm ← precise to 1 mm
   239 mm = 240, to the nearest 10 mm

Check Your Understanding

Complete the chart below.

Measurement	Precision	GPE	Actual measurement is between
1. 37 cm			
2. 29.0 cm			
3. 4.51 L			
4. 300 g			

Add or subtract.

5. 34.2 km + 13.91 km

6. 164.8 cm − 36 mm

7. 16 mg + 4.3 mg

Share Your Ideas Why do we round to the precision of the least precise measurement when we add or subtract?

Complete the chart below.

Measurement	Precision	GPE	Actual measurement is between
8. 42.31 cm			
9. 28 cm			
10. 17.9 kg			
11. 17.00 m			
12. 3.9 L			
13. 53 m			
14. 420 km			
15. 5,000 m			

Add or subtract. Choose paper and pencil or a calculator.

CHOICES

16. 239 km + 67.5 km + 102.9 km

17. 47 m + 9.5 m + 48.5 m

18. 634.5 cm + 8.13 m + 58.72 cm

19. 4.53 kg + 2,473 g + 1.348 kg

20. 16.23 m − 12.9 m

21. 34.6 cm − 0.97 cm

22. 3,486 cm − 27.9 m

23. 4.93 L − 1,879 mL

Think and Apply

24. Three lengths of pipe are joined as shown. What is the total length of pipe?

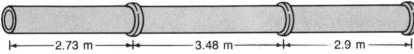

|←——— 2.73 m ———→|←——— 3.48 m ———→|←——— 2.9 m ———→|

25. A rectangular sheet of plywood has a length of 2.66 meters and a width of 1.743 meters. What is the perimeter of the sheet of plywood?

26. Sam measured the length of the classroom and reported it to be 100 meters. The teacher said, "Sam, that's about ten times too long." Sam replied, "You said the greatest possible error was half the unit. I couldn't be off by more than half a meter!" How could Sam have been off by ten times the correct measurement? What is the difference between the greatest possible error in a correct measurement and the mistake Sam made in measuring?

27. A hoist will lift no more than 100 kilograms total weight. Ten bars each weighing 10.0 kilograms are stacked on the hoist. Will the hoist lift that load? Explain your answer.

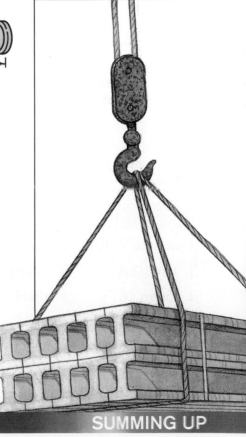

Think of some measurements that must be very precise. Think of some measurements that are less precise. What units are used?

SUMMING UP

What names are used to identify the sides of a right triangle?

Special Ratios

The study of the relationship between the sides and the angles of a right triangle is called **trigonometry.**

Three special ratios can be used to relate the measures of the sides and the angles.

The **sine (sin)** of $m\angle B = \dfrac{\text{length of side opposite } \angle B}{\text{length of hypotenuse}}$

The **cosine (cos)** of $m\angle B = \dfrac{\text{length of side adjacent } \angle B}{\text{hypotenuse}}$

The **tangent (tan)** of $m\angle B = \dfrac{\text{length of side opposite } \angle B}{\text{length of side adjacent } \angle B}$

You can calculate the special ratios for a given angle, using the measures of the sides.

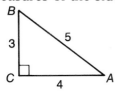

$$\sin m\angle B = \frac{4}{5} = 0.8$$

$$\cos m\angle B = \frac{3}{5} = 0.6$$

$$\tan m\angle B = \frac{4}{3} = 1.\overline{3}$$

You can also use a table of values. The measure of $\angle B$ is 53°, to the nearest degree. What is the $m\angle A$? What is the tan $m\angle A$?

What if the length of each side of $\triangle ABC$ is doubled? Find the special ratios for $\angle B$. What do you notice?

Degrees	Sin	Cos	Tan
51	0.7771	0.6293	1.2349
52	0.7880	0.6157	1.2799
53	0.7986	0.6018	1.3270
54	0.8090	0.5878	1.3764
55	0.8192	0.5736	1.4281

Check Your Understanding

Find each value, to the nearest ten thousandth.

1. tan $m\angle A$
2. cos $m\angle A$
3. sin $m\angle A$
4. tan $m\angle B$
5. sin $m\angle B$
6. cos $m\angle B$

Use the table of values on page 536 to find the measure of each angle.

7. sin $m\angle R = 0.6428$
8. cos $m\angle D = 0.0872$
9. tan $m\angle P = 1$

Share Your Ideas If the tan $m\angle B = 1$, how do the lengths of the legs compare? Explain.

Use the table on page 536 to find each ratio or the measure of ∠M.

10. tan 50° **11.** cos 46° **12.** sin 52° **13.** tan 48°

14. sin 38° **15.** cos 20° **16.** tan 45° **17.** sin 88°

18. tan m∠M = 1.0355 **19.** cos m∠M = 0.6157 **20.** sin m∠M = 0.7771

21. sin m∠M = 0.7193 **22.** cos m∠M = 0.0175 **23.** tan m∠M = 11.4301

24. tan m∠M = 57.2900 **25.** sin m∠M = 0.9455 **26.** cos m∠M = 0.9998

CHOICES Find the trigonometric ratios for each acute angle. Use a calculator or paper and pencil.

27.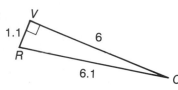

28.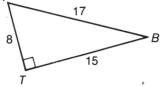

29.

Look Back at 27–29. Find each angle measure, to the nearest degree. Use the table on page 536.

30. m∠C **31.** m∠R **32.** m∠A **33.** m∠P

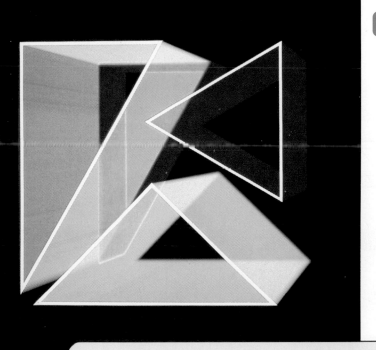

Use △SCT to answer 34–36.

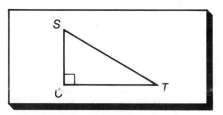

34. What if SC decreases? How does the m∠T change?

35. What if m∠T decreases? How does each trigonometric ratio for m∠T change? Explain.

36. If the cos m∠T is greater than the sin m∠T, how do SC and CT compare? Explain.

△ABC ~ △DEC. How do the trigonometric ratios for m∠A and m∠D compare? Explain.

SUMMING UP

273

In this triangle, sin m∠A = cos m∠B.
Is this true for all right triangles? Explain.

Working with Right Triangles

The first passenger incline in the United States was built in Pittsburgh in 1870. Since then the Mon has carried millions of passengers from Carson Street to the top of Mount Washington. What is the elevation of the incline?

► You can use trigonometric ratios to find a missing side in a right triangle.

Use the table of values on page 536 to find sin 35°.

$$\sin 35° = 0.5736 = \frac{x}{195} \begin{array}{l}\leftarrow \text{opposite side} \\ \leftarrow \text{hypotenuse}\end{array}$$

$$0.5736 \cdot 195 = x$$
$$112 = x \leftarrow \text{to the nearest meter}$$

The incline has an elevation of about 112 meters.

Monongahela passenger incline, Pittsburgh, PA

More Examples

a. Find x, to the nearest unit.

a.

$$\cos 40° = 0.7660$$
$$0.766 = \frac{x}{16} \begin{array}{l}\leftarrow \text{adjacent side} \\ \leftarrow \text{hypotenuse}\end{array}$$

$$0.766 \cdot 16 = x$$
$$12 \text{ cm} = x \text{ to the nearest cm}$$

b. Find y, to the nearest unit.

b.

$$\tan 50° = 1.1918$$
$$1.1918 = \frac{y}{12} \begin{array}{l}\leftarrow \text{opposite side} \\ \leftarrow \text{adjacent side}\end{array}$$

$$1.1918 \cdot 12 = y$$
$$14 \text{ m} = y \text{ to the nearest meter}$$

Find x, to the nearest unit. Use the table of values on page 536.

1.

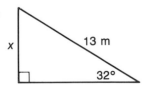

2.

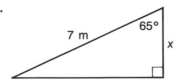

3.

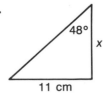

Share Your Ideas Look back at **3.** Find as many other measures as you can.

CHOICES Find each missing angle, to the nearest degree, and each missing side, to the nearest unit. Use paper and pencil or a calculator and the table on page 536.

4.
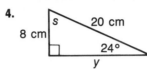
a. s b. y

5.
a. w b. y

6.
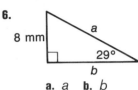
a. a b. b

7.
a. y b. x

8.
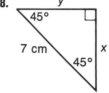
a. x b. y

9.
a. a b. x

Use △ABC to answer 10–13.

10. Write the trigonometric ratios for m∠A and m∠C.

11. If you know m∠A, can you find r, s, and t? Explain.

12. If r = 10, can you find all other missing measures? Explain.

13. What is the minimum data needed to find the measures of all the sides and angles of △ABC?

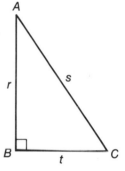

Think and Apply

14. Timothy's kite is flying on a 15-m string. The string is tied to a stake at an angle of 60°. How high is the kite, to the nearest meter?

15. A ramp is used to slide a box up a flight of 8 stairs. Each stair is 27.5 cm deep and 20 cm high. How long is the ramp, to the nearest centimeter? What is its angle of elevation, to the nearest degree?

How high is the building? In how many ways can you solve this problem? Explain.

SUMMING UP

Using Problem Solving

Interview: Calculators and the Museum

Larry O'Reilly is assistant director of exhibits for the Museum of Natural History at the Smithsonian Institution. "When we make an exhibit, we must decide what scale to use. We have a certain amount of room to house the exhibit, so we must make a plan so that everything will fit. With my calculator I can very quickly determine which scale will be the best for building the model."

An exhibit designer uses different scales, such as $\frac{1}{4}$ in.:1 ft scale. (This means $\frac{1}{4}$ in. in the model stands for 1 ft in real life.)

Solve. Use a calculator.

A. Suppose two designers wish to make a model of a scene that is 200 ft by 200 ft. If they want to use $\frac{1}{4}$ in.:1 ft scale, what will be the dimensions of the model?

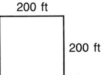

B. **What if** the designers want to use a scale of $\frac{1}{2}$ in.:1 ft? What would be the dimensions of the model?

C. What would be the dimensions of the model for a 200 ft × 200 ft display if they use the scale of $\frac{1}{8}$ in.:1 ft?

D. You need to design a model of a setting that is $\frac{1}{4}$ mi by $\frac{1}{4}$ mi. You have a museum space of 15 ft by 15 ft. What scale would you choose to make the model?

Sharing Your Ideas

1. What steps did you use to determine the dimensions of an exhibit?

2. A designer was able to find the dimensions for $\frac{1}{4}$ in.:1 ft. scale exhibit by using only one calculation. What did the designer do?

Extending Your Thinking

Often a designer will need to put exhibits next to each other. When doing this, the designer will use the same scale for each. Viewers will then be able to see how the sizes of the exhibits relate to each other.

3. Larry has two exhibits. The dimensions of the original scene A are 400 ft by 200 ft. For scene B the dimensions are 500 ft by 250 ft. What scale should be used if his total space is 20 ft by 6 ft? How should he divide the space for each exhibit?

4. Later Larry placed three scenes adjacent to each other. The scenes had these dimensions: scene C, 80 ft by 40 ft; scene D, 150 ft by 60 ft; and scene E, 50 ft by 50 ft. The exhibit space is 14 ft × 3 ft. What scale do you suggest that Larry use? Draw a diagram to show how you would divide up the space.

5. Your adult standing figures are $1\frac{1}{2}$ in. tall. You want to use them in two scenes that are next to each other. The original scenes are 224 ft by 85 ft and 149 ft by 100 ft. If you used the figures, what scale would you use? How large a space would you want to use for the exhibit? How would you divide up the space? Draw a diagram.

Summing Up

6. How did you determine what scale to use when there was more than one exhibit?

7. What suggestions would you give to someone who had to plan how to make an exhibit to scale?

Chapter Review

Write = or ≠ for each ●. pages 250–255

1. $\frac{2}{3}$ ● $\frac{12}{18}$

2. $\frac{9}{8}$ ● $\frac{11}{10}$

3. $\frac{14}{30}$ ● $\frac{33}{68}$

4. $\frac{1\frac{1}{3}}{6}$ ● $\frac{8}{27}$

Write a proportion for each. Then solve. pages 254–261

5. 5 out of 12
   How many out of 20?

6. 132 km in t h
   528 km in 8 h

7. scale 1 cm: 5 km
   drawing 2.5 cm
   actual _____

Copy the polygon _ABCD_. pages 266–267

8. Draw a polygon similar to _ABCD_.

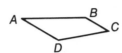

For the triangles at the right, △_ABC_ ~ △_RPS_. pages 268–269

9. Find the missing measures.

10. Name the corresponding angles.

Give the precision and the GPE for each. pages 270–271

11. 137 mg

12. 1.3 L

13. 14.001 m

14. 12.0 kg

Find _x_, to the nearest unit. Find _a_, to the nearest degree. pages 272–275

15.

16.

17.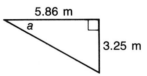

Complete.

18. Distance is a product of rate and ____.

19. If two triangles are similar, corresponding sides are ____.

20. The smaller the unit of measure, the more ____ the measurement.

21. Trigonometric ratios relate sides and angles of ____ triangles.

Words to Know
precise
right
time
proportional

Solve. pages 263–265

22. Luis rode 15 km in 2 h. What was his rate of speed?
    How far would he travel in 3 h (to the nearest km)?

23. To raise money for the Special Olympics, Sarasota
    Elementary School children are tie-dying shirts. There
    are 8 colors available. Each shirt is to be a different
    shade, with no more than 2 colors combined. How many
    shirts should be ordered if every possible color
    combination is used?

Chapter Test

Write = or ≠ for each ⬭.

1. $\dfrac{\frac{1}{2}}{1}$ ⬭ $\dfrac{3}{6}$

2. $\dfrac{28}{8}$ ⬭ $\dfrac{12}{5}$

3. $\dfrac{18}{39}$ ⬭ $\dfrac{12}{26}$

4. $\dfrac{2}{7}$ ⬭ $\dfrac{4}{14}$

5. $\dfrac{2\frac{1}{3}}{10}$ ⬭ $\dfrac{6}{27}$

6. $\dfrac{5}{4}$ ⬭ $\dfrac{125}{100}$

Write a proportion for each. Then solve.

7. $\dfrac{2}{3}$ out of how many?
   7 out of 21

8. scale 1 cm: 5 km
   drawing 4.2 cm
   actual ____

9. 12 for $6.00
   How many for
   $2.00?

10. *d* in 6 h
    42 m in 1 h

11. 20 out of 100
    1 out of how many?

12. 3 for $7.00
    33 for how much?

The triangles in each pair are similar. Find the unknown measures.

13.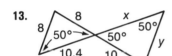

14.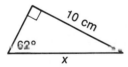

15.

Find x, to the nearest unit. Find a, to the nearest degree. Indicate which triangle has the most precise measurements.

16.

17.

18.

Solve. Round all answers to the nearest tenth.

19. Jen's grandpa has a motorized cart he rides when he goes shopping. To transport the cart, he uses a van. How long a ramp does he need?

20. Carol and Rosa want to be at a beach 2.5 km away by 1 o'clock. If they can walk 1 km in 20 minutes, when do they need to leave?

THINK Two trains left Washington at noon, traveling in opposite directions. The northbound train traveled at a rate of 80 km/h. The southbound train traveled at a rate of 100 km/h. How far apart were the trains at 4 P.M.?

The Fibonacci Sequence

How are the terms of the Fibonacci sequence related? Find the next three terms.

1, 1, 2, 3, 5, 8, 13, . . .

Materials: computer spreadsheet, Logo

The basic unit of a spreadsheet is called a cell. Cell A1 contains the label FIBONACCI. The formulas in cells B3 and B4 find the third and fourth terms. What formula can you enter in cell B5 to find the fifth term?

A. Use a spreadsheet to find the first twenty terms of the Fibonacci sequence. Enter the data shown in your spreadsheet. Then enter formulas in cells B5 to B20 to find the third through the twentieth terms.

B. What is the difference between each two successive terms of the sequence? Use column C to find each difference. Enter the formula B2 − B1 in cell C1. Replicate the formula in cells C2 to C20.

C. How are the numbers in column B related to the numbers in column C? Explain.

D. Which terms of the Fibonacci sequence are odd? even? Which terms are divisible by 3? 4? 5? Describe the patterns of divisibility you find.

SPREADSHEET DEFINITION

	A	B	C
1	FIBONACCI	1	
2		1	
3		B1 + B2	
4		B2 + B3	
5			
6			

SPREADSHEET DISPLAY

	A	B	C
1	FIBONACCI	1	
2		1	
3		2	
4		3	
5		5	
6			

Sharing Your Results

1. Explain the pattern of odd and even numbers in the terms of the Fibonacci sequence.

2. Use the divisibility patterns you found to predict which terms of the Fibonacci sequence are divisible by 7.

Extending the Activity

The ancient Greeks used a ratio in their architecture and art that is called the Golden Ratio. It is approximately 0.61803. Is the ratio of two successive terms of the Fibonacci sequence golden?

3. Use the next column of the spreadsheet to find the ratio of each two successive terms in the Fibonacci sequence. Enter the formula B2/B1 in cell D2. Replicate the formula for each term. Then compare the ratios you find to the Golden Ratio. What do you notice?

4. A Golden Rectangle has the ratio of its width and length equal to the Golden Ratio. Define GOLDEN and enter GOLDEN 20 to draw a Golden Rectangle that has width 20. Explain how Logo finds the length.

```
TO GOLDEN :WIDTH
REPEAT 2 [FD :WIDTH  ←── Type as one line.
          RT 90
          FD :WIDTH * 1.61803
          RT 90]
HIDETURTLE
END
```

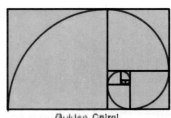

Golden Rectangle

5. Use the recursive procedure below to draw a rectangle composed of squares whose successive sides have a ratio equal to the Golden Ratio. The side of each successive square is 0.61803 times the side of the previous square. Then draw a spiral on the printout by connecting the opposite corners of each square with a 90 degree arc.

```
TO GOLDENSPIRAL :SIDE
IF :SIDE < 3 [STOP HIDETURTLE]
REPEAT 4 [FD :SIDE RT 90]        What does this line do?
FD :SIDE RT 90 FD :SIDE
GOLDENSPIRAL :SIDE * 0.61803
END
```

Golden Spiral

Summing Up

6. Suppose you find the 99th and the 100th terms of the Fibonacci sequence. Predict the ratio of the terms.

7. What is the stopping condition for the procedure GOLDENSPIRAL? Explain why a stopping condition is needed.

Significant Digits and Accuracy

Both of these diameter measurements have 3 **significant digits**. The significant digits tell the number of times the unit to which you measured is used.

12,700 km

2.45 cm

Unit of measure: 100 km	Unit of measure: 0.01 cm
Number of units used: 127	Number of units used: 245
Greatest possible error (GPE): 50 km	Greatest possible error (GPE): 0.005 cm

The measurement for the button is more **precise** because 0.01 cm is a smaller unit of measure than 100 km.

▶ The relative error of the measurement is the ratio of the GPE to the measurement itself. The lower the relative error, the more accurate the measurement.

$$\text{GPE} \rightarrow \frac{0.005}{2.45} \approx 0.00204 \qquad \text{measurement} \rightarrow$$

$$\text{GPE} \rightarrow \frac{50}{12{,}700} \approx 0.0039 \qquad \text{measurement} \rightarrow$$

The measurement for the diameter of the button is more accurate because it has a smaller relative error.

Complete this chart. Use a calculator to compute the relative error.

	Measurement	Precision (Unit of Measure)	Number of Units	Significant Digits	Number of Significant Digits	Approximate Relative Error
1.	32.6 km					
2.	4,000 m					
3.	78,588 km					
4.	21.30 m					
5.	0.018 m					

6. What general statement could you make about the number of significant digits in a measurement and the accuracy of the measurement?

Maintaining Skills

Choose the correct answer. Write A, B, C, or D.

1. What is the property illustrated?
   $6 + {}^-6 = 0$

   A Associative   **C** Additive Inverse

   B Commutative   **D** not given

2. Evaluate $4x + 16$ for $x = {}^-6$.

   A 8   **C** ${}^-16$

   B ${}^-8$ **D** not given

3. Compare. ${}^-4.25$ ⬤ ${}^-6.01$

   A $<$ **C** $=$

   B $>$ **D** not given

4. 3.45×10^3

   A 3,450   **C** 34,500

   B 0.00345   **D** not given

5. What is $\sqrt{64}$?

   A 8   **C** 8^2

   B 8×8 **D** not given

6. What is ${}^-\sqrt{81}$?

   A 18   **C** 9

   B ${}^-18$ **D** not given

7. What is the length of side a?

   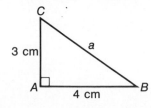

   A 7 cm   **C** 5 cm

   B 9 cm   **D** not given

8. What is the median of 6.2, 3.3, 8.4, 2.1, 2.1, and 0.6?

   A 7.8   **C** 2.7

   B 2.1   **D** not given

9. What is the ratio of ★ to #?
   ★★#####

   A 5:2   **C** 2:7

   B 2:5   **D** not given

10. Solve for n. $\frac{2}{8} = \frac{n}{28}$

    A $n = 4$ **C** $n = 8$

    B $n = 7$ **D** not given

11. Find the missing measure.
    scale = 1 cm : 25 km
    drawing = 2.4 cm   actual = _____

    A 600 km   **C** 60 km

    B 2.4 km   **D** not given

12. $2.42 \text{ L} - 1{,}624 \text{ mL} =$

    A 1,621.58 mL   **C** 796 mL

    B 1,382 mL   **D** not given

Solve.

13. Jefferson Middle School is selling daffodils for $.50 each as a fund raiser. A florist offered to supply the flowers for $16.00 for each bundle of 80. Find the profit on 1 daffodil.

    A $24.00   **C** $.30

    B $.40   **D** not given

14. If 880 daffodils are sold, what is the total profit?

    A $264.00   **C** $440.00

    B $176.00   **D** not given

9 Percent

Sharing What You Know

Wilt Chamberlain, one of basketball's greats, scored 31,419 points in a total of 1,045 games. Julius Erving, better known as Dr. "J", scored 30,026 points in 1,243 games. How can their records be compared? What could you say if you figured that Wilt scored an average of 30.1 points per game and Dr. "J" scored 24.2? Discuss how averages are computed. What are some ways that you use averages?

Using Language

Performances can also be described in terms of **percent.** For example, in 1988 Larry Bird of the Boston Celtics made 88 out of 100, or 88%, of his free throws. A **percent** is a ratio whose denominator is 100. **Percent** comes from the Latin words *per* meaning *by* or *through* and *centum* meaning *hundred.* Which coin is named for the Latin word *centum?* How is its meaning related to its value?

Words to Know   percent, ratio, proportion, cross products, circle graphs, interest, principal, discount, markup

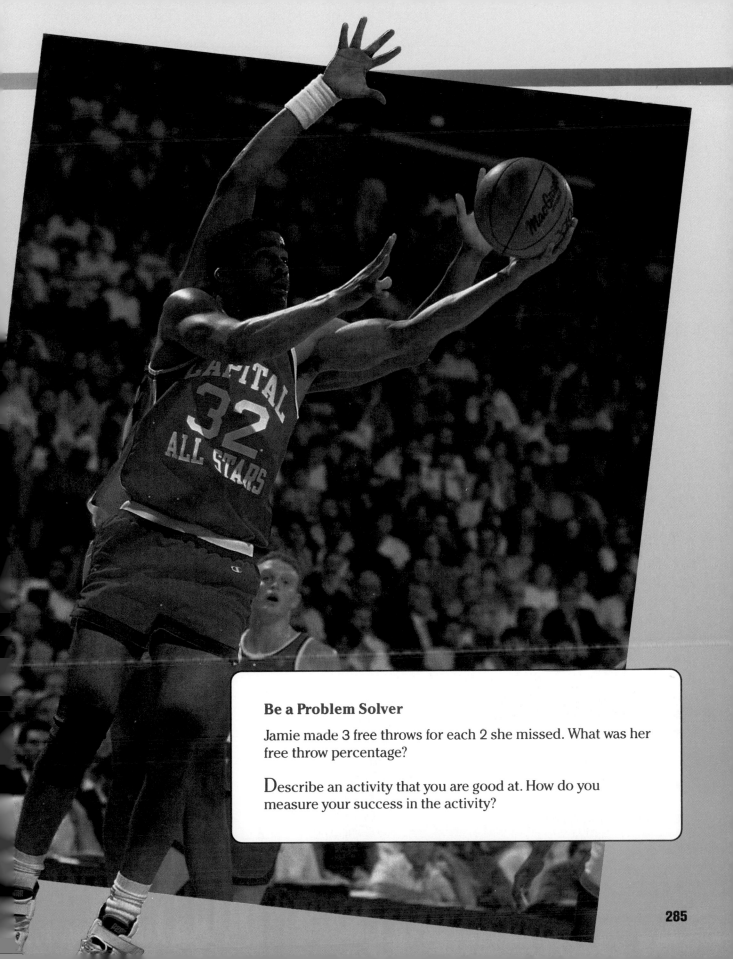

Be a Problem Solver

Jamie made 3 free throws for each 2 she missed. What was her free throw percentage?

Describe an activity that you are good at. How do you measure your success in the activity?

The symbol % is used for percents. Name some things that are usually expressed as percents.

Understanding Percent

In her first varsity football game, Leanne Bollinger scored 3 out of 4 times that she attempted to kick a point after a touchdown. What percent of her attempts were successful?

▶ A percent is a ratio whose second term is 100. To write a ratio as a percent, you can use equal ratios.

$$\frac{3}{4} = \frac{3 \times 25}{4 \times 25} = \frac{75}{100} \qquad \text{So } \frac{3}{4} = 75\%.$$

Leanne scored in 75% of her attempts.

You can also use proportion.

$$\frac{3}{4} = \frac{n}{100}$$

$$4n = 300$$
$$n = 75 \qquad \frac{3}{4} = \frac{75}{100} = 75\%$$

To write a percent as a ratio, divide by 100 and simplify if possible. $24\% = \frac{24}{100} = \frac{6}{25}$

More Examples

a. What percent is shaded?

$$\frac{9}{25} = \frac{n}{100}$$
$$900 = 25n$$
$$36 = n$$

36% is shaded. What percent is not shaded?

b. Write 2.5% as a ratio.

$$\frac{2.5}{100} = \frac{25}{1,000} = \frac{1}{40}$$

Check Your Understanding

Write each as a percent.

1. 71 out of 100
2. 1 out of 10
3. 3 out of 4
4. 7 out of 50
5. 14 out of 14
6. 11 out of 20

Explain each percent.

7. They won 80% of the games.
8. He scored 90% on a test.
9. 15% were absent.

Share Your Ideas Look back at 9. Can you tell how many were absent? Explain.

286

Write each as a percent.

10. 34 out of 100

11. 11 out of 50

12. 4 out of 10

13. 7 out of 25

14. 12 out of 20

15. 1 out of 4

16. 2 out of 5

17. $6 out of $12

18. 93 out of 93

Explain each percent.

19. 2% preferred brand X.

20. 93% voted for the school referendum.

21. It rained 50% of the time.

22. The sales tax rate is 5%.

23. Prices were reduced 10%.

24. The team won or tied 60% of the games.

Follow the rule to find each output.

Rule: Write each ratio as a percent.

	Input	Output
25.	2 out of 5	
26.	4 out of 10	
27.	9 out of 10	
28.	20 out of 20	

Rule: Write each percent as a ratio.

	Input	Output
29.	37%	
30.	10%	
31.	25%	
32.	50%	

Find the percent of each color, letter, or number.

33.

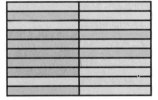

34.

S	T	O	P
T	O	P	S
P	O	T	S
P	O	S	T
S	P	O	T

35.

3	9	6	9	3
9	3	6	3	9
6	6	3	6	6
9	3	6	3	9
3	9	6	9	3

Look back at 33–35.

36. Find the sum of the percents in each exercise. What do you notice? Explain.

37. What if you found the fractional part for each number in **35**? Predict the sum of the fractions. Explain.

Mathematics and History

Different percent notations have been used throughout history. Instead of %, expressions such as per centum, p 100, p cento, and p C° were used. Roman numerals were used for numbers. Express each percent in today's notation.

38. X p cento

40. 35 p 100

39. VI p C°

41. 19 per centum

Explain how you could use percents to compare $\frac{4}{5}$ and $\frac{17}{20}$.

SUMMING UP

Write each ratio as a decimal.

$\frac{3}{10}$ $\frac{93}{100}$ $\frac{1}{3}$

Relating Percents, Ratios, and Decimals

Jean has successfully returned 57 out of 100 serves. Find a decimal and a percent to express 57 out of 100.

57 out of 100 $= \frac{57}{100} = 0.57 = 57\%$

How does a number in decimal form change when you write it as a percent? Study the examples below. Describe the patterns that you see.

a. $\frac{15}{100} = 0.15 = 15\%$

b. $\frac{7}{25} = \frac{7 \times 4}{25 \times 4} = \frac{28}{100} = 0.28 = 28\%$

c. $\frac{1}{3} = 3\overline{)1.00}^{\,0.33\frac{1}{3} = 33\frac{1}{3}\%}$ **d.** $\frac{3}{8} = 8\overline{)3.00}^{\,0.375 = 37\frac{1}{2}\%}$

Look back at the examples above. How can you change a percent to a decimal?

More Examples

e. Write 40% as a ratio.

$40\% = \frac{40}{100} = \frac{2}{5}$

f. Write $2\frac{1}{2}\%$ as a decimal.

$2\frac{1}{2}\% = \frac{2.5}{100} = \frac{25}{1,000} = 0.025$

g. Write 0.7 as a percent.

$0.7 = \frac{7}{10} = \frac{70}{100} = 70\%$

Check Your Understanding

Write each as a percent. Use mental math, paper and pencil, or a calculator.

1. $\frac{1}{2}$ **2.** $\frac{5}{8}$ **3.** $\frac{2}{3}$ **4.** 0.19   **5.** 0.03   **6.** $\frac{4}{5}$

7. $\frac{2}{9}$ **8.** $\frac{21}{50}$ **9.** 0.87   **10.** 0.875   **11.** 0.66   **12.** $0.66\frac{2}{3}$

Write each percent as a decimal and as a ratio in lowest terms.

13. 1%   **14.** 60%   **15.** 75%   **16.** 7.5%   **17.** $12\frac{1}{2}\%$ **18.** $33\frac{1}{3}\%$

Share Your Ideas   How would you find the percent for $\frac{1}{6}$? Explain why you chose that method.

Write each as a percent. Use mental math, paper and pencil, or a calculator.

19. $\frac{3}{4}$ 20. 0.37   21. 0.3   22. 0.1   23. $\frac{1}{3}$ 24. $\frac{4}{9}$

25. $\frac{39}{50}$ 26. 1   27. $\frac{2}{15}$ 28. 0.716   29. $\frac{7}{40}$ 30. $\frac{5}{12}$

Write each percent as a decimal and as a ratio in lowest terms.

31. 50%   32. 6%   33. 31%   34. 30%   35. 60%   36. 84%

37. 12%   38. 76%   39. 65%   40. 95%   41. 2.5%   42. 12.5%

Find *n*. Eact set of numbers represents a ratio, decimal, and percent that are equal.

43. 3%, 0.03, *n*   44. $\frac{3}{4}$, 75%, *n*   45. $0.\overline{6}$, $66\frac{2}{3}$%, *n*   46. 0.71, $\frac{71}{100}$, *n*

47. $\frac{1}{50}$, 0.02, *n*   48. $\frac{5}{8}$, 0.625, *n*   49. $\frac{9}{20}$, 45%, *n*   50. 1, 1.00, *n*

Choose the greatest value.

51. a. $\frac{3}{5}$
    b. 59.7%
    c. 0.65
    d. $\frac{17}{25}$

52. a. 6%
    b. $\frac{1}{20}$
    c. 0.065
    d. $\frac{9}{200}$

53. a. 0.19
    b. $\frac{1}{5}$
    c. 18.3%
    d. $\frac{9}{50}$

54. a. $66\frac{2}{3}$%
    b. $\frac{67}{100}$
    c. 0.66
    d. $0.\overline{6}$

Think and Apply

55. Four thousand seats in the tennis stadium were filled. 1,800 women and 300 children were present. What percent of the seats were filled by women? by children? by men?

56. **What if** you had to order a set of three numbers from least to greatest? Would ratios, decimals, or percents be the easiest to order? Support your answer with examples.

Explain how you would write a decimal as a percent. a percent as a decimal.

Mental Math: Percents

The swim team completed 10 out of 20 laps.
What percent did they complete?

$$\frac{10}{20} = \frac{1}{2} = 50\%$$ The swim team completed 50% of the laps.

It is helpful to know equivalent ratios for commonly used percents.

a. The practice medley is $\frac{1}{3}$ backstroke and $\frac{2}{3}$ freestyle. What is the percent for each?

Think $\frac{1}{3} = 33\frac{1}{3}\%$, and $\frac{2}{3} = 66\frac{2}{3}\%$

The medley is $33\frac{1}{3}\%$ backstroke and $66\frac{2}{3}\%$ freestyle.

You can use ratios for common percents to find other percents.

b. The team is $\frac{2}{5}$ female and $\frac{3}{5}$ male. Find the percent for each.

Think $\frac{1}{5} = 20\%$, so $\frac{2}{5} = 2 \times \frac{1}{5}$, or 40%, and $\frac{3}{5} = 3 \times \frac{1}{5}$, or 60%

The team is 40% female and 60% male.

You can use equivalent ratios to find some percents easily.

c. Lisa attended 47 out of 50 practice sessions. What percent is that?

Think $\frac{47}{50} \times \frac{2}{2} = \frac{94}{100} = 94\%$

Lisa attended 94% of the sessions.

How can you use mental math to find the percent for $\frac{7}{50}$?

Check Your Understanding

Use mental math to write each as a percent.

1. $\frac{2}{3}$

2. $\frac{7}{10}$

3. $\frac{9}{20}$

4. $\frac{4}{5}$

5. $\frac{1}{8}$

6. $\frac{39}{50}$

Use mental math to write each as a ratio in lowest terms.

7. $16\frac{2}{3}\%$

8. 90%

9. 15%

10. 75%

11. $12\frac{1}{2}\%$

12. $87\frac{1}{2}\%$

Share Your Ideas What other mental math strategies can you use to find percents?

Use mental math to write each ratio as a percent.

13. $\frac{1}{10}$ **14.** $\frac{1}{3}$ **15.** $\frac{3}{4}$ **16.** $\frac{3}{8}$

17. $\frac{17}{20}$ **18.** $\frac{3}{5}$ **19.** $\frac{23}{50}$ **20.** $\frac{2}{3}$

Use mental math to write each percent as a ratio in lowest terms.

21. $33\frac{1}{3}\%$ **22.** 20% **23.** 56% **24.** 2%

25. 45% **26.** 83% **27.** 98% **28.** $87\frac{1}{2}\%$

Use $\frac{1}{25} = 4\%$ to find a percent for each.

29. $\frac{2}{25}$ **30.** $\frac{7}{25}$ **31.** $\frac{24}{25}$ **32.** $\frac{24}{50}$

Use $\frac{1}{8} = 12\frac{1}{2}\%$ to find a percent for each.

33. $\frac{3}{8}$ **34.** $\frac{5}{8}$ **35.** $\frac{7}{8}$ **36.** $\frac{7}{16}$

Compare. Use <, >, or = for each ⬤.

37. $\frac{1}{6}$ ⬤ $0.\overline{16}$ **38.** $33\frac{1}{3}\%$ ⬤ $0.\overline{3}$

39. 0.41 ⬤ $\frac{2}{5}$ **40.** 0.01 ⬤ $\frac{1}{10}$

41. 94% ⬤ $\frac{19}{20}$ **42.** $\frac{1}{40}$ ⬤ 2.5%

Think and Apply

43. Tim is swimming backstroke in the 400-meter medley. If he is one of four members on the team, what percent of the team does Tim represent?

44. Chris swam the 50-meter freestyle in 29.4 seconds. Jan's best time was 0.25 seconds faster. What is Jan's best time?

Mixed Review

1. $\frac{-3}{4} \times 1\frac{2}{3}$

2. $-3\frac{1}{2} - 1\frac{1}{2}$

3. $31.6 \div 0.4$

4. $-7\frac{3}{4} + 2\frac{5}{8}$

5. $-31 - (-17.89)$

6. -5.12×6.8

Solve.

7. $3x + 2 = 14$

8. $7 - 2x = 11$

9. $-7x + 7 = -28$

10. $5x - 4 = 1$

11. $10 - x = 13$

Find n if the mean is 20.

12. 30, 15, 26, n

13. 42, n, 12

14. 17, 5, 32, n

15. n, 15, 25

Solve each proportion.

16. $\frac{3}{50} = \frac{x}{300}$

17. $\frac{16}{x} = \frac{96}{18}$

18. $\frac{21}{30} = \frac{x}{70}$

19. $\frac{20}{x} = \frac{4}{30}$

20. $\frac{5}{60} = \frac{7}{x}$

If you know that $\frac{1}{20} = 5\%$, explain how you can find each.

$\frac{3}{20}$ $\frac{7}{20}$ $\frac{17}{20}$

SUMMING UP

Name some decimals and fractions that are between 0 and 0.01. Name some mixed numbers and decimals that are greater than 1.

Less Than 1% or Greater Than 100%

Nutritionists recommend a high-carbohydrate diet for marathon runners. A serving of 300 g of carbohydrates is suggested. If Tom eats 375 g, or $1\frac{1}{4}$ times the recommended serving, what percent of the suggested serving does he consume?

$$1\frac{1}{4} = 1.25 = \frac{125}{100} = 125\%$$

Tom consumes 125% of the suggested serving.

What decimal represents 200%? 250%?

More Examples

a. Write 0.001 as a percent.

Think $0.01 = \frac{1}{100} = 1\%$, and 0.001 is $\frac{1}{10}$ of 0.01.

$$0.001 = 0.1\% = \frac{1}{10}\%$$

b. Write $\frac{1}{2}\%$ as a ratio.

$$\frac{1}{2}\% = \frac{\frac{1}{2}}{100} = \frac{1}{2} \times \frac{1}{100} = \frac{1}{200}$$

c. Write 150% as a ratio and as a decimal.

$$150\% = \frac{150}{100} = 1.5$$

d. Write $\frac{3}{400}$ as a percent.

$$\frac{3}{400} = \frac{n}{100}$$
$$400n = 300$$
$$n = \frac{300}{400} = \frac{3}{4} \quad \text{So } \frac{3}{400} = \frac{3}{4}\%, \text{ or } 0.75\%$$

Write a percent for each.

1. $1\frac{3}{4}$ 2. $2\frac{1}{2}$ 3. 0.009   4. 0.0075   5. $\frac{3}{1,000}$ 6. $\frac{1}{500}$

Write each percent as a decimal and as a ratio in lowest terms.

7. 150%   8. 375%   9. 0.5%   10. 0.25%   11. $\frac{1}{10}\%$ 12. $\frac{3}{4}\%$

Share Your Ideas Explain how $\frac{1}{4}$ and $\frac{1}{4}\%$ are different.

Write a percent for each.

13. $1\frac{1}{2}$ 14. $2\frac{3}{4}$ 15. 1.2 16. 0.55 17. 0.005 18. 0.0025

19. $0.33\frac{1}{3}$ 20. $1\frac{1}{3}$ 21. $\frac{5}{8}$ 22. $\frac{2}{3}$ 23. $1\frac{2}{3}$ 24. $\frac{17}{1,000}$

25. $\frac{1}{200}$ 26. $\frac{3}{250}$ 27. $\frac{7}{500}$ 28. 1.009 29. $1\frac{1}{500}$ 30. 2.0075

Write each percent as a decimal and as a ratio in lowest terms.

31. $\frac{1}{10}\%$ 32. 110% 33. $\frac{1}{5}\%$ 34. 35% 35. 135% 36. 150%

37. $1\frac{1}{2}\%$ 38. $2\frac{3}{4}\%$ 39. 275% 40. 0.5% 41. 7.2% 42. 1.35%

Copy and complete.

	Ratio	Decimal	Percent
43.	$2\frac{1}{2}$		
44.		1.75	
45.			310%
46.	$\frac{1}{200}$		
47.			0.009%

	Ratio	Decimal	Percent
48.	$\frac{4}{5}$		
49.			$\frac{4}{5}\%$
50.	$7\frac{1}{3}$		
51.		0.625	
52.			200%

53. Philip analyzed his diet and found that he got 125% of the recommended daily allowance of vitamin A, 133% of vitamin E, and 200% of vitamin C. Express each percent as a ratio.

54. A sports nutritionist recommends a diet that is 50% carbohydrates, 35% fat, and the balance protein. What percent of protein is recommended?

55. Juma Ikangaa of Tanzania won the New York City Marathon on November 5, 1989. His winning time of 2 h 8 min 1 s was 12 s faster than the record set 8 years before. What was the previous record time?

DATA 56. Use an almanac to compare 6 winners in Olympic marathons. What percent improved the time of the previous marathon by at least 2 min?

Common Error

Correct each error.

57. $\frac{1}{10}\% = 0.1$ ← incorrect

58. $\frac{1}{3}\% = 0.33\frac{1}{3}$ ← incorrect

59. $\frac{1}{2}\% = 0.5$ ← incorrect

Which percent describes a number greater than 1; a number between 0 and 0.01; a number between 0.01 and 1. **a.** 6% **b.** 600% **c.** 0.6%

SUMMING UP

Midchapter Review

Write each as a percent. pages 286–293

1. 25 out of 100
2. 6 out of 10
3. 12 out of 50
4. 3 out of 5
5. 8 out of 16
6. 42 out of 42
7. $\frac{1}{3}$
8. $\frac{9}{20}$
9. 3
10. $\frac{5}{9}$
11. 0.42
12. 0.123
13. $\frac{3}{4}$
14. $1\frac{1}{2}$
15. 0.006
16. $\frac{19}{1,000}$
17. 2.0075
18. $2\frac{2}{3}$

Write each percent as a decimal and as a ratio. pages 288–293

19. 50%
20. $66\frac{2}{3}\%$
21. 32%
22. 14%
23. 80%
24. 6.5%
25. 75%
26. $12\frac{1}{2}\%$
27. $22\frac{2}{9}\%$
28. $\frac{1}{20}\%$
29. $\frac{1}{5}\%$
30. 150%
31. 325%
32. 0.5%
33. 25%

Choose the greatest value. pages 288–289

34. a. 0.12
    b. $\frac{1}{8}$
    c. 13%
    d. $\frac{3}{25}$

35. a. $\frac{3}{20}$
    b. 15.5%
    c. $0.15\overline{5}$
    d. $\frac{9}{60}$

36. a. $33\frac{1}{3}\%$
    b. $\frac{16}{50}$
    c. $\frac{33}{100}$
    d. 0.334

Compare. Use >, <, or = for each ⬭. pages 290–293

37. $\frac{1}{4}$ ⬭ 0.26
38. $\frac{1}{2}$ ⬭ 0.5
39. 0.25 ⬭ $\frac{1}{4}\%$
40. $\frac{3}{10}$ ⬭ 32%
41. $\frac{7}{8}$ ⬭ 87.5%
42. 128% ⬭ $1\frac{7}{26}$
43. 75.1% ⬭ $\frac{3}{4}$
44. $\frac{3}{10}\%$ ⬭ 0.3
45. $\frac{7}{40}$ ⬭ $1\frac{3}{4}\%$
46. $1\frac{1}{5}$ ⬭ 121%
47. $\frac{6}{7}$ ⬭ 84%
48. 0.004 ⬭ $\frac{2}{5}$

Solve.

49. One fourth of the people attending the game bought pennants. What percent bought pennants?

50. Helen's team lost $\frac{1}{5}$ of their games. What percent of the total games did they win?

Exploring Problem Solving

Competitive Teams

Frank's Florists bowl 3 games against Susy's Plumbers each week. The team that scores more points in a game wins that game. A win is also awarded to the team with the greater total for all 3 games. The members are meeting, since one team has been winning most of the games. They want to make the games more competitive.

Here are their scores.

FRANK'S FLORISTS

Name	1	2	3	Total	1	2	3	Total
Frank	123	78	141	342	132	128	80	340
Carl	63	97	82	242	81	97	66	244
June	67	93	77	237	72	92	85	249
Reggie	42	84	54	180	40	79	61	180
Total	295	352	354	1,001	325	396	292	1,013

SUSY'S PLUMBERS

Name	1	2	3	Total	1	2	3	Total
Susy	118	125	117	360	115	123	122	360
Rhonda	95	106	98	299	97	103	102	302
Melvin	116	82	103	301	119	77	102	298
Terry	63	68	51	182	59	62	56	177
Total	392	381	369	1,142	390	365	382	1,137

Thinking Critically

What should the team members do to make the scores of the games more even? Work in a group as you study the scores and make a plan.

Analyzing and Making Decisions

CHOICES

Use a calculator where appropriate.

1. How many wins does each team have? What is each team's average total per game? What is each bowler's average score per game? What other differences are there among the bowlers?

2. **What if** one team is given extra points to start a game? Which team should that be? How many points should be given? Try it. Who would have won the games then?

3. Rearrange the members among the teams to make the teams more competitive. Explain what you did. How would this change the scores of the games already played?

4. How would you make the bowling games more competitive? Explain why you would do this.

Look Back What if 40 people wanted to form a bowling league? How would you do it? What different things would you consider?

295

Problem Solving Strategies

Simulation

There are 3 parking lots for people attending the field games. Starting at 9:00 A.M., courtesy buses leave parking lot A every 5 minutes and stop at lots B and C on the way to the stadium. Travel between each stop takes 5 minutes. Courtesy buses also leave from the stadium every 5 minutes, starting at 9:00 A.M., and they stop at lots C, B, and A. If you were on a courtesy bus leaving parking lot A at 10:00 A.M., how many courtesy buses would you meet going in the other direction? Include the one that pulls in as you leave and the one that is ready to leave as you arrive at the stadium.

Sometimes you can solve a problem by simulating the action with a drawing or chart rather than by acting it out.

Solving the Problem

Think What is the question?

Explore How often does a bus leave each parking lot? How often does a bus leave the stadium? How can you simulate the action? Explain. At 10:00 A.M., where are buses located? Which ones do you need to consider? What happens in 5 minutes? How many buses will be passed in 5 minutes?

Solve How many buses did you meet?

Look Back What pattern developed during the simulation?

Share Your Ideas

1. In both this problem and the bowling problem on page 295, you could simulate the action. Why might someone want to use simulation to solve a real problem?

296

Practice

 Solve. Use a calculator where appropriate.

2. The Barons have the football on their own 20 yard line. On the next 7 plays, they gained 10 yards, lost 5 yards, gained 9 yards, gained 6 yards, gained 2 yards, lost 4 yards, and lost 7 yards. On the next play they kicked the ball and gained 18 yards. Where did the ball land?

3. Victor skied cross-country 6 miles in one hour while Richard went 4 miles. Both skied 9 miles at these rates and arrived at the cabin at the same time. How much earlier than Victor did Richard leave?

4. Alice and Faith are in a 68-mile bike race. Alice leaves at 9:00 A.M. and averages 19 mph. Faith leaves at 9:30 A.M. and averages 22 mph. Who will cross the finish line first? Explain.

5. Chris is playing a square dart game with 4 blue, 4 red, 4 yellow, and 4 green darts. He must place each dart so that every row, column, and the 2 diagonals have four different colored darts in them. Draw a diagram to show how he can do it.

Mixed Strategy Review

6. Sam and Stan each have 30 hits for 100 times at bat. In the last game Stan had 2 hits in 3 at bats. Sam had 3 hits in 5 at bats. Who had the higher batting average? Explain. (To compute a batting average, divide the number of hits by the number of times at bat.)

7. In soccer each goal scores 1 point. With two minutes left to play, the score was tied 4-4. How many different possible scores could there have been at half time?

8. In professional football, a team can score 2 points for a safety, 3 points for a field goal, 6 points for a touchdown, and 1 point for the extra point after each touchdown. The score for a game was 20-12. How might the points have been scored?

9. Mr. Roberts was having trouble selling table-tennis balls at $.25 each. Mr. Roberts took 60% off the price and took in $9.70. How much did he sell them for? How many did he sell at that price?

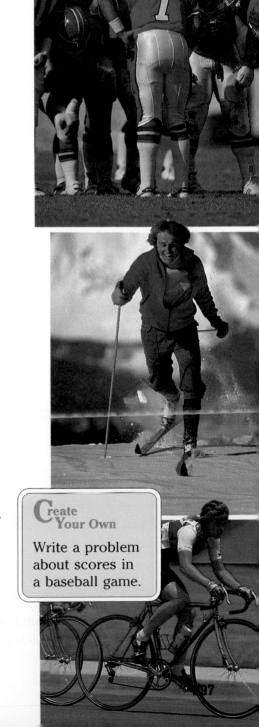

Create **Y**our **Own**

Write a problem about scores in a baseball game.

289

Name the percents for $\frac{1}{2}$, $\frac{3}{4}$, $\frac{2}{5}$, $\frac{9}{10}$, and $\frac{2}{3}$. State other common ratios and their percents.

Solving Percent Problems Using Mental Math

Chris made 25% of the 20 goals scored by the soccer team. How many goals did she make?

$25\% = \frac{1}{4}$

25% of 20 is $\frac{1}{4}$ of 20, or 5.

Chris scored 5 goals.

What if Chris scored 6 times in the next week, making $33\frac{1}{3}\%$ of the goals? How many goals did the team score?

$33\frac{1}{3}\% = \frac{1}{3}$

6 is $\frac{1}{3}$ of the total. $6 \times 3 = 18$, so 6 is $33\frac{1}{3}\%$ of 18.

The team scored 18 goals.

More Examples

a. Find 15% of 20.

Think 10% of 20 is $\frac{1}{10}$ of 20, or 2.
    5% of 20 is half of 2, or 1.
    15% of 20 = 2 + 1 = 3

b. 14 is 200% of n. Find n.

Think 200% = 2
    14 is twice the number.
    So the number is 7.

c. 12 is 50% of what number?

Think $50\% = \frac{1}{2}$

    12 is $\frac{1}{2}$ of the number.
    So the number is 24.

d. n is 4% of 300. Find n.

Think 1% of 300 is $\frac{1}{100}$ of 300, or 3.
    4% is $4 \times \frac{1}{100}$
    So 4% of 300 is 4×3, or 12.

e. 7 is what percent of 28?

Think 7 is $\frac{1}{4}$ of 28, so 7 is 25% of 28.

Check Your Understanding

Use mental math to find each value of *n*.

1. n is 50% of 70.
2. n is 15% of 60.
3. 8 is 25% of n.
4. n is 25% of 8.

5. n is 90% of 20.
6. 9 is $33\frac{1}{3}\%$ of n.
7. 12 is 80% of n.
8. 15 is 200% of n.

Share Your Ideas Explain how you can use mental math to find 10% of 50, 1% of 50, and 100% of 50.

Use mental math to find each missing value.

9. 50% of 74 is *n*.

10. 25% of 44 is *n*.

11. What percent of 70 is 7?

12. What percent of 50 is 10?

13. 150% of 40 is *n*.

14. 10 is 20% of *n*.

15. 200% of 17 is *n*.

16. 50 is 200% of *n*.

17. $33\frac{1}{3}$ of 24 is *n*.

18. 3% of 200 is *n*.

19. $12\frac{1}{2}$% of 32 is *n*.

20. What percent of 12 is 2?

21. 4 is what percent of 10?

22. 4% of 250 is *n*.

23. What percent of 50 is 2?

Choose the correct equation for each. Write *a*, *b*, or *c*.

24. Find 1% of 92.

  a. $0.1 \times 92 = n$
  b. $0.001 \times 92 = n$
  c. $0.01 \times 92 = n$

25. 84 is 75% of what number?

  a. $84 \div 0.0075 = n$
  b. $84 \times 0.75 = n$
  c. $84 \div 0.75 = n$

26. What percent of 45 is 15?

  a. $45 \div 15 = n$
  b. $15 \div 45 = n$
  c. $45 \times 0.15 = n$

Find each input or output.

Rule: Find 200%.

	Input	Output
27.	35	
28.	7.2	
29.		$\frac{4}{5}$

Rule: Find $66\frac{2}{3}$%.

	Input	Output
30.	96	
31.	4.8	
32.		$\frac{6}{7}$

Rule: Find $\frac{1}{10}$%.

	Input	Output
33.	50	
34.	10.1	
35.		$\frac{1}{10}$

Think and Apply

36. Soccer is called football in most of the 140 nations where it is played. Only six nations have won the international World Cup competition. About what percent of the countries that play soccer have won the World Cup?

37. The football coach used a circle graph to analyze the team's offense. Use mental math to find the number of minutes used for each technique.

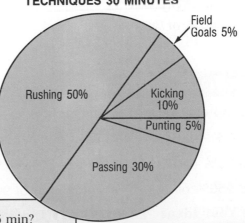

ANALYSIS OF TEAM OFFENSE TECHNIQUES 30 MINUTES

Field Goals 5%
Rushing 50%
Kicking 10%
Punting 5%
Passing 30%

Look back at **37. What if** they have the ball for 15 min? Describe an easy way to find the number of minutes for each technique. Explain why your method works.

SUMMING UP

Would you rather multiply two decimals or multiply two fractions? divide two decimals or divide two fractions? Why?

Solving Percent Problems Using Ratios or Decimals

One thousand youths participated in the first Special Olympics, held in 1968. **What if** 16% of the athletes were 13 years old? How many athletes were age 13?

Find 16% of 1,000.

You can use a decimal to find the answer.
    $0.16 \times 1,000 = 160$

There were 160 participants of age thirteen.

You can also write the percent as a ratio to find the answer.

$$\frac{16}{\overset{}{\underset{1}{\cancel{100}}}} \times \frac{\overset{10}{\cancel{1,000}}}{1} = 160$$

Which way do you prefer? Why?

More Examples

a. Find $33\frac{1}{3}\%$ of 42.

$\frac{1}{3} \times \frac{42}{1} = \frac{14}{1} = 14$

$33\frac{1}{3}\%$ of 42 = 14.

b. What percent is 7 out of 10?

$\frac{7}{10} = 0.7 = 70\%$

7 is 70% of 10.

c. Find 60% of 36.

60% = 0.6
$0.6 \times 36 = 21.6$
21.6 is 60% of 36.

d. 20 is what percent of 80?

$\frac{20}{80} = \frac{1}{4} = 25\%$

20 is 25% of 80.

Use a ratio or a decimal to find each.

1. Find 25% of 64.

2. What number is 37% of 200?

3. What percent is 12 out of 72?

4. Find 75% of 124.

5. 41.4 is 20% of what number?

6. 40 is what percent of 50?

7. Find 250% of 20.

8. Find $66\frac{2}{3}\%$ of 99.

9. 144 is what percent of 100?

Share Your Ideas Look back at **9.** Did you use a decimal or a ratio to find the answer? Explain your choice.

Use a ratio or a decimal to find each.

10. Find $66\frac{2}{3}\%$ of 51. **11.** 93 is what percent of 31? **12.** What is 75% of 36?

13. What is 1% of 720? **14.** Find 25% of 140. **15.** Find 2% of 2,950.

16. What is $\frac{1}{4}\%$ of 100? **17.** What percent is 54 out of 72? **18.** Find 19% of 17.

19. What is 85% of 20? **20.** Find $87\frac{1}{2}\%$ of 48. **21.** What is 45% of 40?

22. 90 is what percent of 15? **23.** Find 14% of 7.1. **24.** Find 15% of 90.

25. Find $14\frac{2}{7}\%$ of 49. **26.** 2.5 is what percent of 0.5? **27.** Find $\frac{3}{4}\%$ of 560.

Use mental math, paper and pencil, or a calculator to find each. Then describe each pattern.

28. 10% of 15 **29.** 5% of 5 **30.** 48% of 40 **31.** 16% of 16
10% of 30 10% of 5 49% of 40 16% of 17
10% of 60 20% of 5 50% of 40 16% of 18
10% of 120 40% of 5 51% of 40 16% of 19

Choose the correct answer for each.

32. If 18% of 18 is 3.24, then

a. 9% of 9 is 1.62

b. 18% of 36 is 12.96

c. 36% of 18 is 6.48

33. If 1% of 73 is 0.73, then

a. $\frac{1}{2}\%$ of 73 is 0.365

b. $\frac{1}{10}\%$ of 73 is 0.0073

c. $\frac{1}{2}\%$ of 146 is 0.0146

34. If 55% of 22 is 12.1, then

a. 110% of 44 is 24.2

b. 55% of 11 is 6.05

c. 11% of 11 is 0.121

Think and Apply

35. Two thousand athletes participated in the second International Special Olympics. Then in 1975, 160% of that number competed in the fourth International games. How many athletes competed in 1975?

36. Track and field is one of the sports in the Special Olympics. Wheelchair–bound athletes compete in a 25-yard race, a 30-yard slalom, and a 100-yard relay. What percent of the relay distance is the race distance?

Would you use a decimal or a ratio to solve each? Explain your choice.
$11\frac{1}{9}\%$ of 108 = n   80% of 20 = n

SUMMING UP

Solving Percent Problems Using Proportions

Andy has a collection of baseball cards. Forty-five cards, or 9%, show catchers. How many cards does Andy have?

You have already solved percent problems, using decimals or ratios. You can also use a proportion.

45 is 9% of what number?

Think A percent is a ratio whose second term is 100.

$$\frac{45}{n} = \frac{9}{100}$$ Write equal ratios.

9n = 4,500   Use cross products.

n = 500   Andy has 500 cards.

More Examples

a. What is 80% of 120?

$$\frac{80}{100} = \frac{n}{120} \quad \textbf{Think } \frac{80}{100} = \frac{4}{5}$$
$$\frac{4}{5} = \frac{n}{120}$$

$$5n = 480$$

$$n = 96$$

b. 6.1 is what percent of 18.3?

$$\frac{n}{100} = \frac{6.1}{18.3}$$
$$\frac{n}{100} = \frac{1}{3}$$

$$3n = 100$$

$$n = 33\frac{1}{3}$$

6.1 is $33\frac{1}{3}$% of 18.3.

Look back at the examples. What is the advantage of using an equal ratio in lowest terms to solve a proportion?

Check Your Understanding

Use a proportion to solve each.

1. 12 is what percent of 15?   **2.** Find 50% of 22.1.   **3.** 72 is $12\frac{1}{2}$% of n.

4. $33\frac{1}{3}$% of n = 8.   **5.** What percent of 18 is 14?   **6.** Find 40% of 75.2.

Choose a method to solve each.

7. 1.2 is 5% of n.   **8.** Find $87\frac{1}{2}$% of 32.   **9.** 85 is what percent of 255?

Share Your Ideas Look back at **9**. Did you use a ratio, a proportion, or mental math to solve? Give a reason for your choice.

Use a proportion to solve each.

10. 22 is 50% of *n*.

11. What percent of 84 is 21?

12. 12 is $33\frac{1}{3}$% of *n*.

13. 110 is 10% of *n*.

14. What percent of 45 is 40?

15. 16 is 16% of *n*.

Choose a method to solve each.

16. What percent of 24 is 24?

17. 27 is what percent of 9?

18. *n* is 20% of 13.

19. 28% of 42 is *n*.

20. 20% of 75 is *n*.

21. 3 is $2\frac{1}{2}$% of *n*.

22. 13 is what percent of 26?

23. 26 is 200% of *n*.

24. 17% of 25 is *n*.

25. $\frac{1}{2}$% of 90 is *n*.

26. What percent of 6.4 is 0.32?

27. 0.6% of 120 is *n*.

Match each proportion with the correct problem. Write A, B, C, D, E, or F.

28. $\frac{28}{100} = \frac{n}{70}$

A. What percent is 19.6 out of 70?

29. $\frac{n}{100} = \frac{19.6}{70}$

B. Find 70% of 28.

30. $\frac{28}{100} = \frac{19.6}{n}$

C. Find 28% of 70.

31. $\frac{28}{100} = \frac{70}{n}$

D. What percent is 250 out of 70?

32. $\frac{n}{100} = \frac{250}{70}$

E. 19.6 is 28% of *n*.

F. 70 is 28% of *n*.

Think and Apply

33. Of the 500 cards in Andy's collection, 25% show pitchers, 8% show outfielders, and 40% show first-base players. How many cards of each does he have?

34. One card cost Andy $13. Another cost only $33\frac{1}{3}$% as much. How much was the other card?

35. Twenty-five percent of Denise's 500-card collection show Baltimore Orioles players. Forty percent of the remaining cards represent Texas Rangers. How many cards show Rangers? Orioles? other teams?

Compare using a proportion to solve percent problems with other methods of solving them. Which way do you prefer? Why?

SUMMING UP

303

Solving Percent Problems Using Equations

The Tigers won the volleyball game by scoring on 18 of their serves. If that was 60% of their serves, how many times did the Tigers serve in the game?

You can use an equation to solve percent problems.

18 is 60% of n.

$18 = 0.6n$ Write 60% as a decimal.

$\dfrac{18}{0.6} = \dfrac{0.6n}{0.6}$ Divide both sides by 0.6 and simplify.

$30 = n$ The Tigers served 30 times.

More Examples

a. 5 is what percent of 45?

$5 = 45n$

$\dfrac{5}{45} = \dfrac{45n}{45}$

$\dfrac{1}{9} = n$

$\dfrac{1}{9} = 11\dfrac{1}{9}\%$

b. n is 14.3% of 7.

$n = 0.143 \times 7$

$n = 1.001$

What if you forgot the percent for $\dfrac{1}{9}$?
How could you use mental math to find it?

Check Your Understanding

Use an equation to solve.

1. 18 is what percent of 24?

2. 13 is 10% of n.

3. $22\dfrac{2}{9}\%$ of 72 is n.

4. 32 is what percent of 160?

5. 108 is 200% of n.

6. What percent of 64 is 72?

Solve using any method you choose.

7. 20 is $83\dfrac{1}{3}\%$ of n.

8. n is 30% of 20.

9. What percent of 40 is $7\dfrac{1}{2}$?

Share Your Ideas   Look back at **7–9**. Did you use a ratio, a decimal, a proportion, mental math, or an equation? Explain each choice.

Use an equation to solve each.

10. 5% of n is 50.　　　**11.** 15 is what percent of 180?　**12.** n is $66\frac{2}{3}$% of 78.

13. $12\frac{1}{2}$% of n is 16.　　**14.** 125% of n is 10.　　　**15.** $1\frac{1}{2}$% of n is 3.

Choose a method to solve each.

16. 10% of n is 5.2.　　**17.** 25% of n is 9.9.　　**18.** 68 is what percent of 17?

19. 4.2 is 1% of n.　　**20.** 59 is $33\frac{1}{3}$% of n.　　**21.** n is $62\frac{1}{2}$% of 56.

22. 33 is what percent of 99?　**23.** 4% of 311.5 is n.　　**24.** $86\frac{1}{2}$% of 1,000 is n.

25. n is $16\frac{2}{3}$% of 1.2.　　**26.** What percent of 20 is 0.2?　**27.** 71 is 0.71% of n.

Match each problem with the correct equation.

28. The Tigers' coach wrote 20 out of 35 articles about the Tigers. What percent of the articles did she write?

29. 20% of the articles she wrote about the Tigers have appeared in the school paper. How many have been in the paper?

30. 20% of 35 photos in the yearbook have captions written by the coach.

31. The coach set a goal for the team to win 200% of last year's wins. If the new goal is 20 wins, how many games were won last year?

A. $0.2 \times 20 = n$

B. $2 \times 20 = n$

C. $35n = 20$

D. $2n = 20$

E. $0.2 \times 35 = n$

F. $20n = 35$

32. The longest recorded volleyball marathon is 118 h 30 min. The record was set by students at Krugersdorf High School in South Africa. How many days did they play volleyball to set the record? What percent of a week does that represent?

33. Bob Schaffer has won over 1,000 games as a one-man team playing against six-man teams. If he has only lost 2 games, about what percent of the games has he won? About what percent of the games has he lost?

34. Women from the University of Hawaii have won 3 out of 7 collegiate volleyball championships. Five out of seven men's winning teams are from California. About what percent of the 14 winning teams are from Hawaii or California?

35. Walking can be a better aerobic exercise than volleyball. The record for the greatest distance walked in 24 hours was set in Belgium by Paul Forthomme. If he walked 140 mi and 1,229 yd in 24 hours, what was the average distance he walked per hour? per minute?

Explain why it is useful to be able to solve percent problems, using different methods.

SUMMING UP

Name some situations where an estimate could be used to solve a percent problem.

Estimating Percents

Wayne Gretsky broke the scoring record of the National Hockey League by scoring 1,850 points for goals and assists. If 641 of the points were goals, about what percent of the points were scored for goals?

Estimate. What percent is 641 out of 1,850?

You can use compatible numbers to estimate.

$\frac{641}{1,850}$ is about $\frac{600}{1,800}$ $\frac{600}{1,800} = \frac{1}{3} = 33\frac{1}{3}\%$

About $33\frac{1}{3}\%$ of Gretsky's points were goals.

What other compatible numbers could you use to estimate a percent for 641 out of 1,850?

More Examples

Use compatible numbers to estimate.

a. 16% of 49 is n.

16% of 49 $\rightarrow \frac{1}{6} \times 48 = 8$

16% of 49 is about 8.

b. What percent of 81 is 21?

$\frac{21}{81} \rightarrow \frac{20}{80} = \frac{1}{4} = 25\%$

21 is about 25% of 81.

c. 23 is 53% of n.
23 is about 50% of n.
So n is about 46.

d. 4% of 197 is n.
1% of 200 is 2.
4% = 4 × 1%   4 × 2 = 8
4% of 197 is about 8.

e. What percent of 42 is 5?
5 is about $\frac{1}{8}$ of 42.
5 is about $12\frac{1}{2}\%$ of 42.

f. 91 is 202% of n.
90 is about 200% of n,
so 100% of n is 90 ÷ 2, or 45.
91 is 202% of about 45.

Check Your Understanding

Estimate each missing value.

1. 15% of $22.65 is n.

2. What percent of 71 is 5?

3. 52% of n is 13.

4. What percent of 61 is 51?

5. $1.50 is 6% of n.

6. n is 26% of 1.

Share Your Ideas What other strategies can you use to estimate percents?

Estimate each value of *n*.

7. 14% of 97.2 is *n*.   **8.** 18% of 53 is *n*.   **9.** 0.9% of 713 is *n*.

10. What percent of 68 is 330?   **11.** What percent of 92 is 18?   **12.** $5\frac{3}{4}$% of 18 is *n*.

13. 209% of 189 is *n*.   **14.** 83% of *n* is 79.   **15.** What percent of 116 is 6?

16. What percent of 217 is 67?   **17.** $31\frac{1}{2}$% of *n* is $62\frac{5}{7}$.   **18.** 48.6 is 243% of *n*.

Use estimation to choose a reasonable answer.

19. 37% of 393 is *n*.   **20.** 0.8% of 67 is *n*.   **21.** 21% of *n* is 386.   **22.** 57% of *n* is 47.

a. 50   a. 0.7   a. 200   a. 50
b. 100   b. 7   b. 2,000   b. 80
c. 135   c. 70   c. 20,000   c. 100

23. What percent of 457 is 917?   **24.** What percent of 179 is 58?   **25.** 5% of 58.7 is *n*.

a. 50%   a. 25%   a. less than 2.5
b. 100%   b. $33\frac{1}{3}$% b. greater than 3
c. 200%   c. 40%   c. less than 3

Is the actual number greater than or less than the estimate?

26. 48% of 29 is about 15.   **27.** 12% of 310 is about 31.   **28.** 11 out of 36 is about $33\frac{1}{3}$%.

29. 64 is 60% of about 100.   ★ **30.** 92 is 150% of about 60.   ★ **31.** 202% of 67 is about 140.

32. The National Hockey League record for career goals is held by Gordie Howe, who scored 801 goals. Estimate how many years it will take Gretsky to score the 161 goals needed to break the record if he has scored 641 in 11 years of play.

33. This year, Lisa scored 25% more goals than last year. If she scored 15 goals this year, how many goals did she score last year?

Visual Thinking

Estimate the percent that is shaded for each.

34.   **35.**

Explain as many ways as you can to estimate percent problems.

SUMMING UP

How many degrees are in a circle? in 50% of a circle? How would you find the number of degrees in 20% of a circle?

Making Circle Graphs

What is your favorite sport? Suppose the 24 votes below were recorded in response to that question. Display the results in a circle graph.

To make a circle graph, use these steps.

- Find the percent of the total each category represents.
- Find the number of degrees for each percent.
- Draw a central angle representing each percent.
- Label each section of the graph.
- Title the graph.

CLASS SURVEY FAVORITE SPORT

SPORT	NUMBER OF VOTES	PERCENT	DEGREES
Swimming	ⅬⱧ I	25%	$\frac{1}{4}$ x 360° = 90°
Skiing	IIII	$16\frac{2}{3}\%$	$\frac{1}{6}$ x 360° = 60°
Golf	III	$12\frac{1}{2}\%$	$\frac{1}{8}$ x 360° = 45°
Tennis	IIII	$16\frac{2}{3}\%$	$\frac{1}{6}$ x 360° = 60°
Running	ⱵⱧ II	$29\frac{1}{6}\%$	$\frac{7}{24}$ x 360° = 105°

TOTAL = 360°

▶You can use a protractor to measure each central angle or use estimation to sketch a graph.

Start by drawing a right angle for swimming. Next sketch an angle slightly larger than a right angle for running. Sketch $\frac{2}{3}$ of a right angle for skiing. Repeat for tennis. Does the section left for golf measure about one half a right angle? Then label and title the graph.

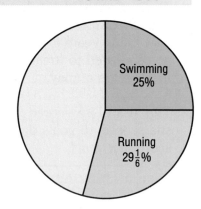

Check Your Understanding

1. Conduct a class survey to find out which sports students name as their favorite. Display your results in a circle graph.

2. Explain how you can estimate a central angle for each.
   a. 10% of a circle
   b. 40% of a circle
   c. $33\frac{1}{3}\%$ of a circle

Share Your Ideas Is it necessary to measure the last angle of a circle graph? Why or why not?

Make a circle graph for each.

3.

EXERCISE SCHEDULE	
Activity	Minutes
Jogging	15
Walking	10
Bicycling	15
Aerobics	20

4.

PHYSICAL EDUCATION GRADES	
Grade	Number of students
A	20
B	16
C	10
D	3
E	1

5.

SCHOOL ATHLETIC BUDGET	
Sport	Amount
Football	$100,000
Soccer	25,000
Track and Field	12,500
Baseball	62,500
Basketball	50,000

6. Number of sports injuries: 90 in football, 60 in running, 100 in boxing, and 50 in bicycling.

7. 200 pairs of sneakers sold: 80 for tennis, 40 for aerobics, 50 for walking, and the rest for jogging.

Use the data from the circle graph to answer 8–11.

8. What information can you obtain from the graph quickly?

9. How many arenas have a capacity of 10,000 and under? 15,000 and under?

10. How many more arenas have a capacity of under 10,001 than have a capacity of over 25,000?

11. Without measuring, find the number of degrees in the central angle for the capacity of 15,001–20,000.

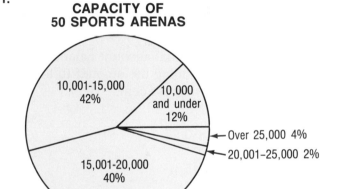

CAPACITY OF 50 SPORTS ARENAS

10,001-15,000 42%
10,000 and under 12%
Over 25,000 4%
20,001–25,000 2%
15,001-20,000 40%

12. Use estimation and a calculator to construct a circle graph of the sports participation survey.

DATA
13. Conduct a class survey of your choice. Display the results on a circle graph. If it is available, use graphing software to display your results.

The Daily News C1

Sports Participation in the U.S.

Activity	Participants
Swimming	72.6 million
Exercise Walking	53.5 million
Bicycling	49.7 million
Using Equipment	32 million
Running or Jogging	23.1 million
Aerobics	21.9 million

Explain step by step how to construct a circle graph.

SUMMING UP

How do banks pay interest on savings accounts? What is the current interest rate on savings? on loans?

Interest

Sara is saving to buy ski equipment. One year ago she put $300 in a savings account that pays interest compounded quarterly. If the interest rate is 6%, how much money is in the account now?

You can use simple interest to estimate the balance. Remember to express time in years.

I = principal × rate × time   principal + interest = balance
  = $300 × 0.06 × 1 $300 + $18 = $318
  = $18 $318 is the estimated balance.

▶ When interest is **compounded**, it is paid on a balance that includes the interest from each preceding period.

To find Sara's actual account balance, calculate the interest for each quarter, adding the amount to the balance each time. Round to the nearest cent.

$I = p \times r \times t$
  $= p \times 0.06 \times 0.25$

  $= p \times$ 0.015

	Interest	Balance
Jan. 1st		$300.00 deposit
Apr. 1st	300 × 0.015 = 4.50	$300 + $4.50 = $304.50
July 1st	304.50 × 0.015 = 4.57	$304.50 + $4.57 = $309.07
Oct. 1st	309.07 × 0.015 = 4.64	$309.07 + $4.64 = $313.71
Jan. 1st	313.71 × 0.015 = 4.70	$313.71 + $4.70 = $318.42

Sara will have $318.42 after one year.

Check Your Understanding

Estimate the interest. Then find the account balance for each. Round to the nearest cent. Use a calculator if you wish.

1. $300 after 1 year at 7% compounded annually
2. $100 after 2 years at 5% compounded quarterly
3. $500 after 1 year at $6\frac{1}{2}$% compounded semiannually

Share Your Ideas   Look back at **3**. Explain how you computed the interest for one period.

Practice

Estimate the interest for each. Use a calculator if you wish.

4. principal = $560
   rate = 6%
   time = 2 yr

5. principal = $1,500
   rate = $7\frac{1}{2}$%
   time = 1 yr

6. principal = $3,400
   rate = 12%
   time = 8 mo

7. principal = $10,500
   rate = $8\frac{1}{2}$%
   time = 2.5 yr

8. principal = $775
   rate = 9%
   time = 9 mo

9. principal = $1,000
   rate = 19.8%
   time = 6 mo

Estimate the interest. Then find the account balance for each. Round to the nearest cent.

10. principal = $3,700
    rate = 6% compounded quarterly
    time = 1 yr

11. principal = $9,400
    rate = 7% compounded semiannually
    time = 2 yr

12. principal = $1,000
    rate = 8% compounded monthly
    time = 6 mo

Think and Apply

Solve. Round to the nearest cent.

13. The ski equipment that Sara wants to buy costs $435. She deposits $100 in the account that has a balance of $318.42. If the account pays 6% compounded quarterly, how many months must she wait until she has enough money to buy the ski equipment?

14. Mary used a credit card to buy cross-country skis for $300. She paid $1\frac{1}{2}$% interest the first month. Find the amount of interest she paid.

15. A money market account that has an annual interest rate of 8.21% pays interest daily at 0.000225. Find the amount of interest paid on $300 for one month.

Is interest you receive computed the same way as interest you pay? Why or why not?

SUMMING UP

Mixed Review

1. $3 \cdot {}^-3$
2. ${}^-2 \div {}^-4$
3. ${}^-5 \times {}^-10$
4. ${}^-6 - {}^-2$
5. $6 - 2$
6. $6 + {}^-2$
7. ${}^-6 + 2$

Write the prime factorization of each.

8. 24
9. 125
10. 222
11. 36

Write each in standard form.

12. $2 \times 3^2 \times 5^3$
13. 3.56×10^3
14. 1.23×10^{-2}
15. $\frac{10^4}{10^2}$

Write each in scientific notation.

16. 0.0015
17. 3,218
18. 15 billion
19. 12 millionths
20. 138×10^2

311

What percents do stores typically use to discount prices for a sale?

Discount and Sale Price

The Ultimate Spa Shop is having a sale. What is the sale price of the treadmill?

A **discount** is the amount that the regular price is decreased.
A **discount rate** is the percent of the decrease.

Exercise bike
1,110. 99
20% Off

$2,100	regular price	**Think**		$2,100	regular price
× 0.25	discount rate	25% = 0.25		− 525	discount
$ 525	discount			$1,575	sale price

The sale price of the treadmill is $1,575.

Another way to find the sale price is to calculate using the percent of the regular price you must pay.
100% − 25% = 75%   What is 75% of $2,100?

Cross-country ski machine
Reduced $\frac{1}{3}$
Sale $ 399.99

More Examples

a. Find the sale price of the exercise bike.

100% − 20% = 80%   What does 80% represent?
0.80 · $1,110.99 = $888.97   to the nearest cent

b. Another exercise bike is advertised at half off. If the sale price is $350, find the regular price.

$350 is half the regular price.
The regular price is $350 × 2, or $700.

Rowing machine
330
33 $\frac{1}{3}$ Off

Check Your Understanding

Use the information on pages 312–313 to find each. Round to the nearest cent.

1. discount off a climber

2. sale price of a rowing machine

3. discount and sale price of a leg table

4. regular price of a cross-country ski machine

Share Your Ideas   Look back at example **a.** Explain two ways to find the amount of discount.

Leg table
700
15% Off

CHOICES Use mental math, paper and pencil, or a calculator to find the discount and the sale price. Round to the nearest cent.

5. regular price = $15
discount rate = $33\frac{1}{3}\%$

6. regular price = $135
Take 15% off.

7. regular price = $710
Take 10% off.

8. regular price = $2,350
discount rate = 25%

9. regular price = $977
discount rate = 20%

10. regular price = $434
Take 35% off.

11. regular price = $98.75
discount rate = 37%

12. regular price = $83.75
Take 50% off.

Copy and complete the chart.

	Regular Price	Discount Rate	Sale Price
13.	$178.90	20%	
14.		30%	$ 46.50
15.	$688		$564.16
16.	$300		$250
17.		$33\frac{1}{3}\%$	$250
18.		$16\frac{2}{3}\%$	$375

Think and Apply

Solve. Round to the nearest cent.

19. The sale price of a cloth exercise mat is $18.49. If the regular price is $21.50, what is the discount rate?

20. Adam bought 3 exercise outfits on sale at 25% off. If the regular price of each outfit was $34, how much did he pay?

21. Extra weights for the leg table are on sale at 20% off. The discount is $5.55. What is the regular price?

Logical Thinking

22. Which would you choose? Why?

a. a discount rate of 15% and then 10% off

b. 25% off

If the discount rate is 10%, explain how to find each: the sale price if the regular price is $50; the regular price if the sale price is $50.

SUMMING UP

Do different stores sell the same item at different prices? Give some examples.

Markup and Selling Price

Ray's Bait and Tackle Shop pays $27 for each fishing rod and sells the rods for 50% more. What is the selling price or retail price of a fishing rod at Ray's shop?

$27	cost		$27.00	cost	
× 0.50	markup rate		+ 13.50	markup	
$13.50	markup		$40.50	selling price	

Ray's shop sells the fishing rods for $40.50 each.

What percent of the cost is the selling price?

More Examples

a. Find the retail price of an item that costs $10.15 and has a markup rate of 40%.

100% + 40% = 140% so the retail price is 140% of the cost.
$10.15 × 1.40 = $14.77

b. Find how much a retailer pays for an item that sells for $259.95 if the markup rate is 100%.

$259.95 is 200% of the amount the retailer pays, so divide by 2 to find the cost.

$259.95 ÷ 2 = $129.98   to the nearest cent

Check Your Understanding

Find the selling price of each. Round to the nearest cent.

1. cost = $5
markup rate = 40%

2. cost = $140
markup rate = 60%

3. cost = $41
markup rate = 50%

Find the cost to a retailer for each.

4. selling price = $3
markup rate = $33\frac{1}{3}$%

5. selling price = $12.95
markup rate = 40%

6. selling price = $21.95
markup = $4.39

Share Your Ideas Look back at **6.** What is the markup rate?

Practice

Use mental math, paper and pencil, or a calculator to find the selling price of each. Round to the nearest cent.

7. cost = $300
markup rate = 50%

8. cost = $1,345
markup rate = 75%

9. cost = $782.75
markup = $139.50

10. cost = $684.40
markup rate = 40%

11. cost = $10.50
markup rate = 23%

12. cost = $58
markup rate = $33\frac{1}{3}$%

13. cost = $168.89
markup = $55

14. cost = $286
markup rate = 100%

15. cost = $250
markup = $250

Copy and complete the chart.

	Cost	Markup Rate	Markup	Retail Price
16.	$1,625	25%		
17.			$15	$95
18.			$130	$630
19.	$145			$224.75
20.		50%	$37.50	
21.		35%	$195.30	

Think and Apply

Solve. Round to the nearest cent.

22. Fishing lures cost the store $2, $3, or $5 each. If the markup rate is 75%, find the selling price of each lure.

23. The selling price of fresh bait is $4.80 per container. If the markup rate is 50%, how much does the shop pay for each container?

24. Explain how you can use mental math to find the selling price for a markup rate of 100%. of 50%.

25. Explain how to find markup rate and discount rate. How are the methods different?

26. A markup rate can be greater than 100%. Can a discount rate be greater than 100%? Explain.

Logical Thinking

27. A store has a markup rate of 50%. At sale time, what is the greatest discount rate the store can offer so that it does not sell items below cost?

Explain how cost, markup rate, and selling price are related.

SUMMING UP

A compact disc sells for $13.95. **What if** the price changes to $15.75? What is the amount of increase in price?

Percent of Increase or Decrease

The Department of Movement Science at a local college teaches a course called Fitness for Life. This semester 250 students took the Fitness for Life course compared with 200 students last semester. What is the percent of increase?

$$\text{percent of increase} = \frac{\text{increase}}{\text{original amount}}$$

$$= \frac{250 - 200}{200} = \frac{50}{200} = \frac{1}{4} = 25\%$$

Enrollment for the class increased 25%.

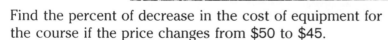

Find the percent of decrease in the cost of equipment for the course if the price changes from $50 to $45.

$$\text{percent of decrease} = \frac{\text{decrease}}{\text{original amount}} = \frac{\$5}{\$50} = \frac{1}{10} = 10\%$$

The price decreased 10%.

What is another name for the percent of decrease in the price of an item?

Check Your Understanding

Write *increase* or *decrease*. Then find the percent of increase or decrease.

1. from 10 to 15
2. from $25 to $30
3. from $65 to $32.50
4. from 100 to 140
5. from 72 to 108
6. from 45 to 81
7. from 500 to 615
8. from 250 to 255
9. from 420 to 140

Share Your Ideas A decrease from 25 to 10 is a 60% decrease. Is an increase from 10 to 25 a 60% increase? Explain.

Write *increase* or *decrease*. Then find the percent of increase or decrease. Use a calculator if you wish.

10. from 40 to 58

11. from 800 to 880

12. from $160 to $320

13. from $50 to $175

14. from 30 to 25

15. from 125 to 240

16. from 90 to 108

17. from 120 to 105

18. from 90 to 30

Use estimation to name the sports team whose number of wins has increased by each amount.

19. about 50%

20. about 10%

21. about $33\frac{1}{3}$%

22. about 25%

23. about 20%

Number of Games Won		
Team	Last Year	This Year
Hockey	31	42
Football	35	52
Basketball	16	21
Tennis	29	32
Baseball	21	25

Find each percent.

24. 260 increased by 40% is the same as what percent of 260?

25. 600 decreased by what percent is the same as 60% of 600?

Think and Apply

26. A major in Athletic Training requires 4 courses relating to first aid and prevention of injury. If this is 40% of the requirement, how many courses are required for that major?

27. The number of students selecting a major in Exercise Physiology has increased 200% since last year. If 51 students chose that major this year, how many selected it last year?

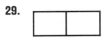

Visual Thinking

Compare the first figure with the second. Then write the percent that each figure has increased.

28.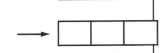

29.

30.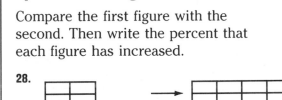

31.

32.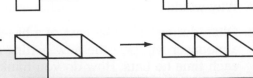

A number is increased by 10% and then decreased by 10%. Is the result the same as when the number is decreased by 10% and then increased by 10%? Explain.

SUMMING UP

Using Problem Solving

Interview: Calculators and Sports

Joe Myers earned a letter in football and basketball at Clarksville High in Clarksville, Tennessee, by keeping statistics for the teams. He also keeps statistics for his father's Little League team and the City Tournament.

Here are some statistics he gathered.

BATTING AVERAGES

Name	Games	At Bats	Hits	Runs	Batting Average
Ogburn	7	15	4	3	.267
Workman	7	25	15	15	___
Turner	7	24	9	10	___
Binkley	7	21	7	8	___
Pace	7	16	3	4	___

A. To find a person's batting average, Joe divides the hits by the number of times at bat. Compute the missing batting averages in the table above.

B. To find the earned run average (ERA—the average number of earned runs a pitcher gives up per game), multiply the earned runs by 9 (the number of innings in a game) and divide by the number of innings pitched. Complete the earned run table.

PITCHING RECORDS

Name	Games	Innings Pitched	Earned Runs	Earned Run Average
Jones	3	16	4	2.25
Harris	4	5	2	___
Ace	2	$12\frac{1}{3}$	3	___

Sharing Your Ideas

1. Why would a sports statistician want to use a calculator?

2. Often during the broadcast of a baseball game, an announcer will give the new batting average of a player each time he bats. How do you think the statisticians are able to do this?

Practice

3. A coach was comparing two of his players. He claimed that Garcia had a higher batting average than McGonegal for the first and second halves of the season, but that McGonegal had a better batting average for the entire year. Can you help the coach?

	FIRST HALF		SECOND HALF	
	At Bats	Hits	At Bats	Hits
Garcia	40	16	256	79
McGonegal	254	93	297	91

Was the coach's statement correct? What were the averages?

4. The 1969 World Series featured the Baltimore Orioles vs. the New York Mets. Bill and Paula wanted to compare the batting averages for the starting line-ups. Bill said, "I'll add the averages and average them." Paula said "You cannot do that. You must add all the at bats and then add all the hits. Then you divide the total hits by the at–bats." Whose method would you use? Find each team's batting average.

NEW YORK METS			
Name	AB	Hits	BA
E. Kranepool	353	84	.238
K. Boswell	362	101	.279
B. Harrelson	395	98	.248
W. Garrett	400	87	.218
R. Swoboda	327	77	.235
T. Agee	565	153	.271
C. Jones	483	164	.340
J. Grote	365	92	.252

BALTIMORE ORIOLES			
Name	AB	Hits	BA
B. Powell	533	162	.304
D. Johnson	511	143	.280
M. Belanger	530	152	.287
B. Robinson	598	140	.234
F. Robinson	539	166	.308
P. Blair	625	178	.285
D. Buford	554	161	.291
E. Hendricks	295	72	.244

Summing Up

5. In problem **3**, is it possible that a player can have a better batting average than another player for each half of a season and have a poorer average for the whole year? Explain.

6. Look at your answers for **4**. How did you determine the teams' batting averages? How would you try to convince the person whose method was incorrect that it was incorrect?

Mathematical Bones

Did you know that statistical studies have shown that the lengths of some of your bones are directly related to your height?

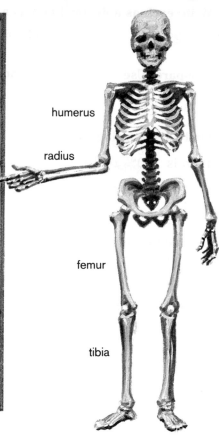

FEMALE

The height is 253.3% of the length of the tibia, increased by 72.572 cm.

The height is 73.502 cm more than 387.6% of the length of the radius.

MALE

The height is 223.8% of the length of the femur, plus 69.089 cm.

The height is 73.57 cm more than 297% of the length of the humerus.

After age 30, the height of a person decreases about 0.06 cm each year.

Labels on skeleton: humerus, radius, femur, tibia

Write an equation for each.

1. the height (H) of a male, given the length of the femur (F)

2. the height (H) of a male, given the length of the humerus (S)

3. the height (H) of a female, given the length of the tibia (T)

4. the height (H) of a female, given the length of the radius (R)

Find the height of each person. You may use a calculator.

5. male, age 14
length of femur: 31 cm

6. male, age 34
length of humerus: 34 cm

7. female, age 14
length of tibia: 31 cm

8. female, age 37
length of radius: 24.5 cm

9. Work with a partner. Measure your height. Then find the lengths of two of your bones, using the information in the chart above.

Maintaining Skills

Choose the correct answer. Write A, B, C, or D.

1. $^-5.26 + 3.45$

  A $^-8.41$ **C** $^-1.81$

  B 1.85   **D** not given

2. Solve for a. $4.5a - 0.3 = 22.2$

  A $a = 101.25$ **C** $a = 0.2$

  B $a = 5$ **D** not given

3. What is 0.0068 written in scientific notation?

  A 6.8×10^3 **C** 68×10^{-3}

  B 6.8×10^4 **D** not given

4. What is the length of side x?

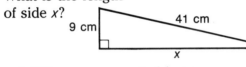

9 cm   41 cm x

  A 1,600 cm   **C** 14 cm

  B 40 cm   **D** not given

5. What is the unit price?
3 cans for $.93

  A $.31   **C** $2.79

  B $.32   **D** not given

6. Solve the proportion. $\frac{2.5}{x} = \frac{0.5}{2}$

  A $x = 0.61$ **C** $x = 10$

  B $x = 0.408$ **D** not given

7. What is t?   55 miles in 1 hour
                 192.5 miles in t hours

  A 2 h   **C** 3.5 h

  B 0.5 h   **D** not given

8. $24\ m + 9.2\ m + 42.6\ cm$

  A 75.8 cm   **C** 54.2 cm

  B 3,362.6 cm   **D** not given

9. What is 405% as a decimal?

  A 40.5   **C** 0.405

  B 4.05   **D** not given

10. What is $12\frac{1}{2}\%$ of 96?

  A 120   **C** 12

  B 16   **D** not given

11. Find n. 30% of $n = 21$.

  A $n = 70$ **C** $n = 42$

  B $n = 6.3$ **D** not given

12. What is the interest?
principal = $6,000
rate = 4% annually
time = 24 months

  A $5,760   **C** $240

  B $57.60   **D** not given

Solve.

13. Five people entered a Ping-Pong marathon. Each person played 2 games with every other person. How many games were played?

  A 40   **C** 25

  B 20   **D** not given

14. Six students stand in a circle and toss a ball to one another. How many tosses are made if each student tosses it to every other student?

  A 15   **C** 30

  B 36   **D** not given

10 Geometric Measurement

THEME Amazing Structures

Sharing What You Know

Did you know that one of the Seven Wonders of the Ancient World still stands outside Cairo, Egypt? The Great Pyramid, tomb of Khufu, stands 450 feet high, even with some of its upper stones missing. It once rose 481 feet high! The pyramid was constructed around 2680 BC and contains over two million blocks of stone, each weighing about 2.5 tons. Discuss how the pyramid might have been constructed. How would mathematics have been used in building such a structure?

Using Language

Some modern day structures are also shaped like pyramids. Look at the pictures of the Washington Monument and the Transamerica Pyramid. How are these structures similar to the Great Pyramid? How are they different? A **pyramid** is a space figure whose base is a polygon and whose faces are triangles with a common vertex. What kinds of polygons serve as the bases for these pyramids? Brainstorm to compile a list of other examples of pyramids.

Words to Know   circumference, perimeter, base, height, area, capacity, surface area, volume

Be a Problem Solver

You have a square base whose dimensions are 6 cubes by 6 cubes. How many more cubes would you need in order to construct a model of a 4-sided pyramid on the base?

Create a design for the highest possible stable structure you can make. What information do you need in order to evaluate the stability of your structure?

Activity

Relating Perimeter and Area

How do perimeter and area change when you double the
length of the sides of a rectangle?

Is there a pattern to how an increase in length of sides
affects perimeter and area?

Working together

Materials: grid paper, rulers

A. Draw a rectangle on grid paper. Record its length, width,
perimeter, and area in a chart like the one below.

Rectangle	Length	Width	Perimeter	Area

B. Draw another rectangle, with sides increased by a factor
of 2, that is, with length and width twice as long as those
of the first rectangle. Record your findings in the table.

C. Draw a third rectangle, with sides increased by a factor
of 3. Record your findings.

Sharing Your Results

Look back at the data you recorded.

1. If the sides of a rectangle are increased by a factor of 2,
by what factor does the perimeter increase? the area?

2. If the sides are increased by a factor of 3, by what factor
does the perimeter increase? the area?

3. **What if** the sides are increased by a factor of 4? of 5? of
12? How will the perimeter and area change in each
case?

4. What conclusion can you draw about the way perimeter
and area are affected when both length and width are
increased?

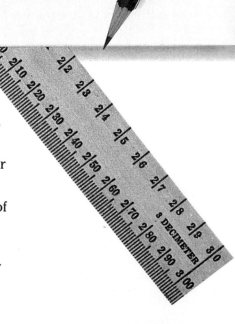

Extending the Activity

A gardener has 20 m of fence.
What is the largest rectangular garden she can enclose?

Work in your group to solve the problem and investigate relationships between perimeter and area. Use grid paper and a calculator whenever it will help.

5. Use grid paper to model the problem above. Let 1 cm represent 1 m. Draw as many rectangles as you can with a perimeter of 20 cm. Record your findings in a table like the one below.

Rectangle	Length	Width	Perimeter	Area
1			20 cm	
2			20 cm	

6. What is the largest rectangle that can be enclosed with 20 m of fence?

7. What is the largest rectangle having a perimeter of 8 cm? of 36 cm? of 26 cm?

8. A rectangle has an area of 16 cm^2. What is the least perimeter it can have? Draw rectangles on grid paper to help solve the problem. Make a table to record your findings.

9. Find the least perimeter for rectangles with areas of 36 cm, 25 cm, and 64 cm.

Summing Up

Compare your results with those of other groups.

10. What is the shape of the largest rectangle with a given perimeter? What is the shape of the rectangle with a given area that has the least perimeter?

11. How is the problem of finding the rectangle having the greatest area related to finding the rectangle having the least perimeter?

Midchapter Review

Give the length and width of the rectangle with the greatest area for each perimeter. pages 326–327

1. 12 cm

2. 40 m

3. 30 cm

Find the area of each shaded region. pages 328–333

4. 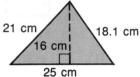 21 cm 18.1 cm 16 cm 25 cm

5. 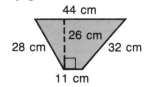 44 cm 26 cm 28 cm 32 cm 11 cm

6. 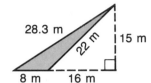 28.3 m 22 m 15 m 8 m 16 m

7. 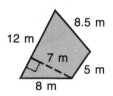 8.5 m 12 m 7 m 5 m 8 m

8. 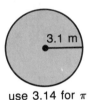 3.1 m use 3.14 for π

9. 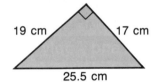 19 cm 17 cm 25.5 cm

10. 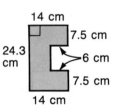 14 cm 7.5 cm 24.3 cm 6 cm 7.5 cm 14 cm

11. 14.8 m use 3.14 for π

12. 5 cm

Choose the correct vocabulary word to complete each sentence.

13. The perpendicular distance from a vertex to a side of a triangle is called the _____.

14. The distance around a polygon is called the _____.

15. The side of a polygon from which the height is measured is called the _____.

16. The interior of a polygon measured in square units is the _____.

17. The distance around a circle is called the _____.

> **Words to Know**
>
> circumference
> perimeter
> base
> height
> area

Solve.

18. A circular flower bed with a radius of 12 m is enlarged to a bed with radius of 14 m. What is the increase in area?

19. A triangular pennant has a base of 22.4 cm and an area of 168 cm². What is the height of the pennant?

Exploring Problem Solving

THINK
EXPLORE
SOLVE
LOOK BACK

Is There a Structure to the Solar System?

Johannes Kepler, a famous astronomer, found a way to relate the length of a planet's year to its distance from the sun.

Mercury: Length of year   88 earth days
Average distance from the sun 57.9 million km

Venus: Length of year   224.7 earth days
Average distance from the sun 107.5 million km

Earth: Length of year   365.26 earth days
Average distance from the sun 149.5 million km

Mars: Length of year   686.69 earth days
Average distance from the sun 227.7 million km

Thinking Critically

Examine the data above. Using the questions below, see if you can discover the pattern between the length of a planet's year and the distance of the planet from the sun. This pattern is known as Kepler's third law.

Use a calculator to help you as you work in a group.

Analyzing and Making Decisions

1. What part of an earth year are Mercury's 88 Earth days? Change all the measurements for Length of Year from days to earth years. Record your answers as decimals.

2. The earth's average distance from the sun is called 1 astronomical unit (AU). What is each planet's distance from the sun in AUs?

3. Make a new chart, using earth years for the length of year and AUs for the average distance from the sun. Do you see any patterns yet?

4. Kepler probably tried many things. He squared the length of a planet's year. He cubed each planet's distance from the sun. Do you see a pattern now? Explain.

Look Back   Saturn is 9.6 AUs from the sun. How long is its year in Earth years?

Problem Solving Strategies

Making and Using Tables

The geometric art sculpture shown here is made of 6 successive concrete blocks, each with a square face. The area of each square face is one-half that of the one behind it. If the sculptor wanted the perimeter of the largest square to be 100 feet in length, what would be the area and the perimeter of the smallest square?

You can use a table or list to keep track of your work when solving a problem. Data that has been organized in a table can easily be examined to help you work through the problem.

Solving the Problem

CHOICES Use a calculator where appropriate.

Think   What is the question? What are the facts?

Explore   What do you need to know about each of the concrete blocks? How many blocks are shown in the sculpture? How should you start your table? If you know the perimeter of the largest square block, how can you find its area?
If you know the area of the largest block, how can you find the area of the next block?
If you know the area of a square block, how can you find the length of one side?
If you know the length of one side, how can you find the perimeter?

Solve   What is the area and perimeter of each square?

Look Back   Was the table helpful in solving this problem?

Share Your Ideas

1. **What if** there was another small square and another large square? What would their perimeters and areas be?

Practice

 Solve. Use a calculator where appropriate.

2. Liz was using cubes to build a model of an ancient pyramid. The base was 10 cubes wide and 10 cubes long. The next layer was 9 cubes wide and 9 cubes long. For each succeeding layer she used 1 cube less for both the length and the width. How many cubes will be needed for the pyramid?

3. Someone told Tim a puzzle that went like this: Once there was a strange clock. One night at 11:30 P.M. it started running backwards at one-half the normal rate. In the morning when the repair crew came to fix the clock, they noticed that it showed the correct time. What time was it?

4. While in Paris, Carrie and Vic climbed the Eiffel Tower, a 984-foot iron framework built for France's Centennial Exposition in 1889. They started their climb at the ground level. They walked up 50 feet in 3 minutes, 75 feet in the next 5 minutes, 100 feet in the next 7 minutes, and so on. How high were they in 63 minutes?

5. At the great Moscow Circus building, the center ring has a diameter of 70 feet. The cleaner, who uses a 5-foot-wide brush, starts on the outer edge to clean a series of circular paths. He stops sweeping after he finishes the path in which $\frac{3}{4}$ of the whole area enclosed by the circle has been cleaned. How many paths did he sweep?

Mixed Strategy Review

6. Doreen always sits in the same section behind third base at the baseball stadium. Her seat is in the fifth row from the front and the ninth row from the back of the section. The seat is the third seat from the right aisle and the eighth seat from the left aisle. If all the rows have the same number of seats, how many seats are in Doreen's section?

7. Ruth took 11 pictures of the Eiffel Tower and 11 pictures of the Louvre. All the pictures are 3 in. by 5 in. The pictures of the Eiffel Tower are oriented vertically and the pictures of the Louvre are oriented horizontally. Her album pages are 10 in. by 12 in. What is the minimum number of pages needed to show the pictures in the proper orientation?

THINK
EXPLORE
SOLVE
LOOK BACK

Create
Your **O**wn

Write a problem about walking up the stairs in a tall building.

Möbius Strip

Materials: five or six 4-inch strips of paper at least 18 inches long, scissors

Make a simple band by gluing or taping the ends of one paper strip together.

1. What do you think will happen if you cut the strip down the middle? Try it.

Cut along middle

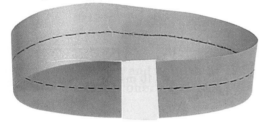

Möbius Strip

Use a new strip. Before joining the ends, give the strip one twist.

This new figure is a **Möbius strip**. It has many interesting properties.

2. Draw a line on the outside of the strip midway between the top and bottom edges. What happens? What does this mean?

3. Draw a similar line on a simple band. Is the result similar?

4. Cut the Möbius strip on the line you drew. Describe your results.

5. What do you think will happen if the strip has more than one twist? Make one, cut it, and describe your results.

6. Finally, cut another Möbius strip lengthwise $\frac{1}{3}$ the distance below one edge. Continue cutting, always staying $\frac{1}{3}$ the distance from the top edge. Describe your results.

7. Why, do you think, does the Möbius strip behave as it does?

Family Math

In the preceding four chapters of our mathematics book, we studied statistics, ratio and proportion, formulas, percent, and geometric measurement.

Let's Go South!

The formula for distance, rate, and time can be useful on a trip.

distance = rate × time	**rate = $\dfrac{\text{distance}}{\text{time}}$**	**time = $\dfrac{\text{distance}}{\text{rate}}$**
To find the distance, multiply the rate, or speed, by the time.	To find the speed, divide the distance by the time.	To find the time, divide the distance by the speed.

Let's go on a trip down the East Coast, using these formulas. Work together as a family to find the answers. As you pass each city, see if you can name its state.

DAY 1—You leave Portland at 10 A.M. You want to be in Boston by noon. What average speed will you need to travel to get there on time?

DAY 2—You left Boston at 8 A.M. and arrived in Newark at 1 P.M. You maintained an average speed of 45 miles per hour. About how many miles did you travel?

DAY 3—You want to drive only 7 hours this day. If you maintain an average speed of 50 miles per hour, between which two cities should you stop?

DAY 4—You stopped to see friends in Raleigh in the morning. Your next stop on the trip is Savannah. If·you travel at an average speed of 50 miles per hour, about how many hours will it take you to get to Savannah?

DAY 5—A person at the gas station in Savannah said that you could make it to Orlando in about $5\frac{1}{2}$ hours. At about what rate of speed do you need to travel to get to Orlando in that amount of time?

Now that you have seen the sights in Orlando, plan a family trip back to Portland. This time, go through Atlanta.

Have a good time!

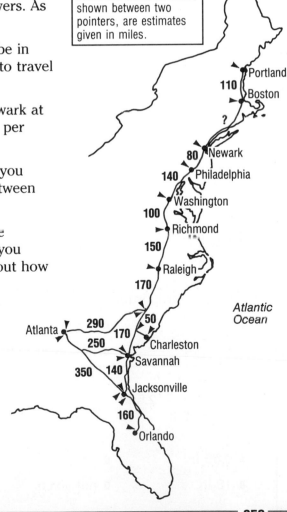

Distances between cities, shown between two pointers, are estimates given in miles.

Cumulative Review

Choose the correct answer. Write A, B, C, or D.

1. What is the mean of 0.2, 0.7, 4.2, 0.7, 3.1, and 0.4?

A 0.7   C 4

B 1.55   D not given

2. What is the range of 12, 10, 9, 4, 5, 7, 9, 2, and 3?

A 7   C 10

B 9   D not given

3. What is the mode of 2, 3, 6, 3, 2, 5, 6, and 2?

A 3,625   C 3

B 6   D not given

4. What is an equal ratio for 11 to 33?

A 3:1   C 6:2

B 1:3   D not given

5. What is the unit price?
a dozen pencils for $.48

A $.03   C $.24

B $.04   D not given

6. Find n. $\frac{28}{40} = \frac{n}{10}$

A $n = 7$ C $n = 4$

B $n = 2$ D not given

7. Solve the proportion. $\frac{m}{9} = \frac{3}{27}$

A $m = 18$ C $m = 1$

B $m = 3$ D not given

8. What is x?
scale: 1 in. = 2.5 ft
actual: 45 ft
drawing: x in.

A 0.55 in.   C 15 in.

B 18 in.   D not given

9. 2.45 kg + 2,634 g + 1.402 kg

A 6,490 g   C 4,281 g

B 30.192 kg   D not given

10. What is 22% written as a ratio?

A 11:100   C 22:100

B 100:22   D not given

11. What is 0.375 as a percent?

A 3.75%   C 375%

B 37.5%   D not given

12. What is 15% of 40?

A 60   C 34

B 6   D not given

13. What is 14.2% of 84?

A 72.072   C 119.28

B 1,192.8   D not given

14. 13 is what percent of 26?

A 50%   C 5%

B 25%   D not given

15. $33\frac{1}{3}$% of what number is 78?

A 234   C 117

B 26   D not given

16. What is the selling price?
regular price = $90.00
rate of discount = 10%

A $100.00   C $9.00

B $81.00   D not given

Choose the correct answer. Write A, B, C, or D.

17. What is the area?

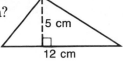

5 cm

12 cm

A 90 cm^2 **C** 30 cm^2

B 60 cm^2 **D** not given

18. What is the area?
Use $\pi \approx 3.14$.

16 m

A 200.96 m^2 **C** 803.84 m^2

B 25.12 m^2 **D** not given

19. What is the area of
the shaded region?
Use $\pi \approx 3.14$.

5 m

A 78.5 m^2 **C** 84.3 m^2

B 21.5 m^2 **D** not given

20. What is the surface area of a cube
whose edge measures 2.2 cm?

A 4.84 cm^2 **C** 29.04 cm^2

B 19.36 cm^2 **D** not given

21. What is
the volume?

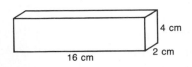

4 cm

2 cm

16 cm

A 22 cm^3 **C** 128 cm^3

B 96 cm^3 **D** not given

Solve.

22. Mr. Perry bought 2 cans of coffee for
$1.19 each, 5 cans of soup for $.35 per
can, and a gallon of milk for $2.05. How
much change did he receive from
$20.00?

A $6.15   **C** $16.41

B $13.82   **D** not given

Solve.

23. Mrs. Owen brought 2 new employees
into her office. They shook hands with
11 people already working there. How
many handshakes occurred?

A 22   **C** 44

B 11   **D** not given

24. The 22 students in Mr. Schultz's class
were sampling 3 juices in 2 different
concentrations. For them to sample
each, how many glasses were needed?

A 99   **C** 33

B 44   **D** not given

Solve.

Mr. Hynnes is planning a floor design made
of 36 squares in 6 rows of 6 squares. The
corners will be black as well as the
diagonals from each corner. All other
squares will be white.

25. How many squares are white?

A 15   **C** 24

B 20   **D** not given

26. How many black squares have another
black square on only 2 sides?

A 2   **C** 10

B 4   **D** not given

11 Probability

THEME   What Would You Expect?

Sharing What You Know

"Sorry, you can't go swimming today! You heard the weather forecast. There is an 80% chance of thunderstorms." In what ways would a weather forecast like this influence your plans for the day? How do weather predictions affect construction workers? school bus drivers? plans for an outdoor concert? How do weather conditions on Earth affect space exploration?

Using Language

Even with an 80% chance of thunderstorms we cannot be absolutely certain that thunderstorms will occur. But we can say that thunderstorms are highly **probable**. The word *probable* is derived from the Latin word *probabilis,* meaning likely. **Probability** describes the chance or likelihood that an event will happen. Discuss the probability that classes will be canceled tomorrow. What factors affect that probability?

Words to Know   outcome, random experiment, sample space, event, favorable outcomes, probability, compound event, fundamental counting principle, independent events, dependent events, mutually exclusive events, factorial notation, permutation, combination

Be a Problem Solver

There is an 80% chance that there will be precipitation. There is a 50% chance that the precipitation will be snow. What is the chance that it will snow?

Select and describe a highly probable event. Exchange descriptions with a partner and compare the probability of the outcomes.

Which spinner is a fair spinner?
Explain why.

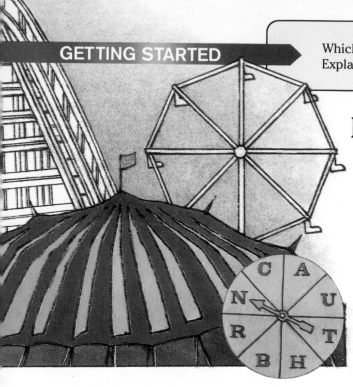

Probability

What do you expect when you spin this spinner? Since all the **outcomes**, or results, are equally likely, spinning the spinner is called a **random experiment.**

All the possible outcomes for an experiment are called the **sample space**. There are 8 possible outcomes for spinning the spinner—C, A, U, T, H, B, R, N.

An **event** may be one or more possible outcomes. It may also include impossible outcomes.
There are 2 **favorable outcomes** for the event of spinning a vowel—A, U.

▶ The **probability**, or chance, that an event, E, will occur can be expressed as a ratio.

$$P(E) = \frac{\text{number of favorable outcomes}}{\text{number of possible outcomes}}$$

The probability of spinning a vowel = **P(A or U)** $= \frac{2}{8} = \frac{1}{4}$

The probability of spinning T, H, or B = **P(T, H, or B)** $= \frac{3}{8}$

What is the probability of spinning a consonant?

Is it possible to spin the letter Q?
An impossible event has a probability of 0.
Is it certain that one of the letters C, A, U, T, H, B, R, or N will be spun, assuming the spinner does not stop on a line?
An event that is certain to happen has a probability of 1.
The probability of any event ranges from 0 to 1. Why?

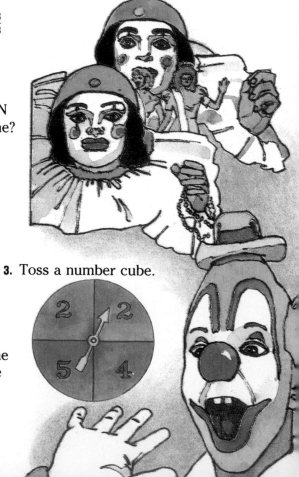

Check Your Understanding

Identify the sample space for each experiment.

1. Flip a coin.   **2.** Pick a number from 1 to 10.   **3.** Toss a number cube.

Find the probability of each event. Use the spinner.

4. P(an even number)   **5.** $P(3)$ **6.** $P(4)$

Share Your Ideas The sum of the probabilities of all the outcomes in an experiment is always 1. **Look back** at the number spinner and show that this is true.

Identify the sample space for each experiment and find the number of favorable outcomes for each event.

Picking a whole number less than 10

7. Pick a number whose name has 4 letters.

8. Pick a number whose name has 5 letters.

9. Pick a number whose value equals the number of letters in its name.

Picking a marble

10. Pick a red marble.

11. Pick a blue or green marble.

12. Pick a brown marble.

13. Pick a yellow or brown marble.

Find the probability of each event.

Toss a number cube with faces numbered **1** through **6**.

14. P(multiple of 8)

15. P(multiple of 1)

16. P(not a factor of 6)

Pick a card at random.

17. P(odd number)

18. P(not blue)

19. P(blue even number)

20. P(number < 9)

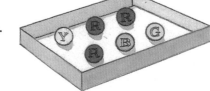

Pick a marble from the box above.

21. P(red)   **22.** P(brown)   **23.** P(white)

Find each probability. Which are equal?

24. Toss a number cube: P(even number); P(prime number).

25. Spin the spinner: P(consonant); P(vowel).

26. Choose a letter at random from your name: P(the letter E from your last name); P(the letter E from your first name).

27. Create an experiment using red, blue, and yellow such that P(red) > P(blue) and P(yellow) = P(blue).

28. Do you have an equal chance of picking any given letter of the name from the name of your city or town?

29. Sally is taking a multiple-choice test with 5 choices for each question. She guesses on one question after eliminating one choice. What are her chances of guessing correctly? incorrectly?

If you are choosing from 5 toppings for a pizza, could there be more than 5 outcomes in your sample space? Explain.

SUMMING UP

Activity

Exploring Relative Frequency

Suppose you predict the probability of an event. How can you experiment to test your prediction? **What if** your results are not consistent with your prediction? What should you conclude?

Working together

Materials: index cards, colored pens, calculator, bag

Each repetition of an experiment is called a **trial**. To test a prediction, compute the relative frequency of the event after a number of trials. Compare the probability you predicted with the relative frequency.

$$\text{Relative frequency} = \frac{\text{number of favorable outcomes}}{\text{total number of trials}}$$

A. Using a red pen, number ten index cards from 1 to 10. Using a green pen, number ten more in the same way.

B. Mix the cards together in a bag.

C. Predict the probability of picking a green number at random.

D. Each member of the group should pick a card from the bag, record the color, and replace it. Repeat this experiment until each member has picked 10 cards.

E. Record your results in a chart as shown.

Student	Number of Trials	Number of Favorable Outcomes	Relative Frequency
Total			

Sharing Your Results

1. How did your relative frequency compare with your prediction?

2. How did your group's relative frequency compare with your prediction?

3. Which result was closer to your prediction? Why might this be so?

4. What do you expect is the probability of picking a 7? How could you test this?

Extending the Activity

When the relative frequency of an event is not close to its predicted probability, there are several possible explanations.

a. The experiment was not repeated enough times.

b. The prediction was faulty.

c. An unknown condition has influenced the outcome. For example, if the green cards are slightly smaller than the red cards, picking a red card might be more likely.

Conduct the following experiment and record your results, using a chart as you did before. Use a calculator if you wish.

5. Choose 11 digits at random to use for 10 trials.

6. Use successive pairs of the digits you have chosen to form 2-digit numbers. For example, if the digits are 2, 8, 5, 6, 7, 4, 3, 1, 9, 2, 5, work with 28, 85, 56, and so on.

7. Experiment: Square each 2-digit number and subtract 1. Favorable outcome: a number divisible by 4

8. Predict the probability of a favorable outcome based on your 10 trials. Conduct 10 more trials using 11 new numbers.

9. Compare the relative frequency for the total number of trials with your prediction. How can you explain any difference that may exist?

10. **What if** only odd digits had been chosen? How would this change the experiment? Would the results be valid?

Summing Up

11. A coin is tossed three times with the result being heads each time. What are the chances another toss will be heads? Explain.

12. If the fourth toss is heads, would your prediction change for the next toss? Why?

How many ways are there to choose a pad and a pen?

Fundamental Counting Principle

The eighth grade is organizing a field day. In the morning, students may choose volleyball, softball, tennis, or soccer. In the afternoon there will be a choice of swimming or boating. How many different all-day schedules are there?

You can use a tree diagram to display the possible choices.

Morning Volleyball   Softball   Tennis   Soccer

Afternoon Swimming Boating   Swimming Boating   Swimming Boating   Swimming Boating

The first choice has **4** possible outcomes.
The second choice has **2** possible outcomes.

▶ To find the total number of outcomes for an all-day schedule, use the fundamental counting principle. Find the product of the number of possible outcomes for each choice.

⌐ possible afternoon choices
4 · 2 = 8
⌐ possible morning choices

Name the 8 possible choices for an all-day schedule.

What is the probability of choosing softball or soccer in the morning and swimming in the afternoon? The counting principle can be used to compute this probability, assuming all outcomes equally likely.

Favorable outcomes
Morning: 2
Afternoon: 1 } 2 · 1 = 2

Possible outcomes
Morning: 4
Afternoon: 2 } 4 · 2 = 8

$P(E) = \dfrac{\text{favorable outcomes}}{\text{possible outcomes}}$

$= \dfrac{2}{8}$, or $\dfrac{1}{4}$

Check Your Understanding

Find the total number of outcomes for each event.

1. Bread: rye, whole wheat
   Meat: chicken, turkey, beef

2. Sport: tennis, Ping-Pong
   Opponent: Sue, Joe, Jill, Ellen

3. Pen: red, blue
   Marker: orange, yellow
   Pad: red, blue, white

4. Find the probability of turkey on rye in **1**. Use a tree diagram to justify your answer.

Share Your Ideas Explain how you could find the probability of tossing a head on a coin and tossing a 6 on a number cube.

Use the counting principle to answer each question.

5. Inez has a stamp book with 12 pages of stamps. She also has 4 books of coins. In how many ways can she choose a page of stamps and a book of coins?

6. There are 6 routes from Hope to Farley and 3 routes from Farley to Benton. In how many ways can you travel from Hope to Benton?

7. In how many ways can you choose 1 out of 3 items and 1 out of 6 colors?

8. How many outcomes exist for tossing a coin and tossing a number cube?

9. Make a tree diagram for **6.**

Look at the menu at the Dragon Restaurant. Use it for 10–13.

10. One selection is made from each section. How many different orders are possible?

11. One selection is made from each section. How many orders are possible without seafood?

12. One selection is made from each section. How many orders can include eggplant?

13. Jamie and Helen order all 3 appetizers, 1 main course, and 1 vegetable. How many different orders could they have made?

The DRAGON RESTAURANT

MENU

APPETIZER
Egg Roll
Shrimp Toast
Wonton Soup

VEGETABLES
Snow Peas
Eggplant
Bean Curd

MAIN COURSE
Beef with Broccoli
Scallops in Garlic Sauce
Chicken with Cashews

NOODLES AND RICE
Fried Rice
Shrimp Lo Mein
Pan-fried Noodles

Use a coin and the spinner to find the probability of each event, $P(A, B)$.

14. *A*: Spin yellow.
    B: Toss a head.

15. *A*: Spin an even number.
    B: Toss a tail.

16. *A*: Spin a red odd number.
    B: Toss a head.

17. *A*: Spin a number > 9.
    B: Toss a head.

18. A company installs phones with 2-digit extensions. Repeated digits are allowed. How many extensions are possible?

19. If extensions are assigned randomly, what is the probability of getting an extension using only 5's and 6's?

20. What if the extensions had 4 digits with repeated digits allowed? What is the probability of being assigned an extension with only odd digits?

Create your own problem about making 2 or more choices. Exchange it with a friend to solve.

SUMMING UP

Names are drawn from a box. If a name is not drawn first, is it then more likely to be drawn second? Discuss.

Independent and Dependent Events

Events that contain more than one outcome are **compound events.**

Suppose two events, A and B, happen one after the other. If the outcome of A affects the probability of B, the events are **dependent.**

At the carnival 2 record albums are given as prizes. Six names are in the box for the drawing. What is the probability that a girl's name is drawn first, followed by a boy's name?

$P(\text{girl's name}) = \frac{3}{6}$, or $\frac{1}{2}$

If a girl's name is drawn first, how many names are left? How many are boys' names?

$P(\text{boy's name after girl's name}) = \frac{3}{5}$

When two events are dependent, the probability that they both will occur is expressed as a product.

$$\mathbf{P(A, B) = P(A) \times P(B/A)}$$ $P(B/A)$ is the conditional probability of B, assuming A has happened.

$P(\text{girl's name, boy's name/girl's name}) = \frac{1}{2} \times \frac{3}{5} = \frac{3}{10}$

What if the first name is replaced before drawing the second?

$P(\text{girl's name}) = \frac{3}{6}$, or $\frac{1}{2}$ $P(\text{boy's name}) = \frac{3}{6}$, or $\frac{1}{2}$

If the outcome of A does *not* affect the probability of B, the events are **independent.**

To find the probability of a compound event consisting of two or more independent events, find the product of the probability of each event.

$$\mathbf{P(A, B) = P(A) \times P(B)}$$ $P(\text{girl's name, boy's name}) = \frac{1}{2} \times \frac{1}{2} = \frac{1}{4}$

Check Your Understanding

Look Back at the carnival drawing above. The first name drawn is not replaced. Find each probability.

1. $P(\text{girl's name, girl's name})$

2. $P(\text{boy's name, girl's name})$

Share Your Ideas   Use examples of your own to explain the difference between $P(B/A)$ and $P(B)$.

Write *independent* or *dependent* for each.

3. A die is rolled twice.

4. A coin is flipped three times.

5. Two children are born into a family—a boy, then a girl.

6. Choose one coin, replace it, and choose again.

7. Choose one of three books and one of two page numbers.

8. Choose one marble and then another without replacement.

**Each card is drawn at random and not replaced.
Find the probability of each compound event.**

9. $P(1, 5)$

10. $P(\text{even, odd})$

11. $P(\text{prime, 6})$

12. $P(\text{prime, prime})$

13. $P(\text{prime, perfect square})$

14. $P(1, 9)$

15. $P(1, 2, 3)$

16. $P(1, 5, 9)$

17. $P(1, 1, 4)$

**Use the cards shown. Find the probability of each compound
event if each card is replaced before the next is drawn.**

18. $P(\text{prime, 6})$

19. $P(\text{even, even})$

20. $P(\text{odd, 9, 4})$

Think and Apply

21. The Animal Shelter brought a litter of puppies to the carnival for adoption. Four are brown and three are black. What is the probability that the first two puppies chosen are both black?

22. What is the probability that the first three puppies chosen will be a black puppy and then two brown puppies?

23. You flip a coin. The first eight flips come up heads. Does that change the probability of tails on the next flip? Explain.

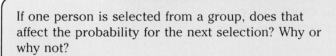

If one person is selected from a group, does that affect the probability for the next selection? Why or why not?

SUMMING UP

If you toss a number cube, in how many ways can you toss a 2? a 6? How many ways are there to toss a 2 or a 6?

Mutually Exclusive Events

A bag contains 3 red marbles, 2 blue marbles, and 5 green marbles. Choose a marble at random. What do you expect? What are the chances you will choose a blue or green marble?

Since you cannot choose *both* a blue and a green marble at the same time, these events are called **mutually exclusive.**

To find the probability of *A* or *B* when *A* and *B* are mutually exclusive, find *P(A) + P(B).*

The probability of choosing a blue marble is $\frac{2}{10}$.

The probability of choosing a green marble is $\frac{5}{10}$.

$P(\text{blue or green}) = P(\text{blue}) + P(\text{green}) = \frac{2}{10} + \frac{5}{10} = \frac{7}{10}$

The chances are 7 out of 10 of choosing a blue or green marble.

What is the probability of choosing a yellow, blue, or green marble?

Another Example

A number cube is tossed. Find the probability of tossing a 6 or a 3.

$P(6 \text{ or } 3) = P(6) + P(3)$

$= \frac{1}{6} + \frac{1}{6} = \frac{2}{6}, \text{ or } \frac{1}{3}$

Check Your Understanding

Find each probability.

1. *P*(London or Rome)

2. *P*(city in North America or Asia)

3. *P*(city in South America or Australia)

4. *P*(city in Europe or Africa)

5. *P*(Toronto or Athens or Berlin)

Share Your Ideas Explain the difference between mutually exclusive events and independent events. Give an example of each, using the bag of marbles described above.

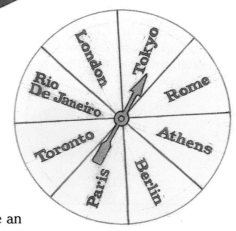

Practice

A number cube is tossed. Find the number of favorable outcomes for each event. Then find *P(A or B)*.

6. *A*: 2
   B: 5

7. *A*: even
   B: 1

8. *A*: prime
   B: 4

9. *A*: factor of 6
   B: 5

10. *A*: 6
   B: 7

11. *A*: odd
   B: 2

An octahedron is tossed. Its sides are numbered 1 to 8. Find each probability.

12. *P*(an even number or 1)

13. *P*(a prime or 4)

14. *P*(2 or 5)

15. *P*(a perfect square or 7)

16. *P*(a perfect cube or 9)

17. *P*(1, 6, 7, or 8)

Write *true* or *false* for each. If false, explain your thinking.

18. Mutually exclusive events happen at the same time.

19. Two mutually exclusive events can never both have a probability of 1.

20. Two mutually exclusive events can both have a probability of 0.

Think and Apply

A department store is offering free monogramming on luggage.

21. How many 3-initial monograms are possible?

22. The floor model has initials assigned at random. What is the probability its monogram begins with A or G?

23. A customer's account has a 2-digit code on it. The first digit is never 0. What is the chance the code is 12 or 22?

A and *B* are mutually exclusive events. Explain how to find *P(A or B)*.

Mixed Review

1. $\frac{7}{12} \cdot 1\frac{1}{2}$

2. $3\frac{4}{5} \div \frac{7}{10}$

3. $1\frac{3}{14} + \frac{8}{28}$

4. $4\frac{7}{10} - 2\frac{2}{5}$

5. $12 - {}^{-}51$

6. ${}^{-}36 + {}^{-}55$

7. ${}^{-}4.2 \cdot 6.8$

8. ${}^{-}14.4 \div 0.12$

9. $121 \div 11^2$

10. $6 + 81 \div 3^3$

Complete.

11. 6 kL = _____ L

12. 0.25 kg = _____ g

13. 3,000 mL = _____ L

14. 6 cm = _____ mm

15. 4,321 m = _____ km

Evaluate each expression for $n = {}^{-}2$.

16. $4n + 2$

17. $3(42 \div n)$

18. ${}^{-}5n + 8$

19. $12 + 36n$

20. $16n - 12n$

SUMMING UP

Midchapter Review

Give the number of favorable outcomes and the probability of each event. pages 358–359

1. Spin R. **2.** Spin a letter in the alphabet.

3. Spin P. **4.** Spin a letter in the first half of the alphabet.

Use the counting principle to answer each. pages 362–363

5. In how many ways can you choose 1 out of 6 items and 1 out of 4 colors?

6. How many outcomes exist for spinning the spinner above and tossing a number cube?

7. For a coin and the spinner above, find the probability of tossing heads and spinning R.

The spinner shown above is spun twice. Find P(A, B). pages 364–365

8. *A*: Spin R. **9.** *A*: Spin P.
   B: Spin G.   *B*: Spin Y.

Find each probability. pages 366–367

10. $P(1 \text{ or } 6)$ **11.** $P(7 \text{ or } 10)$

12. $P(7 \text{ or } 8 \text{ or } 9)$ **13.** $P(\text{prime or even})$

Complete.

14. The chance that an event will occur is its _____.

15. All the possible outcomes for an experiment are called the _____.

16. Two events that cannot occur at the same time are _____.

17. To test a prediction, compute the _____ after a number of trials.

18. Two events are _____ when the probability of the second is affected by the outcome of the first.

Words to Know
mutually exclusive
probability
sample space
dependent
relative frequency

Solve.

19. Sal is traveling from Clark to Springfield through Madison. If there are 2 roads he can use from Clark to Madison and 6 he can use from Madison to Springfield, how many different routes can he follow?

20. Look back at **19.** Make an organized list of the different routes from Clark to Springfield through Madison. Use *A, B, C, D, E, F, G,* and *H* for each road.

Exploring Problem Solving

Test the Waters

Water samples are being tested for the presence of a contaminant called C. It costs $100 to run one test.

Thinking Critically

How can you test for C, using the fewest tests?

Analyzing and Making Decisions

1. If you test one sample, what are the possible outcomes of the test?

2. **What if** you took a part of each of two samples and combined them? What are the 4 possible combinations?

3. Look at each possible combination from question **2**. What result would a test show for each? How many tests would you have to run for each possible combination to find out if each original sample contained C?

4. The probability of a water sample containing C is $\frac{1}{4}$. What is the probability that a sample does not contain C? What is the probability that each of the combinations in question **2** will occur? What is the total when you add all these probabilities? Does that make sense?

5. We know the probability of each possible combination. We know how many tests each combination takes. On the average, how many tests would you have for each possibility?
Example: Both samples do not contain C.

   Probability   Number of Tests

   $$\frac{9}{16} \quad \times \quad 1 \quad = \frac{9}{16} \text{ test}$$
   (on the average)

   Add the averages to find the average number of tests it takes to test two samples when the samples are combined.

6. How many tests does it take to test two samples when they are not combined? Which method of testing, testing one sample or combining parts of two samples, is more efficient when the probability that C is present is 1 in 4?

Look Back Suppose you test 320 samples. About how much would it cost if you tested each sample separately? if you tested combined parts of two samples?

369

Problem Solving Strategies

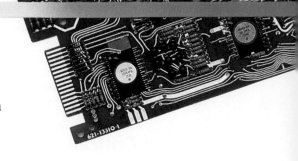

Organized Listing

You have been developing your own integrated circuits. Two companies will manufacture the product. The Epsilon Company charges $2,000 plus $80 per circuit. Eta Inc. charges $1,500 plus $95 per circuit. When should you order from Epsilon? When should you order from Eta?

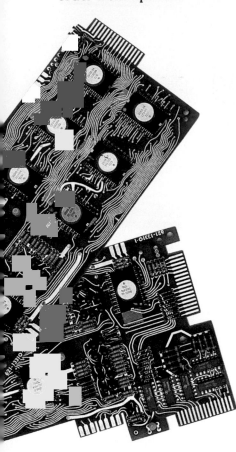

For some problems a list can help you look at the possibilities and solve the problem.

Solving the Problem

Think What is the question? What are the facts?

Explore If you only wanted one circuit, which company would be cheaper? Explain. Which company should be cheaper for smaller orders? for larger orders? How could making a list help you tell which company would be cheaper for which size orders? To make your list, would you start with one circuit? If not, where would you start? How would you know when to change your order from one company to the other?

Solve When should you order from Epsilon? When should you order from Eta?

Look Back Did you pick a good place to start making your list? Why or why not?

Share Your Ideas

1. **What if** Epsilon charged $2,500 plus $85? How would that change your answer?

2. What information could help you determine what number of units you should start with in making your list?

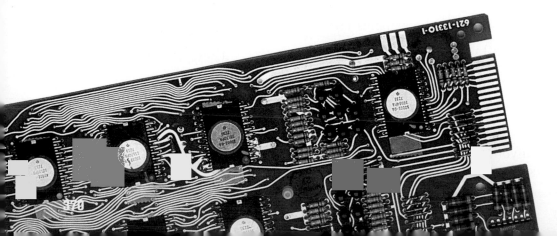

Practice

CHOICES **Solve.   Use a calculator where appropriate.**

A calendar uses two cubes to show every date in a month. The cubes can be moved, exchanged, or rotated around to show all the dates. A 6 can be inverted to make a 9.

3. What three numbers must be on each cube?

4. Write the numbers that might be on each cube.

5. Denise is considering two different jobs. The first job pays $22,000 the first year with raises of $4,000 each year after. The second job pays $26,000 the first year with raises of $2,000 each year after. When will Denise make as much money in the first job as in the second?

6. Lin is playing a computer game. The computer picks 1 of the 3 cubes and tosses it. No matter which cube the computer picks, Lin can have a better chance of tossing a greater number. Which cube should he pick for each pick the computer might make?

Cube 1	2, 4, 9, 2, 4, 9
Cube 2	3, 5, 7, 3, 5, 7
Cube 3	1, 6, 8, 1, 6, 8

Mixed Strategy Review

7. The average of 8 test scores is 72. One point of extra credit is given to the first score, 3 points to the second score, 5 to the third score, and so on. What is the new average?

8. On a multiple-choice test, students receive 4 points for each correct answer, lose 1 point for an incorrect answer, and receive 0 points if the question is not answered. On a 25-question test, Jeff scored 65. How might he have answered the questions?

Create
Your Own

Write a problem that can be solved by writing a list.

371

How can you write the product of 6 and 6? How can you write the product of all the whole numbers from 1 to 6?

Factorials

Exponential notation is used to write a product when all the factors are the same. **Factorial notation** is used to write a product when the factors are consecutive whole numbers.

▶ *n!*, read **n factorial,** means the product of all whole numbers from n to 1.

$$n! = n(n - 1)(n - 2) \ldots 3 \cdot 2 \cdot 1$$
$$10! = 10 \cdot 9 \cdot 8 \cdot 7 \cdot 6 \cdot 5 \cdot 4 \cdot 3 \cdot 2 \cdot 1 = 3{,}628{,}800$$
$$5! = 5 \cdot 4 \cdot 3 \cdot 2 \cdot 1 = 120$$

Using factorials is a convenient way to write certain expressions.

a. Express $8 \cdot 7 \cdot 6 \cdot 5 \cdot 4$, using factorials.

$$8 \cdot 7 \cdot 6 \cdot 5 \cdot 4 = \frac{8 \cdot 7 \cdot 6 \cdot 5 \cdot 4 \cdot 3 \cdot 2 \cdot 1}{3 \cdot 2 \cdot 1} = \frac{8!}{3!}$$

b. Express $12 \cdot 11$, using factorials.

$$12 \cdot 11 = \frac{12 \cdot 11 \cdot 10 \cdot 9 \cdot 8 \cdot 7 \cdot 6 \cdot 5 \cdot 4 \cdot 3 \cdot 2 \cdot 1}{10 \cdot 9 \cdot 8 \cdot 7 \cdot 6 \cdot 5 \cdot 4 \cdot 3 \cdot 2 \cdot 1}$$
$$= \frac{12!}{10!}$$

Think

Multiplying the numerator and denominator by the same number does not change the value of the expression.

What if you want to express $12 \cdot 11 \cdot 10$, using factorials? What denominator would you use?

Evaluate factorials in division expressions by simplifying factors.

c. Evaluate. $\frac{10!}{8!}$

$$\frac{10 \cdot 9 \cdot \cancel{8} \cdot \cancel{7} \cdot \cancel{6} \cdot \cancel{5} \cdot \cancel{4} \cdot \cancel{3} \cdot \cancel{2} \cdot \cancel{1}}{\cancel{8} \cdot \cancel{7} \cdot \cancel{6} \cdot \cancel{5} \cdot \cancel{4} \cdot \cancel{3} \cdot \cancel{2} \cdot \cancel{1}} = 10 \cdot 9 = 90$$

d. Evaluate. $\frac{7!}{6!}$

$$\frac{7 \cdot \cancel{6} \cdot \cancel{5} \cdot \cancel{4} \cdot \cancel{3} \cdot \cancel{2} \cdot \cancel{1}}{\cancel{6} \cdot \cancel{5} \cdot \cancel{4} \cdot \cancel{3} \cdot \cancel{2} \cdot \cancel{1}} = 7$$

Check Your Understanding

Write an expression for each, using factorials.

1. $13 \cdot 12 \cdot 11 \cdot 10$

2. $7 \cdot 6 \cdot 5 \cdot 4 \cdot 3 \cdot 2 \cdot 1$

3. $25 \cdot 24$

Evaluate each expression.

4. $3!$

5. $\frac{9!}{7!}$

6. $\frac{100!}{99!}$

7. $6!$

8. $\frac{8!}{8!}$

Share Your Ideas Does $7! - 3! = 7 \cdot 6 \cdot 5 \cdot 4$? Why or why not?

Write an expression for each, using factorials.

9. $9 \cdot 8 \cdot 7 \cdot 6 \cdot 5$

10. $19 \cdot 18 \cdot 17$

11. $32 \cdot 31$

12. $56 \cdot 55 \cdot 54 \cdot 53$

13. $27 \cdot 26 \cdot 25 \cdot 24$

14. $5 \cdot 4 \cdot 3 \cdot 2$

15. $12 \cdot 11 \cdot 10$

16. $73 \cdot 72 \cdot 71 \cdot 70 \cdot 69$

17. $100 \cdot 99$

 Evaluate each expression. Use mental math or paper and pencil.

18. $4!$

19. $9!$

20. $1!$

21. $7!$

22. $8!$

23. $2!$

24. $\dfrac{5!}{3!}$

25. $\dfrac{12!}{11!}$

26. $\dfrac{16!}{14!}$

27. $\dfrac{10!}{9!}$

28. $\dfrac{9!}{5!}$

29. $\dfrac{13!}{10!}$

30. $\dfrac{6!}{6}$

31. $5 \cdot 4!$

32. $\dfrac{20!}{17!}$

33. $(3!)^2$

34. $8! - 7!$

35. $\dfrac{12!}{9! \cdot 3!}$

36. $\dfrac{14!}{10! \cdot 4!}$

37. $\dfrac{15!}{12! \cdot 3!}$

Evaluate each expression. Use a calculator if you wish.

38. $\dfrac{50!}{47!}$

39. $\dfrac{38!}{35!}$

40. $\dfrac{19!}{12!}$

41. $\dfrac{60!}{56!}$

42. $\dfrac{10!}{2!}$

43. $\dfrac{100!}{98!}$

44. $\dfrac{53!}{50!}$

45. $\dfrac{27!}{24!}$

46. $\dfrac{38!}{34!}$

47. $\dfrac{11!}{5!}$

Think and Apply

48. If x is a positive integer, what does $\dfrac{(x + 1)!}{x!}$ equal? Substitute different values for x.

49. Simplify the expression $\dfrac{100!}{95!}$. How can you use a calculator to evaluate the expression?

50. Some calculators have a factorial key. If your calculator has one, find the greatest integer for which your calculator will compute a factorial value. What happens if you try to find $n!$ for a greater value of n?

51. You can use a computer spreadsheet to evaluate factorials. Enter the data shown in your spreadsheet. To show $2!$ replace 0 in cell C1 with 1. Then recalculate each time to find $3!$ to $20!$. Write an estimate for $20!$ in standard form.

Logical Thinking

52. Three playing cards are adjacent to one another. There is a 3 just to the right of a 2. There is a 3 just to the left of a 3. There is a diamond just to the left of a heart, and a diamond just to the right of a diamond. Name each of the cards.

	A	B	C	D
1		START	0	
2				
3	N	IF (C1 = 0, 1, B3 + 1)	N!	IF (C1 = 0, 1, B3*D3)

$10^6 = 1,000,000$ and $6! = 720$. Do you think 10^n will always be greater than $n!$? Explain.

SUMMING UP

First–, second–, and third–place winners of the race are announced. Will the names be listed in a certain order? What do you expect?

Permutations

In how many ways can five runners line up for a race?

You can use the counting principle to compute the total number of possible arrangements.

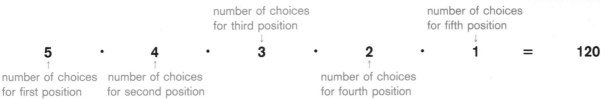

		number of choices for third position				number of choices for fifth position		
		↓				↓		
5	·	**4**	·	**3**	·	**2**	·	**1** = 120
↑		↑				↑		
number of choices for first position	number of choices for second position			number of choices for fourth position			

The runners can line up in 120 ways.

▶ A **permutation** is an arrangement in which order is important. The permutation ABCDE is different from the permutation BCADE.

More Examples

a. In how many ways can you elect a president and a vice–president from 20 students?

$$_{20}P_2 = 20 \cdot 19 = 380$$
↑ └number to be elected
total number in class

b. How many 3–digit codes can be made with no repeating digits?

$$_{10}P_3 = 10 \cdot 9 \cdot 8 = 720$$
↑ └number of digits in code
total number of digits

You can use factorials to express answers to permutation problems.

$$_8P_3 = 8 \cdot 7 \cdot 6 = \frac{8 \cdot 7 \cdot 6 \cdot 5 \cdot 4 \cdot 3 \cdot 2 \cdot 1}{5 \cdot 4 \cdot 3 \cdot 2 \cdot 1} = \frac{8!}{5!}$$

Check Your Understanding

Find the number of permutations for each.

1. In how many ways can the two male roles be filled if 12 boys audition?

2. In how many ways can the pitcher and catcher be chosen if 7 girls try out?

Use factorials to express each number.

3. $_{100}P_{20}$ **4.** $_{65}P_{13}$ **5.** $_{19}P_6$ **6.** $_{28}P_{25}$

Share Your Ideas   Sarah picks 5 books out of 10 to buy. Does this situation describe a permutation? Explain.

Practice

Find the number of permutations for each.

7. In how many ways can you make a 2–digit code if digits are not repeated?

8. If repeated digits are allowed, how many 2–digit codes are possible?

9. In how many ways can a gold medal, a silver medal, and a bronze medal be awarded to 20 Olympic contestants?

10. How many possible arrangements exist for 6 spectators seated in a row?

 Compute each number of permutations. Choose paper and pencil or a calculator.

11. $_{14}P_3$

12. $_{100}P_2$

13. $_{65}P_1$

14. $_{6}P_4$

15. $_{9}P_2$

16. $_{36}P_3$

17. $_{18}P_2$

18. $_{70}P_5$

19. $_{300}P_2$

Use factorials to express each number of permutations.

20. $_{16}P_9$

21. $_{30}P_{14}$

22. $_{26}P_5$

23. $_{40}P_{12}$

24. $_{61}P_3$

25. $_{38}P_7$

26. In how many ways can 16 books out of 25 be arranged on a shelf?

27. In how many ways can Lydia arrange 8 photos in a column if she places her favorite one on top?

Think and Apply

28. Bicycle license plates have 4 digits. How many different plates exist if no repeating digits are used?

29. How many plates have only odd digits?

30. If license plates are randomly assigned to bikers, what is the probability of getting a plate with only odd digits?

31. Look at the list of 3-digit telephone exchanges in your phone book. What is the greatest number of local listings possible using those exchanges?

Compute $_4P_4$ and $_4P_3$. How do they compare?
Explain your results.

Mixed Review

1.
$$\begin{array}{r} 41.739 \\ 2.008 \\ +\ 6.71 \\ \hline \end{array}$$

2. $64.37 - 4.08$

3. $1\frac{1}{3} \cdot 7\frac{3}{4}$

4.
$$\begin{array}{r} 32\frac{1}{3} \\ +\ 16\frac{4}{7} \\ \hline \end{array}$$

5.
$$\begin{array}{r} 4.037 \\ \times\ 7.1 \\ \hline \end{array}$$

6. $\$32.50 \div 4.5$

7. $27\frac{1}{4} \div 6\frac{1}{2}$

8. $\frac{7}{8} + \frac{1}{6} + \frac{3}{4}$

9. $13.28 - 0.014$

10. $\frac{2}{3} \cdot \frac{5}{8}$

Estimate.

11. $2.7 + 16.58 + 11.87$

12. $12\frac{1}{8} - 7\frac{5}{6}$

13. $5.32 \cdot 2.7$

14. $164.7 \div 21$

15. $\$.86 \cdot 3$

Solve.

16. $\frac{2}{3} = \frac{n}{12}$

17. $\frac{n}{15} = \frac{12}{30}$

18. $\frac{6}{n} = \frac{10}{11}$

19. $\frac{n}{12} = \frac{4}{2.4}$

20. $\frac{7}{12} = \frac{14}{n}$

The first 10 people to enter the theater will receive a free T-shirt. Does it matter whether Jill is the first or the tenth one to enter?

Combinations

In how many ways can you pick 3 out of 5 sweaters to take on a ski trip?

The possible combinations of 5 sweaters, *ABCDE*, taken 3 at a time, are shown below.

ABC   ABD   ABE   ACD   ACE   ADE
BCD   BCE   BDE   CDE

There are 10 combinations possible.

▶ A **combination** is a selection in which order is *not* important.
Choosing *ABC* is the same as choosing *BAC*.

The number of combinations of 5 things taken 3 at a time, written $_5C_3$, is related to $_5P_3$.

$$_5C_3 = \frac{_5P_3}{_3P_3} = \frac{5 \cdot \overset{2}{\cancel{4}} \cdot \cancel{3}}{\cancel{3} \cdot \cancel{2} \cdot 1} = 10$$

Explain why $_5C_3$ is less than $_5P_3$. Do you think this is always true? Why or why not?

Another Example

Find the number of combinations of 7 books taken 2 at a time.

$$_7C_2 = \frac{_7P_2}{_2P_2} = \frac{7 \cdot \overset{3}{\cancel{6}}}{\cancel{2} \cdot 1} = 21$$

Check Your Understanding

Write *permutations* or *combinations* for each.

1. Award first and second prize to 2 out of 10 runners.

2. Pick 4 out of 5 shirts from a drawer.

3. Arrange 10 floats for a parade.

4. Take home 5 out of 90 library books.

Compute each number of combinations.

5. $_{10}C_3$ 6. $_6C_4$ 7. $_5C_2$ 8. $_7C_3$

Share Your Ideas   Compute $_5C_3$ and $_5C_2$. How do they compare? Explain your results. Compute $_6C_4$. What do you expect $_6C_2$ will be?

Write *permutations* or *combinations* for each. Then solve.

9. In how many ways can you choose 2 students from 14?

10. In how many ways can you arrange 5 different chairs in a row?

11. Find the number of ways to call 6 people in a row.

12. Find all the ways to pick 3 out of 5 pizza toppings.

13. How many ways are there to mail 2 out of 10 albums?

14. How many ways are there to choose 6 out of 12 people?

15. Find the number of ways to paint two rooms 2 out of 7 colors.

16. How many ways are there to elect a president and secretary from 10 people?

 Compute. Choose paper and pencil or a calculator.

17. $_{11}C_3$

18. $_{17}C_5$

19. $_{13}C_2$

20. $_{60}P_2$

21. $_5C_4$

22. $_{16}C_{14}$

23. $_{12}P_3$

24. $_{15}P_4$

Find the number of combinations for each.

25. 2 letters from COUNTRY

26. 3 digits from 4, 5, 6, 7, 8

27. 2 socks from 20

28. 4 stamps from 10

29. 5 pens from 7

30. 2 cooks from 8 people

Think and Apply

After the class barbecue, 3 people are needed to clean up. The class has 9 boys and 11 girls.

31. How many 3-person committees are possible?

32. How many cleanup committees of only boys are possible?

33. If chosen at random, what is the probability the committee will be 3 boys?

34. What is the probability it will be either all boys or all girls?

Test Taker

When you are not sure of how to solve a problem, you can increase your chances of choosing the correct answer by eliminating ones that are obviously incorrect. Find one or more answers that are clearly incorrect for each problem. Then solve.

35. P (tossing a head twice)

   a. 1   b. $\frac{1}{2}$ c. 0   d. $\frac{1}{4}$

36. P (tossing 3 or 7 on a number cube)

   a. 7   b. $\frac{3}{7}$ c. 0   d. $\frac{1}{6}$

37. Find the number of ways to go from A to B. A ⬭⬭ B

   a. 12   b. 7   c. 1   d. 24

Explain the difference between a permutation and a combination.

SUMMING UP

Using Problem Solving

Finding the Area of an Irregular Figure

What do you think is the area of the figure? How could you find out what it is?

Working together

Work in a small group to solve this problem.

Materials: tracing paper, grid paper

A. You can use probability to find the approximate area of this figure. This method is called the Monte Carlo method.

- First enclose the irregular figure within a regular figure.

- Then close your eyes and draw dots randomly within this total figure.

- Count the dots that fall within the irregular figure and those that fall within the remaining part of the regular figure.

- Add to find the total number of dots.

- Find the percentage of dots that fall in the irregular figure. Calculate the percent this way:

$$\frac{\text{Number of Dots Within the Irregular Figure}}{\text{Total Dots Within the Whole Figure}}$$

- Multiply that percent by the area of the whole regular figure. That will give you the approximate area of the irregular figure.

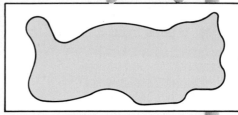

B. Trace the figure on page 379. Use the Monte Carlo method to find the area of the irregular figure.

Sharing Your Ideas

1. What figure did you draw around the irregular figure? Why did you choose that figure?

2. How many dots did you use? How did you make sure they were random? If any dots accidentally went outside the regular figure you drew, should you count them?

378

Extending Your Thinking

3. Draw an irregular figure and exchange it with a partner. Use the Monte Carlo method to find its area.

4. You can check the Monte Carlo method. Make some figures for which you know the area and enclose them in a rectangle. Use the Monte Carlo method to determine the area of each "irregular" figure.

5. You can use grid paper and coordinates to help you find the area of an irregular figure. Draw a 20 unit × 20 unit square on grid paper. Draw an irregular figure inside it. Number a set of index cards from 1 to 19. Draw a card for the horizontal coordinate. Put the card back and draw another card for the vertical coordinate. Plot a point for each pair of numbers you drew. Draw at least 40 pairs of numbers and plot them. How does this method work?

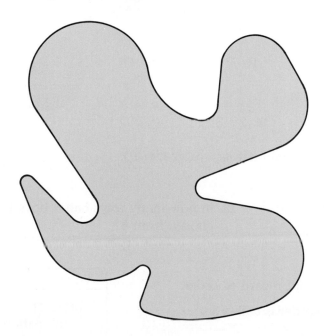

Summing Up

6. Why must you draw a figure for which you can compute the area around the irregular figure? Explain.

7. Did you find the Monte Carlo method worked on the figures for which you knew the area? Why or why not?

8. How might you use a computer to help you find the area of an irregular figure?

Chapter Review

Find the probability of each event. pages 358–359

1. $P(S)$ 2. $P(C)$ 3. P (vowel)

Use the counting principle to answer each. pages 362–363

4. In how many ways can you choose 1 out of 5 sweaters and 1 out of 6 pairs of socks?

5. How many outcomes exist for choosing 1 out of 9 marbles and 1 out of 10 cards?

You toss a coin and toss a number cube. Find each probability. pages 364–365

6. P (head, 6)   7. P (head)   8. P (tail, 7)

A marble is chosen and not replaced. A second marble is chosen. Find each probability. pages 364–365

9. $P(B, R)$ 10. $P(B, B)$ 11. $P(R, R)$

Find each probability. pages 366–367

12. $P(2 \text{ or } 8)$ 13. $P(16 \text{ or } 14 \text{ or } 2)$ 14. $P(10 \text{ or } 12 \text{ or } 1)$

Evaluate each expression. pages 372–373

15. $5!$ 16. $\dfrac{20!}{18!}$ 17. $\dfrac{10!}{10!}$ 18. $2 \cdot 3!$

Find each number of permutations or combinations. pages 374–377

19. $_5P_2$ 20. $_{10}C_4$ 21. $_7P_3$

22. In how many ways can 4 books be stacked?

23. In how many ways can 4 boys be chosen from 6?

Complete.

24. A _____ is an arrangement without regard to order.

25. A grouping of things in a certain order is called a _____.

26. The _____ of all the whole numbers from n to 1 is called n factorial.

Words to Know
product
combination
permutation
factorial
sum

Solve. pages 369–371

27. A box contains 7 blue pens and 3 red ones. What is the probability that Sarah will choose 2 red pens at random if she does not replace the first one chosen?

28. Make a table showing all the possible outcomes for tossing a number cube and tossing a coin. What is the probability of tossing heads and 6?

Chapter Test

Find the probability of each event.

1. $P(5)$ 2. P (even)   3. $P(9)$

Use the counting principle to answer each.

4. There are 2 ways to travel from A to B and 5 ways to travel from B to C. How many ways are there to travel from A to C?

5. In how many ways can Joe pick 1 out of 3 books and 1 out of 10 notebooks?

6. How many different ways are there to choose 1 out of 5 boys and 1 out of 6 girls?

The letters T, E, E, A, and S are placed in a bag. You choose a letter and toss a coin. Find each probability.

7. $P(E$, tail)   8. P (vowel, head)   9. $P(S)$

Two cards are chosen without replacement. Find the probability of each.

10. $P(O, O)$ 11. $P(G, N)$ 12. $P(S, O)$

A number cube is tossed. Find each probability.

13. P (even or odd)   14. $P(2$ or $6)$ 15. $P(1$ or 2 or $3)$ 16. $P(5$ or $8)$

Write each expression, using factorials.

17. $8 \cdot 7 \cdot 6 \cdot 5$ 18. $21 \cdot 20$ 19. $10 \cdot 9 \cdot 8 \cdot 7$

Find each number of permutations or combinations.

20. $_5C_4$ 21. $_5P_2$ 22. $_7P_2$ 23. $_6C_3$

Solve.

24. Three red and two blue marbles are in a bag. When is the probability of choosing two reds greater—if the first marble is or is not replaced after being chosen?

25. List all the possible outcomes of choosing a marble from the bag in **24** and tossing a coin. What is the probability of choosing a red marble and tossing tails?

THINK   How many more license plates can be made with 3 digits and 3 letters than with 4 digits and 2 letters if no digit or letter is repeated?

Computer Link

Batter Up!

What is the meaning of a .300 batting average? Do you think the player could have a game with no hits?

Use the computer to simulate or model the situation.

Materials: Logo

A. The ATBAT procedure simulates a player coming to bat and either getting a hit or making an out. Define ATBAT and then call it by entering PRINT ATBAT .300 several times. Describe your results.

```
TO ATBAT :AVRG
MAKE "T (1 + RANDOM 1000) / 1000
IF :T < :AVRG [OP "HIT] [OP "OUT]
END
```

B. Susie has a batting average of .350. How many hits do you expect her to get in 5 games? Use 1 game = 4 at bats. Enter the command below and tally how many times HIT prints. Find the batting average for your results. Compare it to the average you input. Are they the same? Why or why not?

```
REPEAT 20 [PR ATBAT .350]
```

C. Define the GAME procedure below. Enter GAME .300. Record whether the player had a hit or not. Repeat 9 times. How many games out of 10 were hitless? Were your results what you expected? Why or why not?

```
TO GAME :AVRG
REPEAT 4 [PR ATBAT :AVRG]
END
```

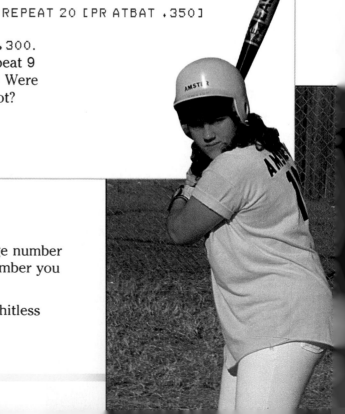

Sharing Your Results

1. Combine the class results. What was the average number of hitless games? Is the average close to the number you expected? Explain.

2. Make a general statement about the number of hitless games a player can expect to have in a season.

382

Extending the Activity

A hitting streak can be defined as the number of consecutive games in which a player gets at least one hit. If you know the batting average of a player, can you predict how many games a hitting streak is likely to last?

3. Use the GAME procedure from page 382 to simulate a season of twenty games with four at bats per game. Count the number of consecutive games that have at least one hit for each batting average. Record your work.

   a. .200   **b.** .250   **c.** .300   **d.** .350

4. Repeat two times to collect three sets of data for each batting average. Combine the class results. Then predict the length of a hitting streak that is most likely for each batting average.

5. Which player is expected to have the longest streak? Do your results show the player with that batting average has the longest streak? Why or why not?

6. Did any player bat one thousand in a game? Do you think this is likely to happen? Explain.

7. Use your own batting average or the batting average of a friend. How long a hitting streak is likely for that batting average?

Summing Up

8. What aspects of a real situation have been ignored in the simulation? What modifications would you suggest to make the simulation more realistic?

EXTENSION

Pascal's Triangle and Probability

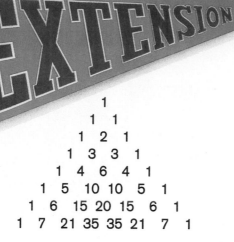

```
            1
          1   1
        1   2   1
      1   3   3   1
    1   4   6   4   1
  1   5  10  10   5   1
1   6  15  20  15   6   1
1   7  21  35  35  21   7   1
```

Blaise Pascal (1623–1662) was interested in numbers and number patterns, starting at a very early age. His use of the triangle of numbers shown here is the work for which he is most often remembered.

This array of numbers can be very helpful in solving some probability problems.

The chart below gives the possible outcomes for flipping one or more coins. Complete the number of outcomes for two, three, and four coins.

Number of Coins Tossed	Sample Space	Number of Outcomes				
		0 heads	1 head	2 heads	3 heads	4 heads
1	T H	1	1			
2	TT HT HH TH					
3	TTT HTT HHT HHH THT HTH TTH THH					
4	TTTT HTTT HHTT THHH HHHH THTT HTHT HTHH TTHT HTTH HHTH TTTH THHT HHHT THTH TTHH					

Compare the numbers recorded in each column of outcomes with Pascal's triangle.

Use your observations to find the following.

1. Toss 5 coins. What is the number of possible outcomes with

  a. no heads   **b.** 1 head   **c.** 2 heads   **d.** 3 heads

2. Toss 6 coins. What is the number of possible outcomes with

  a. 3 heads   **b.** 4 heads   **c.** 5 heads   **d.** 6 heads

Any situation in which there are two possibilities for each possible outcome, such as heads or tails for tossing a coin, can use Pascal's triangle to compute probability.

3. What is the probability of tossing 3 coins and getting 2 heads?

4. What is the probability of a family of 4 children having 3 boys?

5. What is the probability of 5 true or false questions being all false?

Maintaining Skills

Choose the correct answer. Write A, B, C, or D.

1. Which ratio is equal to 3 to 4?

    A 2 to 3   **C** 6 to 10

    B 6 to 8   **D** not given

2. Find n. $\frac{n}{64} = \frac{18}{32}$

    A $n = 36$ **C** $n = 8$

    B $n = 32$ **D** not given

3. What is 18% as a ratio?

    A $\frac{1}{8}$ **C** $\frac{18}{100}$

    B $\frac{1}{4}$ **D** not given

4. 9 is 150% of what number?

    A 13.5   **C** 6

    B 12   **D** not given

5. What is 24% of 62?

    A 15   **C** 1,488

    B 14.88   **D** not given

6. What percent of 52 is 10.4?

    A 20.4%   **C** 2%

    B 80%   **D** not given

7. What is the area of ABCD? 3 cm

    A 54 cm^2 **C** 27 cm^2

    B 45 cm^2 **D** not given

8. What is the circumference? Use $\pi \approx 3.14$.

    A 21.98 cm   **C** 4.396 cm

    B 43.96 cm   **D** not given

9. 25 kg = _____ dm^3

    A 25   **C** 250

    B 2.5   **D** not given

10. What is P(odd number)?

    A $\frac{1}{2}$ **C** $\frac{3}{5}$

    B $\frac{3}{4}$ **D** not given

11. What is the probability of choosing an even number or choosing a 3?

    1   2   3   4   5   6   7

    A $\frac{3}{7}$ **C** $\frac{4}{7}$

    B $\frac{4}{6}$ **D** not given

Make a list to solve 12 and 13.

12. Phil practices violin every third day and piano every other day. The last time he had to practice both on the same day was Thursday. What day of the week will this next occur?

    A Friday   **C** Wednesday

    B Tuesday   **D** not given

13. Mrs. Baum has exact change but no pennies to pay the $.75 bridge toll. How many different ways could she pay this toll?

    A 15   **C** 16

    B 18   **D** not given

Transformations and Constructions

Sharing What You Know

Have you ever studied patterns in quilts, wallpaper, or woven fabrics? Often these patterns repeat each other, sometimes mirroring each other, sometimes shifting from one direction to another. Study the design of the quilt on this page. How are the shapes in the design related to each other? What directions could you write to tell someone how to create the pattern that you see here?

Using Language

Designs on fabrics or wallpaper often use **symmetry** to create pleasing effects. In mathematics, there is **point symmetry** and **rotational symmetry.** What do you think is the difference between them? How do you think they are similar?

Words to Know construction, tessellation, perpendicular lines, rotational symmetry, point symmetry, transformation, translation, reflection, rotation, locus, bisector

Be a Problem Solver

Imagine that you are creating designs using triangles. What figures can you create by flipping a triangle?

Create a design using geometric figures. Describe your design in words.

Activity

Exploring Geometric Patterns

The artist M. C. Escher used geometric patterns called **tessellations** to create unusual drawings. A tessellation uses a single shape repeatedly to cover a plane without gaps or overlapping.

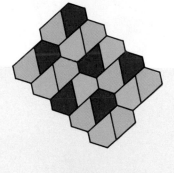

Working together

Materials: stiff paper or tagboard, scissors, straightedge, colored pencils or markers

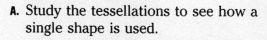
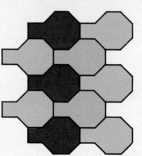

A. Study the tessellations to see how a single shape is used.

B. Draw several different triangles and quadrilaterals. Cut them out and use each shape as a pattern to make a tessellation.

C. Use color to highlight your designs.

Sharing Your Results

1. Compare your tessellations with those of other groups.

2. Explain your method for making each design.

3. Which shapes were easiest to use? Explain.

4. Were you unable to use some shapes for making a tessellation? Explain.

Extending the Activity

5. Do you think every triangle can be used to tessellate a plane? every quadrilateral? Discuss.

6. Look at the tessellation at the right. Which angles meet at each vertex? What is the sum of these angle measures?

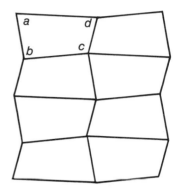

7. **Look back** at a triangular tessellation you made. Identify the angles that meet at each vertex. What is the sum of their measures?

8. Draw and cut out a regular pentagon. Can you use it to tessellate a plane? Why or why not?

9. Can you predict which regular polygons can be used to tessellate a plane? Consider the sum of their angle measures and discuss your ideas.

10. **What if** you combine two polygons, such as an octagon and a square, to create a shape for a design? Which ones would you choose? Test your ideas by making a design.

Summing Up

11. How does the sum of the angle measures determine which regular polygons can be used in a tessellation?

12. Discuss the uses of geometric designs in the world around you. Why are such designs used so often? How else could things be designed?

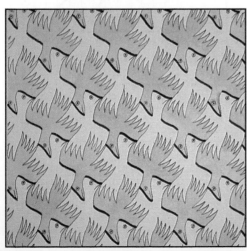

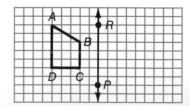

How does figure A move into positions 1, 2, or 3? Describe each movement.

Translations and Reflections

A **transformation** is a change in the size, shape, or position of a figure. A change in position can be described as a flip, a slide, or a turn.

▶ A **translation** is a change in position resulting from a slide without any turn. A translation can be described using a rule on a grid.

△ABC translates into △DEF by moving each point right 2 and up 4. What is the rule that translates △DEF into △ABC?

▶ A **reflection** is a change in position resulting from a flip. A reflection can be described using a **line of reflection**.

Each point of △ABC is reflected about $\overleftrightarrow{RP}$ into △DEF. How could you use paper folding to locate the line of reflection? Trace both triangles and test your idea.

Sometimes a line of reflection is also a **line of symmetry.** $\overleftrightarrow{GJ}$ is a line of symmetry for FGHJ. What reflection can you describe?

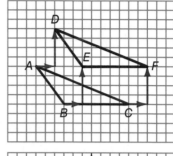

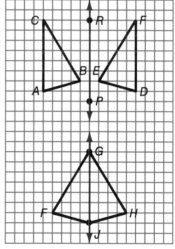

Check Your Understanding

Write *reflection, translation,* or *neither* for each.

1.
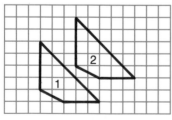

2.
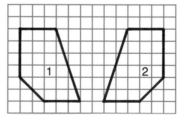

3.
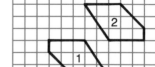

4. Draw a figure on grid paper and translate it down 3 and left 6.

5. Reflect *ABCD* about $\overleftrightarrow{RP}$.

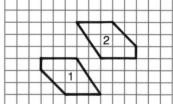

Sharing Your Ideas How does a figure change in a reflection? in a translation?

Write *reflection*, *translation*, or *neither*.

6.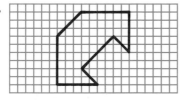

7.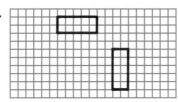

8.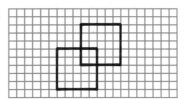

Draw a line of reflection for each.

9.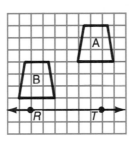

10.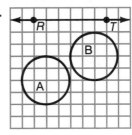

11.

Describe each translation from A to B.

12.

13.

14. Copy the figures in **12** on grid paper. Draw the result of translating shape A down 5 and right 2. Draw the result of reflecting shape B about $\overleftrightarrow{RT}$.

15. Copy the figures in **13** on grid paper. Draw the result of translating shape A left 6 and down 0. Draw the result of reflecting shape B about $\overleftrightarrow{RT}$.

Think and Apply

16. How would you use reflection if you were designing a car?

17. How would you use symmetry if you were checking a knee injury in football?

18. What transformations might you use if you were designing wallpaper?

Visual Thinking

19. A square has four lines of symmetry. How many lines of symmetry do each of these figures have?

a.

b.

c.

d.

e.

Is a figure always congruent to its image after translation? after reflection? Explain.

SUMMING UP

391

Copy this pattern on grid paper. Repeat or change the pattern to make a design. What transformations did you use?

Graphing Translations and Reflections

A translation can be defined by the changes in the x- and y-coordinates of the points on the figure.

Figure 1 has been translated to figure 2.
5 has been added to each x-coordinate.
6 has been subtracted from each y-coordinate.

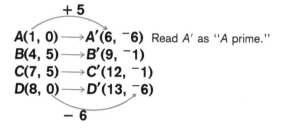

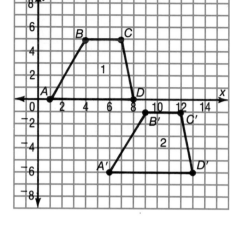

$A(1, 0) \longrightarrow A'(6, \, ^-6)$ Read A' as "A prime."
$B(4, 5) \longrightarrow B'(9, \, ^-1)$
$C(7, 5) \longrightarrow C'(12, \, ^-1)$
$D(8, 0) \longrightarrow D'(13, \, ^-6)$

Figure 3 is reflected about the x-axis to figure 4. When a figure is reflected about the x-axis, the y-coordinates are multiplied by $^-1$. The x-coordinates are unchanged.

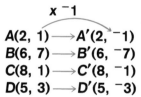

$A(2, 1) \longrightarrow A'(2, \, ^-1)$
$B(6, 7) \longrightarrow B'(6, \, ^-7)$
$C(8, 1) \longrightarrow C'(8, \, ^-1)$
$D(5, 3) \longrightarrow D'(5, \, ^-3)$

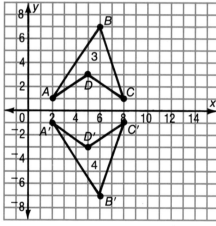

What if a figure is reflected about the y-axis? Each y-coordinate is unchanged. How does the x-coordinate change?

Use the figures shown above. Draw each transformation on grid paper. List the coordinates of each transformation.

1. Reflect figure 1 about the x-axis.

2. Reflect figure 2 about the y-axis.

3. Translate figure 3. Add 8 to each x-coordinate.

4. Translate figure 4. Subtract 5 from each y-coordinate.

Share Your Ideas Figure A is translated horizontally. What changes are made in the coordinates? What changes result in a vertical translation?

Copy figure 1 on grid paper. Draw each transformation. List the coordinates of the vertices of each.

5. Reflect figure 1 about the *y*-axis. Label the reflection figure 2.

6. Translate figure 1 by subtracting 6 from each *y*-coordinate. Label this translation figure 3.

7. Reflect figure 3 about the *y*-axis. Label this reflection figure 4.

8. What transformation will transform figure 4 into figure 2? Describe the changes in the *x*- and *y*-coordinates.

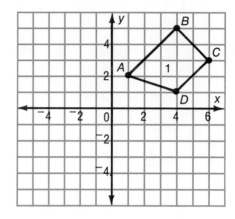

Copy figure 1 on grid paper. Use it to solve 9–10.

9. Name the transformation that moves *A* to *A'* (1, ⁻2) and *C* to *C'* (6, ⁻2).

10. Name two transformations that could move *D* to *D'* (4, ⁻1).

Think and Apply

11. The wings of a model plane are to be attached to the body with *A* at *A'* and *B* at *B'*. What combination of transformations will position one wing on each side of the body?

12. **What if** the wings are to be positioned with *A* at *B'* and *B* at *A'*? What combination of transformations will position one wing on each side of the body?

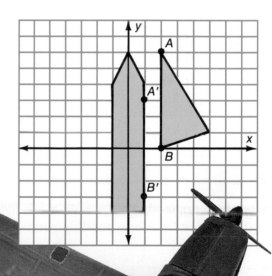

Logical Thinking

13. A figure is reflected about the *x*-axis, then about the *y*-axis, and again about the *x*-axis. If it is then reflected about the *y*-axis again, what is its final position?

How do coordinates change when a figure is reflected about the *x*-axis and then the *y*-axis?

SUMMING UP

What fraction of a full turn moves the hour hand of a clock from 3 to 6? Where is the hour hand after it moves a $\frac{3}{4}$ turn starting from 9?

Rotations

This computer-generated design uses rotation to generate a shape that looks almost like a snowflake.

▶ A **rotation** is a transformation resulting from a turn about a center point. A figure can be rotated clockwise (CW) or counterclockwise (CCW).

Drawing a Rotation Image

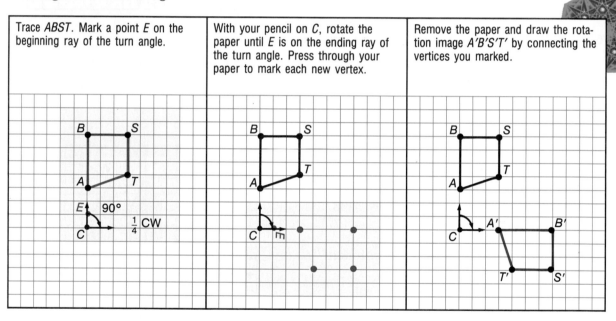

| Trace *ABST*. Mark a point *E* on the beginning ray of the turn angle. | With your pencil on *C*, rotate the paper until *E* is on the ending ray of the turn angle. Press through your paper to mark each new vertex. | Remove the paper and draw the rotation image *A'B'S'T'* by connecting the vertices you marked. |

What turn angle about *C* would move figure 1 into position 2? Is there more than one possible rotation?

1. Copy the figure on grid paper. Draw a rotation with a $\frac{3}{4}$ CCW turn angle about *C*.

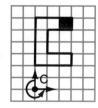

Write the turn angles needed for each.

2. *P* is rotated to *Q*.
3. *S* is rotated to *Q*.
4. *R* is rotated to *P*.
5. *S* is rotated to *R*.

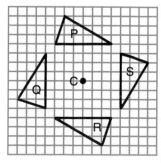

Share Your Ideas Can you always find two turn angles that will produce the same rotation image? Why or why not?

Name two turn angles about C for each rotation.

6. Rotate figure A to position B.

7. Rotate figure A to position D.

8. Rotate figure A to position A.

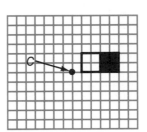

Copy the figure on grid paper. Draw the rotational image for each turn angle about C.

9. $\frac{1}{4}$ CW

10. 180° CCW

11. 270° CCW

12. $\frac{4}{4}$ CW

13. $\frac{6}{4}$ CCW

14. 990° CW

Which figures are rotation images? For those that are, name the turn angles.

15.

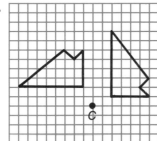

16.

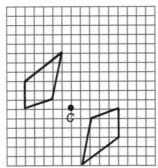

17.

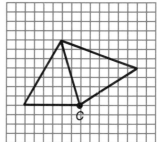

A figure has **rotational symmetry** if it can be rotated less than 360° to coincide with the original figure. A figure also has **point symmetry** if it coincides with the original figure after a turn of exactly 180°. A figure that has point symmetry looks the same upside down and right side up.

18. Which figures have rotational symmetry?

19. Which figures also have point symmetry?

20. Look back at the computer design on page 394. What kind of symmetry does it have?

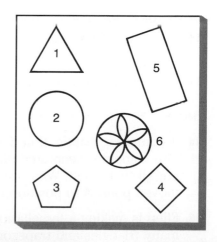

Suppose you need to explain what a rotation is to someone who does not know. What could you say?

SUMMING UP

Midchapter Review

Write _reflection, translation,_ or _rotation_ for each. pages 390–395

1.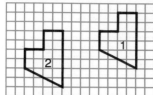

2.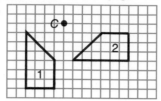

3.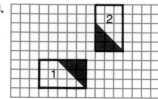

Copy each figure on grid paper. Draw each translation or reflection. pages 390–391

4.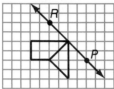

5.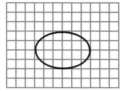

6.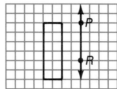

7.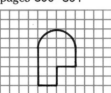

Reflect about $\overleftrightarrow{RP}$.

Translate up 3, left 5.

Reflect about $\overleftrightarrow{RP}$.

Translate down 2, right 6.

A figure has coordinates (3, 3), (0, 3), (0, 6). Draw the figure on grid paper. pages 392–393

8. Draw the reflection of the figure about the *x*-axis.

9. Draw the reflection of the figure about the *y*-axis.

Copy the figure on grid paper. Draw the result of each rotation about C. pages 394–395

10. $\frac{1}{2}$ turn CCW

11. $\frac{3}{4}$ turn CW

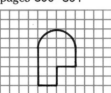

Complete.

12. A pattern that uses one shape to cover a plane completely is a _____.

13. The letter H has _____ symmetry and _____ symmetry.

14. Rotations, reflections, and translations are all _____.

Words to Know
point   line
transformations
tessellation
rotational

Solve.

15. A computer malfunction destroyed all but a small part of a computer-generated diagram. Two points, *A* and *B*, are all that is left. What transformations could have moved point *A* to position B?

16. Ellen is making a tessellation. The table shows how many triangles and trapezoids she uses. If she uses 36 triangles, how many trapezoids does she use?

15.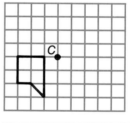

Triangle	3	6	9	12	15
Trapezoid	1	2	3	4	5

Exploring Problem Solving

Design a Logo

Most companies have an identifying mark that they place on their products, advertising material, and stationery. These identifying designs are called logos. Many logos have been designed by using basic geometric constructions.

Thinking Critically

How would you design a logo that uses your initials? How would you design a logo that illustrates a product? Use a compass and a straightedge. Apply your knowledge of geometric constructions.

Analyzing and Making Decisions

1. What geometric figures do you see in the logos? What else do you notice about them?

2. What is the first thing you would do in making a logo? Sketch a few ideas for logos.

3. Design a logo that uses your initials. Design a logo that illustrates a product. Use a straightedge and a compass. Apply your knowledge of geometric constructions.

EMMONDS ELECTRIC

MR. JOHN Q. DOE
142 NORTH MAI

Look Back Look at your logo and those made by other students. What geometric figures were most often used? What else is special about the logos?

SIGHT AND SOUND SPECIALISTS

A·U·D·I·O
V·I·S·U·A·L
STEREO EQUIPMENT
142 MAIN STREET

Problem Solving Strategies

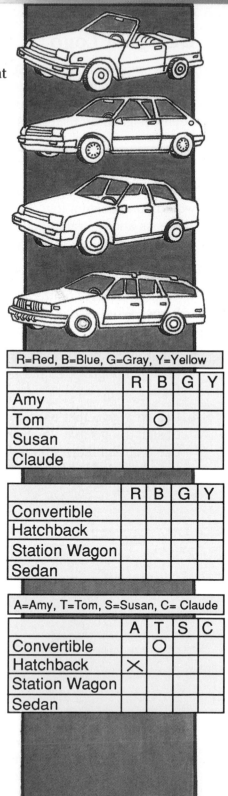

Logic

Tom, Susan, Claude, and then Amy (in that order) came to rent the last four cars at Bugle Rent-A-Car. There was one of each available model: a convertible, a hatchback, a sedan, and a station wagon. There was a red car, a blue car, a gray car, and a yellow car. Use the clues below and match the model and color of the car with the person who rented it.

1. Amy did not want the hatchback, but she did not have any choice.

2. After Tom left, he wished he had rented the blue car or the convertible.

3. When Susan left, the sedan was still there.

4. Susan rented either the gray car or the hatchback.

5. Claude rented the yellow car.

For some problems, you can use a grid to record what you know. Sometimes several grids will be helpful.

Solving the Problem

Think What do you need to find out? In what order did the people rent the cars?

Explore Make a grid. Why might it be helpful to have two or three sections? Read each clue. Record the information in your chart. Why is it important to know in what order the people rented the cars? Read through the clues several times.

Solve Who rented which car and what color was it?

Look Back How can reading back through the clues help you check your answer?

Share Your Ideas

1. Which did you identify first, the person and the color or the person and the model of the car?

2. How were you able to find out what color car Tom rented?

R=Red, B=Blue, G=Gray, Y=Yellow

	R	B	G	Y
Amy				
Tom		O		
Susan				
Claude				

	R	B	G	Y
Convertible				
Hatchback				
Station Wagon				
Sedan				

A=Amy, T=Tom, S=Susan, C= Claude

	A	T	S	C
Convertible		O		
Hatchback	X			
Station Wagon				
Sedan				

Practice

Solve. Make a grid where appropriate.

3. Arnold, Bruce, and Charles, and their sisters Denise, Linda, and Flo work together to design signs. They work in teams of a girl and a boy, but brother and sister never work together. Use these clues to determine who are brother and sister.

   a. Arnold and Denise worked on the capital sign.

   b. Bruce and Florence worked on the courthouse sign.

   c. Arnold and Linda worked on the museum sign.

   d. Charles and Denise worked on the restaurant sign.

4. I am the curator of the art museum. On my staff there is an assistant curator, a designer, and a writer. Our names are Mrs. Arnold, Mrs. Carter, Mr. Jones, and Mr. Hopkins. Mrs. Arnold and the assistant curator are both married. I review copy with the writer on Tuesdays. Mr. Jones and I meet every Friday. Mr. Hopkins would like my job when I leave. Mrs. Arnold does not review copy. Mr. Jones is not married. Match each person's name and job.

5. Maria, Elaine, Fran, Al, Bernie, and Charles help to clean the art room. They work in pairs, but brother and sister never work together. In the morning, Maria and Al are on one team, and Bernie and Fran are on another. In the afternoon, Elaine and Al are on one team, and Charles and Maria are on another. Who is related to whom?

6. Arturo, Wanda, Malcolm, and Victor each went to a different exhibit in the art museum. Each saw one of the following: basketry, mosaics, quilts, or rugs.

   a. Victor saw Wanda looking at the basketry exhibit.

   b. Arturo did not see the quilts.

   c. Arturo and Malcolm did not see the rug exhibit.

Which exhibit did each person see?

Mixed Strategy Review

7. Paula would like to design a $31 coupon book containing 5 coupons. Using different combinations of coupons, a person could make all the dollar values from 1 to 31. How much should each coupon be worth?

Create
Your Own

Write a logic problem for someone else to solve.

Activity

Exploring Geometric Relationships

A good way to visualize geometric relationships is to imagine that a point can move, and, like the point of a pencil, leaves a path that shows where it has been. The path of points is called a **locus.**

Working together

Materials: ruler, compass

A. Sketch the locus of points 4 cm from a fixed point *P*. Begin by marking *P*. Draw several points, each 4 cm from *P*. Complete the locus by drawing a smooth line connecting the points.

B. Mark two points, *R* and *S*. Sketch the locus of all points equidistant from *R* and *S*.

C. Construct a circle with radius 5 cm. Sketch the locus of all points 3 cm from the circle.

D. Draw $\overleftrightarrow{RT}$. Sketch the locus of all points 3 cm from $\overleftrightarrow{RT}$.

Sharing Your Results

1. Compare your sketches with those of other groups. Are they all alike?

2. **Look back** at the locus you sketched for **A.** Use a compass to construct a circle with center at *P* and radius 4 cm. How well does your sketch match the construction?

3. Describe the locus you drew in **B.** What is the relationship between the locus and $\overline{RS}$?

4. Visualize a locus of all points 3 cm from a line segment. How would this compare with the locus you sketched in **D**?

Extending the Activity

Try to visualize and then describe each locus in space.

5. Imagine looking down on a tetherball attached to a pole. When the ball is hit, what path does it follow? Remember that the rope wraps around the pole, so the distance from the pole to the ball becomes shorter and shorter. Try to visualize and then sketch the locus of points that represents the path of the ball in space.

6. What geometric idea describes the locus of all points in space equidistant from two points, *A* and *B*?

7. What geometric figure is the locus of all points in space equidistant from a point *P*?

8. What shape is formed by all the points in space 5 centimeters from a line, $\overleftrightarrow{RV}$? Name a familiar object that has this shape.

9. **What if** you consider only a segment of the line, $\overline{RV}$? Describe the locus of all points in space 2 millimeters from $\overline{RV}$. Name a familiar object that has this shape.

Summing Up

10. Think about the relationship between points and geometric figures. If a circle has a radius of 3 cm, what can you say about all the points of the circle?

11. If two lines are parallel, what is true of all the points on one line?

12. Marking a number of points helps you see the shape of a figure. How can you determine whether your sketch of a locus is correct?

How can you find out whether two line segments are congruent? How can you find out whether two angles are congruent?

Congruent Triangles

The triangles in this paper sculpture are congruent. Two triangles are congruent if corresponding sides and angles are congruent.

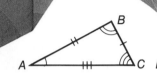

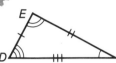

$\angle A \cong \angle F$ $\overline{AB} \cong \overline{EF}$
$\angle B \cong \angle E$ $\overline{BC} \cong \overline{ED}$
$\angle C \cong \angle D$ $\overline{AC} \cong \overline{DF}$

You can be sure that two triangles are congruent by using one of these three rules.

▶ **Side-Side-Side rule (SSS)**

Two triangles are congruent if their corresponding sides are congruent.

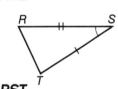

$\triangle FGH \cong \triangle XYZ$

▶ **Side-Angle-Side rule (SAS)**

Two triangles are congruent if two corresponding sides and the included angle are congruent.

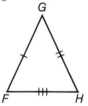 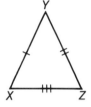

$\triangle CDE \cong \triangle RST$

▶ **Angle-Side-Angle rule (ASA)**

Two triangles are congruent if two corresponding angles and the included side are congruent.

 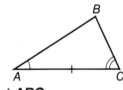

$\triangle MNO \cong \triangle ABC$

Which triangles are congruent to △ABC? Tell which rule applies.

1.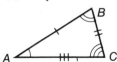

2.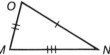

3.

Share Your Ideas   If you show that two triangles are congruent by Side-Angle-Side, what can you say about the other corresponding parts?

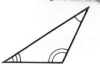

Which pairs of triangles are congruent? Tell which rule applies.

4.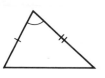

5.

6.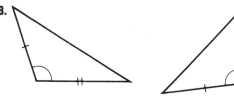

7.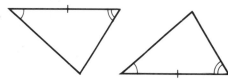

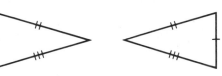

8.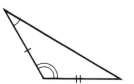

9.

10.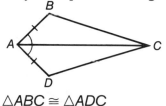

11.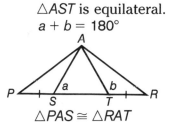

Tell why each pair of triangles is congruent.

12.
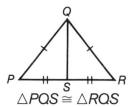
$\triangle ABC \cong \triangle ADC$

13.
$\triangle PQS \cong \triangle RQS$

14. $\triangle AST$ is equilateral.
$a + b = 180°$

$\triangle PAS \cong \triangle RAT$

Think and Apply

15. What if two corresponding angles and one side are congruent as shown? Are the triangles congruent? Why or why not?

16. Use a ruler and protractor to draw $\triangle ABC$ with $m\angle A = 45°$, $\overline{AB} = 5$ cm, and $\overline{BC} = 4$ cm. Is more than one drawing possible? How can you use this fact to explain why there is no SSA rule?

Visual Thinking

17. Draw and cut out two congruent triangles. Position them to form a parallelogram. How many different parallelograms can be made with any pair of congruent triangles?

Explain why there is no AAA rule. What can you say about two triangles whose corresponding angles are equal?

SUMMING UP

How can you show these figures are congruent?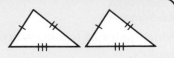

Constructing Congruent Figures

To draw congruent figures, a ruler, protractor, and other drawing instruments may be used. To **construct** congruent figures, only a compass and a straightedge may be used.

Follow these steps to construct a segment congruent to $\overline{LR}$.

| Draw any segment $\overline{PS}$, longer than $\overline{LR}$. 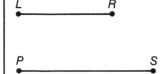 | Place the compass tip on L and draw an arc through R.  | Use the same compass opening. Place the compass tip on P and draw an arc intersecting $\overline{PS}$. Label D. $\overline{PD} \cong \overline{LR}$. 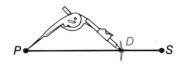 |

Explain why $\overline{PD}$ is congruent to $\overline{LR}$.

Follow these steps to construct an angle congruent to $\angle ABC$.

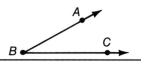

| Draw any ray, $\overrightarrow{DE}$. Place the compass tip on B and draw an arc intersecting $\overrightarrow{BA}$ and $\overrightarrow{BC}$. Label Q and P. Place the compass tip on D and use the same opening to draw an arc intersecting $\overrightarrow{DE}$. Label R. 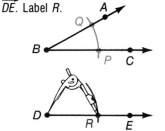 | Place the compass tip on P. Adjust the opening and draw an arc through Q. Use the same compass opening. Place the tip on R and draw a second arc intersecting the first. Label S. 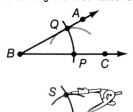 | Draw $\overrightarrow{DS}$. $\angle SDE \cong \angle ABC$ 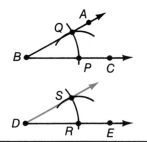 |

Trace each figure. Construct a figure congruent to each.

1.

2.

3.

Share Your Ideas   Look back at the angle construction above. How could you use congruent triangles to explain why $\angle SDE \cong \angle ABC$? Consider $\triangle QBP$ and $\triangle SDR$.

Trace each figure. Construct a figure congruent to each.

4. B   A

C

5.

F

D

6. K   E

R

**Use a ruler to draw a segment with the given length.
Then construct a congruent segment.**

7. 6 cm   **8.** 12 cm   **9.** 21 cm   **10.** 3.8 cm   **11.** 59 mm

**Use a protractor to draw an angle with the given measure.
Then construct a congruent angle.**

12. 15°   **13.** 31°   **14.** 120°   **15.** 61°   **16.** 145°

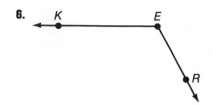

Look back at 4–6. Construct each figure.

17. Construct segment FK such that $\overline{FK}$ is twice as long as $\overline{FD}$.

18. Construct an angle, $\angle PST$, whose measure is the difference between the measures of $\angle KER$ and $\angle ABC$.

19. Construct an angle, $\angle RSP$, whose measure is the sum of $\angle ABC$ and the supplement of $\angle KER$.

Think and Apply

20. A designer adjusts a pattern to fit the customer's needs. The angle and line shown represent part of a pattern. Trace the figures in the positions shown and construct $\overleftrightarrow{PR}$ above $\overleftrightarrow{PQ}$ so that $\angle QPR$ is congruent to $\angle ABC$.

21. If $\overleftrightarrow{BA}$ and $\overleftrightarrow{PQ}$ are parallel, will $\overleftrightarrow{BC}$ be parallel to $\overleftrightarrow{PR}$? Explain your thinking. (Hint: Extend $\overleftrightarrow{BC}$ to intersect $\overleftrightarrow{PQ}$.)

P   Q

C

B

A

Explain how a compass is used in constructing congruent figures.

SUMMING UP

What does the word *bisect* mean? Use a dictionary to find the origins of the word.

Bisecting Figures

Corrine is working on a design for a paper airplane contest. She begins by folding a square piece of paper along the diagonal. The folded line is the angle bisector of the 90° angle.

▶ The **bisector** of a figure divides it into two congruent parts.

Follow these steps to construct the bisector of any segment, $\overline{BQ}$.

Open the compass slightly more than half the length of $\overline{BQ}$. With the tip on B, draw an arc intersecting $\overline{BQ}$.	Use the same compass opening. With the tip on Q, draw an arc intersecting $\overline{BQ}$. Label A and V.	Draw $\overrightarrow{AV}$. Label H. $\overrightarrow{AV}$ bisects $\overline{BQ}$, so H is the midpoint of $\overline{BQ}$. $\overline{BH} \cong \overline{HQ}$, $\overrightarrow{AV} \perp \overline{BQ}$ $\overline{AV}$ is the **perpendicular bisector** of $\overline{BQ}$.
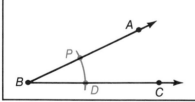	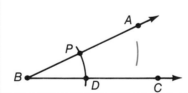	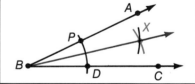

Follow these steps to construct the bisector of any angle, $\angle ABC$.

With the compass tip on B, draw an arc intersecting both rays. Label P and D.	With the compass tip on P, draw a second arc as shown.	Use the same compass opening. Place the tip on D and draw a third arc as shown. Label X. Draw $\overline{BX}$. $\angle ABX \cong \angle XBD$ $\overline{BX}$ is the **angle bisector** of $\angle ABC$.

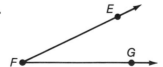

Trace each segment and angle. Extend the sides of the angles if necessary. Construct the bisector of each segment and angle.

1. C ... D

2. E ... F ... G

3. H ... I ... J

Share Your Ideas Look back at the constructions above. How is the length of $\overline{BQ}$ related to the length of $\overline{BH}$? How is m$\angle ABC$ related to m$\angle XBC$?

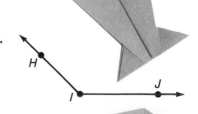

Trace each segment and angle. Extend the sides of the angles if necessary. Construct the bisector of each segment and angle.

4.

5.

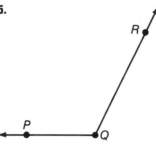

6.

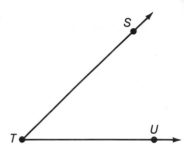

Use a ruler or protractor to draw each segment or angle. Construct each bisector.

7. 5 cm   **8.** 38 mm   **9.** 8 cm   **10.** 12.3 cm   **11.** 95 mm

12. 30°   **13.** 42°   **14.** 120°   **15.** 180°   **16.** 240°

Think and Apply

17. Use a protractor to draw a 160° angle. Then use that angle to construct a 40° angle.

18. Look back at **17.** Use a different method to construct a 40° angle.

The construction of a perpendicular bisector creates congruent triangles. Study the construction below. Think about how the compass settings are used.

19. Why is △PAQ congruent to △PBQ?

20. Why is ∠APQ congruent to ∠BPQ?

21. Why is △APR congruent to △BPR?

22. Why is $\overline{AR}$ congruent to $\overline{BR}$?

The construction of an angle bisector also creates congruent triangles.

23. Why is △YPR congruent to △YQR?

24. Why is ∠PYR congruent to ∠QYR?

How can you be sure that a construction bisects a segment or angle?

SUMMING UP

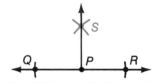

$\overleftrightarrow{AB} \perp \overrightarrow{DC}$ What can you say about ∠ABC and ∠ABD?

Constructing Perpendicular and Parallel Lines

Follow these steps to construct a line perpendicular to a given line through any point, *P*, on the line.

Place the compass tip on *P*. Draw two arcs that intersect the line, using the same compass opening. Label the intersections *Q* and *R*.	Draw two intersecting arcs from *Q* and *R*. Label *S*. Draw $\overleftrightarrow{SP}$. $\overleftrightarrow{SP} \perp \overleftrightarrow{QR}$

Follow these steps to construct a line perpendicular to a given line through any point, *P*, not on the line.

Place the compass tip on *P*. Draw an arc intersecting the line at two points. Label the intersections *Q* and *R*.	Do not change the compass opening. On the same side of the line, draw two intersecting arcs from *Q* and *R*. Label *S*. Draw $\overleftrightarrow{PS}$. $\overleftrightarrow{PS} \perp \overleftrightarrow{QR}$

Construct a line parallel to a given line, $\overleftrightarrow{RT}$.

Construct a line through *P* perpendicular to $\overleftrightarrow{RT}$. Label *Y*.	Construct a line through *Y* perpendicular to $\overleftrightarrow{PY}$. Label *X*. $\overleftrightarrow{YX} \parallel \overleftrightarrow{RT}$

Check Your Understanding

Construct each figure.

1. Draw $\overleftrightarrow{DL}$ and mark a point, *P*, 4 cm above $\overleftrightarrow{DL}$. Construct $\overleftrightarrow{PB}$ parallel to $\overleftrightarrow{DL}$.

2. Draw $\overleftrightarrow{ST}$ and mark a point, *P*, on $\overleftrightarrow{ST}$. Construct $\overleftrightarrow{QP}$ perpendicular to $\overleftrightarrow{ST}$.

Share Your Ideas   When parallel lines are cut by a transversal, pairs of congruent angles are formed. How can you use congruent angles to show that $\overleftrightarrow{DL} \parallel \overleftrightarrow{PB}$ in 1?

Trace each figure.

3. Construct a line perpendicular to $\overleftrightarrow{DC}$ through A.

4. Construct a line parallel to $\overleftrightarrow{DC}$ through A.

• A

D   C

5. Construct a line perpendicular to $\overleftrightarrow{AB}$ through J.

A   J   B

Construct each figure.

6. Draw a line AB. Construct $\overleftrightarrow{MA}$ perpendicular to $\overleftrightarrow{AB}$. Construct segment AD, congruent to segment AB, on $\overleftrightarrow{MA}$. Connect D and B. What figure is DAB?

7. Draw a line AB. Construct two lines perpendicular to $\overleftrightarrow{AB}$ through A and through B. Construct two segments, $\overline{AC}$ and $\overline{BD}$, congruent to segment AB. Connect C and D. What figure is ABDC?

8. Look back at **7.** Try to construct a different figure, following the directions given.

Think and Apply

9. The construction of perpendicular lines results in congruent triangles, as shown. Name the congruent triangles and tell which rule applies.

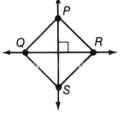

10. When parallel lines are cut by a transversal, alternate interior angles are congruent. How can you construct a line parallel to any line, $\overleftrightarrow{ST}$, by constructing congruent angles? (Hint: Draw any line intersecting $\overleftrightarrow{ST}$.)

$\overleftrightarrow{AB} \perp \overleftrightarrow{CD}$, and $\overleftrightarrow{AB} \perp \overleftrightarrow{FG}$. What can you say about $\overleftrightarrow{CD}$ and $\overleftrightarrow{FG}$? $\overleftrightarrow{RV} \parallel \overleftrightarrow{ST}$, and $\overleftrightarrow{RV} \parallel \overleftrightarrow{LM}$. What can you say about $\overleftrightarrow{ST}$ and $\overleftrightarrow{LM}$?

Mixed Review

1. $4.35 \cdot 6.1$

2. $66.381 \div 0.07$

3. $2.08 + 5.37$

4. $0.037 - 0.009$

5. $3.8 - {}^-4.2$

6. $^-6.30 + {}^-49.7$

7. $^-3.53 \cdot 6.9$

8. $^-187.98 \div 3.9$

Solve for n.

9. $\frac{3}{5} = \frac{n}{40}$

10. $\frac{n}{8} = \frac{7}{4}$

11. $\frac{6}{n} = \frac{8}{48}$

12. $\frac{1.8}{3} = \frac{n}{5}$

Estimate.

13. $5\frac{11}{12} + 3\frac{1}{8}$

14. $7\frac{1}{5} \cdot 4\frac{2}{3}$

15. $8\frac{7}{15} - 3\frac{9}{16}$

16. $7\frac{1}{4} \div 1\frac{11}{12}$

17. $\frac{7}{8} + \frac{3}{4}$

18. $\frac{5}{6} - \frac{1}{5}$

19. $16.27 - 11.9$

20. $13.89 + 4.09$

SUMMING UP

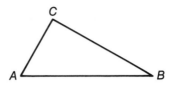

△ABC ≅ △STW   What does this tell you about sides and angles?

Constructing Congruent Triangles

Congruent triangles have corresponding parts that are congruent. You can use the rules for congruence to construct a triangle congruent to △ABC.

Using the SSS rule

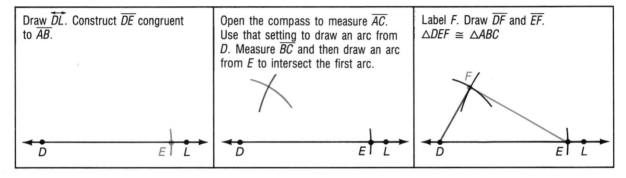

| Draw $\overleftrightarrow{DL}$. Construct $\overline{DE}$ congruent to $\overline{AB}$. | Open the compass to measure $\overline{AC}$. Use that setting to draw an arc from D. Measure $\overline{BC}$ and then draw an arc from E to intersect the first arc. | Label F. Draw $\overline{DF}$ and $\overline{EF}$. $\triangle DEF \cong \triangle ABC$ |

Using the ASA rule

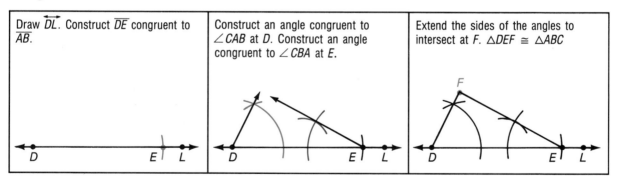

| Draw $\overleftrightarrow{DL}$. Construct $\overline{DE}$ congruent to $\overline{AB}$. | Construct an angle congruent to $\angle CAB$ at D. Construct an angle congruent to $\angle CBA$ at E. | Extend the sides of the angles to intersect at F. $\triangle DEF \cong \triangle ABC$ |

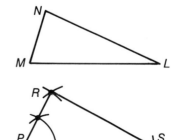

Construct a triangle congruent to △LMN.

1. Use the SSS rule.   2. Use the ASA rule.

Study the construction of △PRS.

3. List the steps used to construct △PRS congruent to △ABC above, using the SAS rule.

Share Your Ideas   Explain why there are an infinite number of triangles with angle measures of 30°, 60°, and 90°.

Trace each of these triangles and construct a congruent triangle.

4. Use SSS.

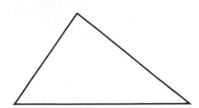

5. Use ASA.

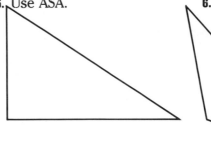

6. Use SAS.

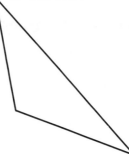

Use the given segments and angles for 7–10.

7. Construct an equilateral triangle, using $\overline{EF}$.

8. Construct a triangle, using $\overline{AB}$ and $\overline{CD}$ as sides and angle PQR as the angle between these sides.

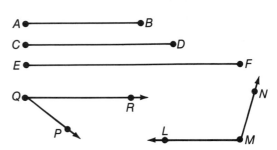

9. Construct a triangle, using angles PQR and LMN and $\overline{AB}$ as the side between them.

10. Construct a triangle, using $\overline{AB}$, $\overline{CD}$, and $\overline{EF}$. How many different triangles can you construct?

Trace each figure and construct a figure congruent to it. Use triangles to do the construction.

11.

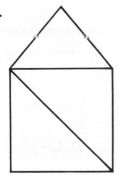

12.

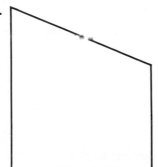

★13.

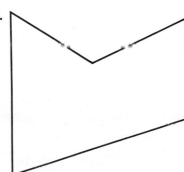

What measures do you need to construct a triangle congruent to a given triangle?

SUMMING UP

ABCD is a regular polygon. What do you know about the sides and angles of ABCD?

Constructing Polygons

Geometric designs can be found in decorative art, industrial designs, and corporate logos. Many of these complex designs are based on polygon constructions.

Follow these steps to construct a rectangle, *RSTV*, with sides congruent to $\overline{AB}$ and $\overline{CD}$.

1. Construct $\overline{RS}$ congruent to $\overline{AB}$.

2. Construct $\overline{RV}$ and $\overline{ST}$ congruent to $\overline{CD}$ and perpendicular to $\overline{AB}$.

3. Connect *T* and *V*.

How do you know *RSTV* is a rectangle?

Follow these steps to construct a regular hexagon, *ABCDEF*, with sides congruent to $\overline{GH}$.

1. Construct a circle with radius $\overline{OA}$ congruent to $\overline{GH}$.

2. Using the same compass setting, mark six arcs around the circumference.

3. Connect the points in order as shown.

Check Your Understanding

Use the figures shown.

1. Construct a rectangle with sides congruent to $\overline{AB}$ and $\overline{CD}$.

2. Construct a square with sides congruent to $\overline{AB}$.

3. Construct a regular hexagon with sides congruent to $\overline{AB}$.

Share Your Ideas Look back at the hexagon construction. How could you use it to construct equilateral triangles?

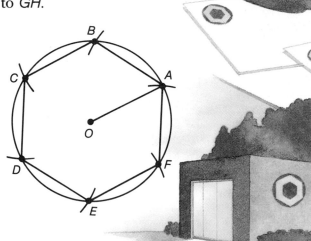

Copy the figures shown for 4–7.

4. Construct a square with sides congruent to $\overline{EF}$.

5. Construct a rectangle with sides congruent to $\overline{CD}$ and $\overline{EF}$.

6. Construct a regular hexagon with sides congruent to $\overline{AB}$.

7. Construct a parallelogram with sides congruent to $\overline{AB}$ and $\overline{CD}$ and an angle congruent to $\angle PSR$.

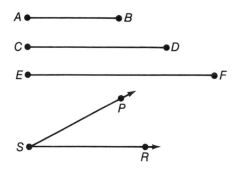

Copy △RST and use it for 8–10.

8. Construct the perpendicular bisector of each side of △RST. Extend the bisectors to intersect at a point, P.

9. Construct a circle with center at P and R on the circumference.

10. What do you notice about circle P and △RST?

11. Copy △RST again and construct the altitude to each side. What do you notice?

12. Draw any triangle you choose. Repeat the construction in **11**. What seems to be true about the altitudes of a triangle?

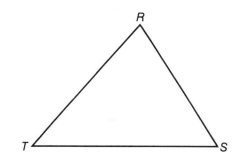

13. **Look back** at the construction of a regular hexagon on page 412. Explain why △OAB is an equilateral triangle.

14. Describe how you could construct a regular hexagon without drawing a circle.

15. Create your own design, using polygon constructions. Exchange it with a classmate and describe how his or her design was made.

16. Is the conclusion true? *RSTV* is a quadrilateral. m$\angle RST = 90°$ $\overline{RS}$ is not parallel to $\overline{TV}$. Therefore, *RSTV* is a trapezoid.

List the basic constructions that are used in the construction of polygons.

SUMMING UP

Using Problem Solving

Topology

Topology is the study of the properties of shapes. These properties are not changed when the figures are stretched or twisted.

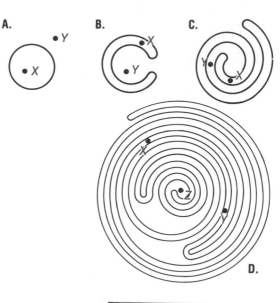

A.

B.

C.

A. In the figures **A**, **B**, and **C**, *X* is inside the figure and *Y* is outside. Look at figure *D*. The letter *X* is outside the shape. If it were moved across one line, would it be inside or outside the figure? What if *X* were moved across 2 lines? Would it be inside or outside?

B. The letter *Y* is inside the figure. What happens if you move *Y* across one line? across two lines?

C. Look at *Z*. If you move it straight to where *Y* is, how many lines does it cross?

D. Look at figure *E*. The edges have been covered so that you cannot tell which is the inside or the outside of the figure. If *X* is inside the figure, is *Y* inside or outside? What about *Z*?

E. Draw an irregular figure. Place two letters inside the figure and one outside it. Cover or erase the edges. Exchange your drawing with a partner. Tell your partner which letter is inside the figure. Your partner is to determine whether the other letters are inside or outside the figure.

D.

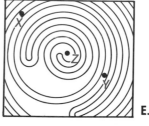

E.

Sharing Your Ideas

1. A letter that is inside a figure crosses how many lines when moved outside the figure? A letter that is outside a figure crosses how many lines when it is moved inside a figure?

2. A letter that stays either inside or outside crosses how many lines?

Practice

3. Figure F has 2 T–intersections at **A** and **B.** Copy the figure. Then begin to trace this figure. Each time you connect with a point that you have already drawn, you have completed one path. Can you trace the entire figure with only one path? If not, how many did you need?

4. Look at figures **G** and **H.** How many T–intersections does each have? How many paths must you draw to complete each figure?

5. Make several figures like these with T–intersections. (Don't forget T–intersections on the side.) Exchange them with a partner. Try to guess how many paths it will take to trace the figure, considering the number of T–intersections.

F.

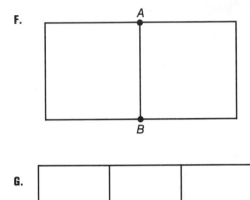

G.

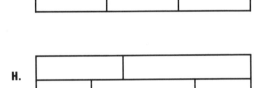

H.

Summing Up

6. Did you see a pattern? If so, what is it?

Chapter Review

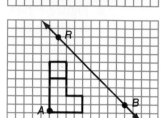

Write *reflection, translation,* or *rotation*. pages 390–395

1. A to B **2.** A to C **3.** A to D

Copy the figure on grid paper. Draw each transformation on the figure. pages 390–395

4. down 2, right 3 **5.** Rotate $\frac{1}{2}$ turn CW about A. **6.** Reflect about $\overleftrightarrow{RB}$.

Construct each figure. pages 404–409

7. Construct $\overline{RT}$ congruent to $\overline{DS}$.

8. Construct the bisector of $\overline{RT}$.

9. Construct $\angle LMO$ congruent to $\angle ABC$.

10. Construct the bisector of $\angle LMO$.

11. Draw a line, $\overleftrightarrow{AM}$, and mark a point, R, 5 cm above the line. Construct a line through R parallel to $\overleftrightarrow{AM}$.

12. Draw a line, $\overleftrightarrow{MA}$. Mark a point, X, on the line and a point, Y, 4 cm above the line. Through each point, construct a line perpendicular to $\overleftrightarrow{MA}$.

Construct triangles congruent to △*KLM*. pages 402–403, 410–411

13. Use the SSS rule. **14.** Use the SAS rule.

Construct each polygon. Draw segments *AB* (3 cm), *CD* (5 cm), and *EF* (7 cm). pages 412–413

15. a rectangle with sides congruent to $\overline{AB}$ and $\overline{CD}$.

16. a regular hexagon with sides congruent to $\overline{AB}$.

Complete.

17. A construction is done with _____ and _____ only.

18. A design that covers a plane by repeating the same figure is a _____.

19. If two lines intersect to form four equal angles, the lines are _____.

Words to Know
perpendicular
straightedge
tessellation
compass   ruler
transformation
protractor

Solve. pages 397–399

20. An architect wants to construct two lines through P. One of the lines must be parallel to $\overleftrightarrow{SL}$ and the other must be perpendicular to $\overleftrightarrow{SL}$. Show how the architect can construct those lines.

21. Can these statements both be true? *ABCD* is a quadrilateral. *ABCD* is not a parallelogram.

Chapter Test

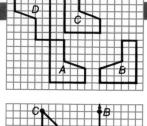

Write *reflection, translation,* or *rotation.*

1. *A* to *B*   **2.** *A* to *C*   **3.** *A* to *D*

Copy the figure on grid paper. Draw each transformation of the figure.

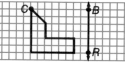

4. up 3, right 4   **5.** Rotate $\frac{1}{4}$ turn CW about *C.*   **6.** Reflect about $\overleftrightarrow{RB}$.

A figure has coordinates (⁻1, ⁻2), (4, 2), (4, 3), (⁻1, ⁻1). Name the new coordinates.

7. The figure is reflected about the *x*-axis.   **8.** The figure is reflected about the *y*-axis.

A figure has coordinates (2, 2), (⁻1, 2), (0, 1), (1, 1). Draw the figure on grid paper.

9. Draw the reflection of the figure about the *x*-axis.

10. Draw the reflection of the figure about the *y*-axis.

Construct each figure. Use ∠*RQB*.

11. Construct a line segment $\overline{ST}$ congruent to $\overline{QB}$.

12. Construct the bisector of $\overline{ST}$.

13. Construct an angle, ∠*ABC*, congruent to ∠*RQB*.

14. Construct the bisector of ∠*ABC*.

15. Draw a line, $\overleftrightarrow{LM}$, and mark a point, *A*, 3 cm above the line. Construct a line through *A* parallel to $\overleftrightarrow{LM}$.

16. Draw a line, $\overleftrightarrow{ST}$. Mark a point, *B*, on the line and a point, *C*, 5 cm above the line. Through each point, construct a line perpendicular to $\overleftrightarrow{ST}$.

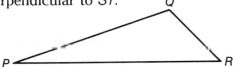

Construct each figure. Use △*PQR*.

17. a regular hexagon with sides congruent to $\overline{PR}$

18. a triangle congruent to △*PQR*

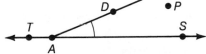

Solve. Use the figure at the right for 19.

19. An artist is laying out a design. She wants to construct $\overleftrightarrow{LM}$ through *P* parallel to $\overleftrightarrow{TS}$ and to construct an angle equal to ∠*SAD* with one ray on $\overleftrightarrow{LM}$ and *P* as a vertex. Show how she could do the construction.

20. Can these statements both be true?
$\overleftrightarrow{AB} \perp \overleftrightarrow{CB}$ m∠*CBA* = 180°

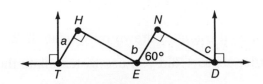

THINK   △*THE* ≅ △*END*   Find *a, b,* and *c.*

417

Computer Link

Coordinates and Geometric Motions

You can use the rectangular coordinate system in Logo to move the turtle to different points on the screen. SETPOS [0 0] moves the turtle to the center of the screen.

AT THE COMPUTER

Materials: Logo

A. Define the procedure T that graphs transformations of points. Then enter T 0 0. What are the coordinates of the vertices of the triangle that is drawn?

```
TO T :A :B
PU SETPOS LIST 10+:A 15+:B
PD SETPOS LIST 60+:A 40+:B
SETPOS LIST 60+:A 15+:B
SETPOS LIST 10+:A 15+:B
END
```

B. Now call T with each pair of inputs shown below. Then try your own inputs. Compare the figures you drew. How are they alike? How are they different?

- T 0 40
- T -70 0
- T -70 40
- T 30 40

C. The coordinates for the points graphed by T 30 40 are computed by adding 30 to each x coordinate and 40 to each y coordinate. Write expressions for the x and y coordinates in each transformation.

T 30 40: $(x, y) \rightarrow (x + 30, y + 40)$
T -70 0: $(x, y) \rightarrow ($ _____ , _____ $)$
T -70 40: $(x, y) \rightarrow ($ _____ , _____ $)$

D. How would you use T to tessellate the plane?

Sharing Your Results

1. The transformation of points defined by T is called a translation. Does a translation correspond to movement of an object in the plane? If so, describe the properties of such a movement.

2. How are all triangles drawn by T related? Why?

3. What inputs to T did you use to tessellate the plane?

Extending the Activity

Other transformations can be defined by multiplying coordinates of points.

4. Edit the T procedure and define the M procedure. Enter M 1 1. What are the coordinates of the vertices of the triangle that is drawn?

```
TO M :A :B
PU SETPOS LIST 10*:A 15*:B
PD SETPOS LIST 60*:A 40*:B
SETPOS LIST 60*:A 15*:B
SETPOS LIST 10*:A 15*:B
END
```

5. **a.** Enter M with inputs for A and B as shown.

   ● M -1 1   ● M 1 -1   ● M -1 -1

   b. Complete each expression to describe how the coordinates were computed. Describe each transformation represented. Do any of them correspond to movement of an object?

   Motion

   M -1 1: (x, y) ⟶ (_____, _____)   _____

   M 1 -1: (x, y) ⟶ (_____, _____)   _____

   M -1 -1: (x, y) ⟶ (_____, _____)   _____

6. **a.** Enter M with inputs for A and B as shown.

   ● M 2 2   ● M 2 1   ● M 1 2   ● M 1 -2

   b. Describe each transformation represented. Do any of them correspond to moving an object? How are these triangles different from those drawn in 5?

7. Try different values for the inputs to M. Classify the triangles that are drawn according to the input values.

Summing Up

8. What operations on coordinates transform a figure into a congruent figure?

9. Try this challenge. Describe the transformation that is defined by this expression. Are figures transformed into congruent figures?

   (x, y) ⟶ (y, x)

Transformations:
Expansion and Reduction

An **expansion** is a transformation that creates a larger similar figure.

Square B at the right is an expansion of square A.

The coordinates of the vertices of square A are (1,1), (2,1), (2,2), and (1,2).

What are the coordinates of the vertices of square B? By what factor has each coordinate of square A been increased?

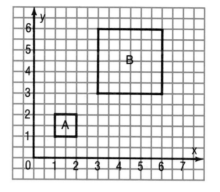

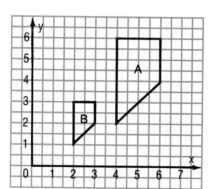

A **reduction** is a transformation that creates a smaller similar figure.

Trapezoid B at the left is a reduction of trapezoid A.

By what factor has each coordinate of trapezoid A been reduced?

Graph an expansion and a reduction for each figure, using the indicated operation on each coordinate.

1.

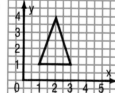

   a. Multiply by 3.

   b. Multiply by $\frac{1}{2}$.

2.

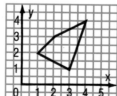

   a. Multiply by 2.

   b. Multiply by $\frac{1}{3}$.

3.

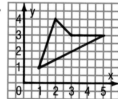

   a. Multiply by 4.

   b. Multiply by $\frac{1}{2}$.

4. Look back at **2. What if** the transformation was formed by multiplying each coordinate by ⁻2? How would the figure be different? Try it and describe your results.

Maintaining Skills

Choose the correct answer. Write A, B, C, or D.

1. What is 3.2% written as a decimal?

   A 0.32   **C** 3.2

   B 0.032   **D** not given

2. What is $\frac{1}{400}$ written as a percent?

   A 40%   **C** 25%

   B 2.5%   **D** not given

3. What is 55% of 20?

   A 11   **C** 1.1

   B 22   **D** not given

4. Find n. 30% of $n = 21$.

   A $n = 6.3$ **C** $n = 70$

   B $n = 7$ **D** not given

5. What is the interest if the principal is $840, the rate is 10%, and the time is 2.5 yr?

   A $84.00   **C** $210.00

   B $168.00   **D** not given

6. What is the area?

   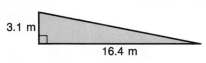
   3.1 m
   16.4 m

   A 50.84 m^2 **C** 101.68 m^2

   B 25.42 m^2 **D** not given

7. What is the area? Use $\pi \approx 3.14$.

   9 cm

   A 254.34 cm^2 **C** 56.52 cm^2

   B 28.26 cm^2 **D** not given

8. Cards with the names of each month are placed in a bag. A card is drawn and then replaced. What is the probability of choosing a month beginning with the letter J and then a month beginning with the letter M?

   A $\frac{1}{72}$ **C** $\frac{1}{144}$

   B $\frac{1}{24}$ **D** not given

9. Evaluate. $\frac{7!}{3!}$

   A 840   **C** 210

   B 2,520   **D** not given

10. How many ways are there to choose 3 out of 5 problems?

    A 60   **C** 20

    B 10   **D** not given

11. What transformation is illustrated?

    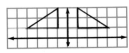

    A rotation   **C** translation

    B reflection   **D** not given

Solve.

12. Earl needs a quarter for a parking meter. He changes a dollar bill and receives at least one quarter and nickels. How many different ways could he receive change?

    A 3   **C** 5

    B 6   **D** not given

13. **What if** he receives at least one quarter and dimes and nickels in change? How many different ways could he then receive change?

    A 20   **C** 13

    B 21   **D** not given

Pre-Algebra: Equations and Inequalities

THEME Traveling Around the World

Sharing What You Know

What birds, animals, or fish migrate long distances? Discuss some of the migratory paths of these creatures. Some animals, such as frogs and toads, travel only short distances between their summer homes and winter homes; others, such as the arctic tern, can migrate as many as 11,000 miles! Monarch butterflies leave Canada and the northern United States to winter in California and Mexico, traveling distances of about 2,000 miles. What are some ways that people migrate? Why might people want to change environments?

Using Language

Migrating creatures follow paths back and forth between two points. We could say that these paths are **inverses** of each other. In mathematics, **inverse operations** undo each other. For example, multiplication and division are inverse operations and addition and subtraction are inverse operations. Explain in your own words what **inverse** means.

Words to Know additive inverse, multiplicative inverse, Identity Property of Addition, inequality

Be a Problem Solver

Pick a number greater than zero. Add 5; multiply by 3; subtract 15; divide by 3. What is your answer? Will you get a different answer if you start with a different number? Why or why not?

Write a description of a migration route you would follow if you were a migrating creature. Give your reasons for choosing that route.

How are these related?
a gain of 10 yards and a loss of 10 yards
borrowing two dollars and repaying two dollars

Inverses

When Gary traveled from New York to London, he set his watch ahead 5 hours. On the return trip he set his watch back 5 hours.

$^+5$ and $^-5$ are additive inverses or opposites.

► The additive inverse of a is ^-a.
Additive Inverse Property The sum of a number and its additive inverse is zero.

$$5 + {}^-5 = 0 \qquad \frac{-1}{2} + \frac{1}{2} = 0 \qquad a + {}^-a = 0$$

► The multiplicative inverse of a is its reciprocal, $\frac{1}{a}$.
5 and $\frac{1}{5}$ are multiplicative inverses.
Multiplicative Inverse Property The product of a number and its multiplicative inverse is 1.

$$5 \cdot \frac{1}{5} = 1 \qquad \frac{-2}{3} \cdot \frac{-3}{2} = 1 \qquad a \cdot \frac{1}{a} = 1$$

Zero does not have a multiplicative inverse. Why?

► Study these examples to review the properties of addition and multiplication.

Property	of Addition	of Multiplication
Identity	$\frac{3}{4} + 0 = \frac{3}{4}$	$\frac{-1}{6} \cdot 1 = \frac{-1}{6}$
Commutative	$3 + {}^-5 = {}^-5 + 3$	$2 \cdot \frac{1}{4} = \frac{1}{4} \cdot 2$
Associative	$\frac{1}{2} + \left(4 + \frac{1}{8}\right) = \left(\frac{1}{2} + 4\right) + \frac{1}{8}$	$\frac{1}{2} \cdot \left(\frac{2}{3} \cdot \frac{3}{4}\right) = \left(\frac{1}{2} \cdot \frac{2}{3}\right) \cdot \frac{3}{4}$
Distributive	$2(3 + {}^-5) = (2 \cdot 3) + (2 \cdot {}^-5)$	

Check Your Understanding

Write the additive inverse and multiplicative inverse for each.

1. $^-3$ 2. $\frac{3}{8}$ 3. $\frac{-2}{5}$ 4. 12   5. $^-3\frac{1}{2}$ 6. 1

Identify the property illustrated.

7. $5 + 7 = 7 + 5$ 8. $\frac{2}{3} \cdot \frac{3}{2} = 1$ 9. $4(1 + 6) = 4 + 24$ 10. $3 \cdot (5 \cdot 2) = (3 \cdot 5) \cdot 2$

Share Your Ideas Explain how inverses are related to the Identity Property of Addition and the Identity Property of Multiplication.

Write the additive and the multiplicative inverse for each.

11. $^-2$ 12. $\frac{1}{5}$ 13. $\frac{4}{7}$ 14. 34 15. $^-2\frac{2}{5}$ 16. $^-1.7$

Name the property illustrated.

17. $\frac{3}{5} + 0 = \frac{3}{5}$ 18. $\frac{^-1}{2} + \frac{1}{2} = 0$ 19. $\frac{7}{8} + \frac{1}{8} = \frac{1}{8} + \frac{7}{8}$ 20. $3 \cdot \frac{1}{2} = \frac{1}{2} \cdot 3$

21. $\frac{^-3}{4} \cdot \frac{^-4}{3} = 1$ 22. $\frac{1}{5} \cdot 1 = \frac{1}{5}$ 23. $\frac{1}{5} \cdot 5 = 1$ 24. $2 + (7 + 9) = (2 + 7) + 9$

25. $(3 \cdot 4) + (3 \cdot 1) = 3(4 + 1)$ 26. $2(7 + {}^-1) = (2 \cdot 7) + (2 \cdot {}^-1)$

Choose the correct answer. Write a, b, c, or d.

27. The additive inverse of $3\frac{1}{2}$ is _____.

   a. $\frac{7}{2}$ b. $\frac{^-7}{2}$
   c. $\frac{^-2}{7}$ d. $\frac{2}{7}$

28. 2 is an inverse of _____.

   a. $\frac{1}{2}$, not $^-2$ b. $^-2$, not $\frac{1}{2}$
   c. $\frac{^-1}{2}$ and $\frac{1}{2}$ d. $^-2$ and $\frac{1}{2}$

29. A number n is less than zero. The additive inverse of n is _____.

   a. positive   b. greater than n
   c. negative   d. a and b

30. The Multiplicative Inverse Property is shown by _____.

   a. $\frac{^-1}{10} \cdot {}^-10 = 1$ b. $\frac{^-1}{10} \cdot 10 = {}^-1$
   c. $1 \cdot \frac{1}{10} = \frac{1}{10} \cdot 1$ d. a and b

Think and Apply

31. Find the additive inverse of the multiplicative inverse of $\frac{^-3}{4}$.

32. Find the multiplicative inverse of the additive inverse of $\frac{^-3}{4}$.

Visual Thinking

33. Place tracing paper over each route. Is there a path that you can follow to trace the route without lifting your pencil or retracing any part? If there is, the route is an Euler ("oiler") path. Which are Euler paths?

34. For each Euler path, count the number of line segments or arcs that meet at your starting and ending points. What pattern do you find?

a.   b.   c.

d.   e.   f.

Use a number line to graph $^-2$, 5, the additive inverse of each, and the multiplicative inverse of each. Describe your results.

SUMMING UP

Find each sum.
a. $4 + {}^-4$ **b.** $5 + {}^-7$ **c.** ${}^-2 + {}^-3$ **d.** $4 + {}^-1$

Adding to Solve Equations

The Galapagos Islands host thousands of visitors each year. The islands are named for their giant tortoises. Today eleven subspecies of tortoises are native to the Galapagos. Three have become extinct. How many subspecies were there originally?

You can write an equation to find out.
Let x = original number of subspecies.

$x - 3 = 11$	Rewrite the equation using addition.
$x + {}^-3 = 11$	The additive inverse of ${}^-3$ is 3.
$x + {}^-3 + 3 = 11 + 3$	Add 3 to both sides of the equation.
$x + 0 = 14$	Simplify.
$x = 14$	Solution

Check $14 - 3 = 11$ Replace x with 14 in the original equation.

There were originally 14 subspecies of tortoises.

What if you get a false statement when you check. What should you do?

More Examples

a.
$$n + 5.2 = {}^-2.9$$
$$n + 5.2 + {}^-5.2 = {}^-2.9 + {}^-5.2$$
$$n = {}^-8.1$$

Check ${}^-8.1 + 5.2 = {}^-2.9$

b. Fifteen is six less than y.
$$15 = y - 6$$
$$15 = y + {}^-6$$
$$15 + 6 = y + {}^-6 + 6$$
$$21 = y \qquad \text{**Check** } 15 = 21 - 6$$

Check Your Understanding

Solve and check.

1. $x + 9 = 37$

2. $w + 28 = {}^-7$

3. $n - 5 = {}^-7$

4. $x - 9 = {}^-12$

5. ${}^-13 + y = 10$

6. $15 = {}^-9 + n$

7. $c - 5\frac{1}{2} = 0$

8. $8 = d - 3.1$

Share Your Ideas Look back at example **b.** Does the solution $21 = y$ mean the same as $y = 21$? Could you have written the original equation as $y - 6 = 15$? Why or why not?

Solve and check.

9. $n + 9 = 15$

10. $x - 24 = 7$

11. $y + 2 = {}^-11$

12. $t - 5 = {}^-3$

13. $x + 11 = 0$

14. $n - 10 = 0$

15. $5 = y + 1$

16. $3 = y - 1$

17. $y - 1 = {}^-6$

18. $t + 2 = {}^-21$

19. ${}^-17 = y + 1$

20. ${}^-23 = n - 2$

21. ${}^-15 + x = {}^-3$

22. ${}^-11 + y = {}^-11$

23. ${}^-5 + x = 0$

24. $4 + x = 0$

25. $n + 32 = {}^-17$

26. $x - 25 = {}^-20$

27. $34 + d = {}^-1$

28. $51 + n = {}^-23$

29. ${}^-25 + x = {}^-13$

30. ${}^-31 + d = 17$

31. ${}^-21 = 8 + y$

32. ${}^-43 = {}^-10 + n$

33. $n + 2.1 = 10.2$

34. $n - 5.2 = 17.9$

35. $x - 2\frac{1}{2} = \frac{1}{2}$

36. $y + 1\frac{3}{4} = 2$

Write an equation for each sentence. Then solve.

37. A number n plus 5 equals 12.

38. A number x minus 2 equals 10.

39. The sum of a number y and 3 is ${}^-1$.

40. The difference of a number n and 5 is 6.

41. 5 more than a number x is 20.

42. 2 less than a number m is 11.

43. 14 is 2 more than a number x.

44. 27 is 5 less than a number y.

45. The sum of a number n and ${}^-17$ is 23 more than ${}^-75$.

46. The difference of a number x and 25 is 4 less than 18.

Think and Apply

47. The Galapagos National Park affords wildlife 2,800 more square miles of land than it does people who live on the islands. If people occupy 100 square miles, what is the area of the Galapagos Islands?

48. The sea temperature in the Galapagos was raised as much as 18°F in the 1980s following a climatic change called El Niño. If the water temperature was 88°F after El Niño, what was the normal sea temperature near the islands?

49. The marine iguana is a reptile that is found only in the Galapagos Islands. It is 3 to 4 feet in length and weighs about 20 pounds. Galapagos tortoises weigh as much as 500 pounds. How many times greater is the weight of a tortoise than the weight of an iguana?

Explain how you can use an additive inverse to solve an equation.

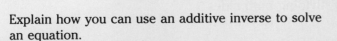

If three times a number equals ⁻21, is the number positive or negative? How do you know?

Multiplying to Solve Equations

When Julie traveled to France, she exchanged 10 dollars for 62 French francs. How many francs did she get for each dollar?

Let n = number of francs exchanged for 1 dollar.

$$10n = 62$$
$$\frac{1}{10} \cdot 10n = \frac{1}{10} \cdot 62$$
$$n = 6.2$$

The multiplicative inverse of 10 is $\frac{1}{10}$.

Multiply both sides of the equation by $\frac{1}{10}$.

Solution

Check $10 \cdot 6.2 = 62$ Replace n with 6.2 in the original equation.

Julie received 6.2 French francs for each dollar.

More Examples

a. Two thirds of a number is ⁻32. Find the number.

Let n = the number.

$$\frac{2}{3}n = {}^-32$$
$$\frac{3}{2} \cdot \frac{2}{3}n = \frac{3}{2} \cdot {}^-32$$
$$n = {}^-48$$

Check $\frac{2}{3} \cdot {}^-48 = {}^-32$

b. The quotient of a number and ⁻5 is 9. Find the number.

Let x = the number.

$$-\frac{x}{5} = 9$$
$$-\frac{1}{5}x = 9$$
$$-5 \cdot -\frac{1}{5}x = {}^-5 \cdot 9$$
$$x = {}^-45$$

Check $-\frac{{}^-45}{5} = 9$

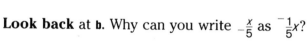

Look back at **b.** Why can you write $-\frac{x}{5}$ as $-\frac{1}{5}x$?

Solve and check.

1. $4x = {}^-32$ **2.** $^-3n = {}^-12$ **3.** $\frac{1}{2}x = 10$ **4.** $5 = \frac{5}{8}y$

5. $\frac{n}{3} = {}^-27$ **6.** $^-42 = 6x$ **7.** $^-4x = 0$ **8.** $14y = {}^-14$

9. $^-2 = \frac{y}{-2}$ **10.** $\frac{3}{4}x = 24$ **11.** $1\frac{1}{3}y = 4$ **12.** $1.6n = 8$

Share Your Ideas   Is multiplying by $\frac{1}{3}$ the same as dividing by 3? Can you solve $3x = 30$ by dividing both sides of the equation by 3? Explain.

Solve and check.

13. $3x = 27$

14. $^-5y = 5$

15. $6x = {}^-18$

16. $^-2x = {}^-40$

17. $\frac{1}{3}n = 5$

18. $\frac{3}{4}x = {}^-12$

19. $\frac{x}{5} = 2$

20. $\frac{a}{^-2} = 7$

21. $48 = 16x$

22. $51 = {}^-3n$

23. $10y = 0$

24. $0 = {}^-5y$

25. $14x = {}^-56$

26. $^-15x = {}^-75$

27. $21n = {}^-105$

28. $^-33x = 99$

29. $\frac{2}{3}x = 24$

30. $30 = \frac{1}{2}x$

31. $35 = \frac{1}{7}n$

32. $\frac{x}{10} = 10$

33. $37x = 0$

34. $^-2.4n = {}^-7.2$

35. $\frac{1}{2}x = 2.5$

36. $0.25x = \frac{1}{2}$

Write an equation for each. Then solve and check.

37. Three times a number n is 45. Find the number.

38. What number n divided by 2 equals 9?

39. The product of a number x and $^-5$ is $^-60$. Find x.

40. The quotient of a number y and $^-5$ equals the difference of 21 and $^-17$.

Think and Apply

The first world travelers by hot air balloon were Jean François Pilâtre de Rozier and François Laurent. A replica of their balloon is shown soaring above the Eiffel Tower.

41. In the race to commemorate the bicentennial of their historic flight, 16 balloons were launched. The race was won by a flight of 428 miles. The second-place winner traveled 326 miles. How many miles greater was the winning flight?

42. The sway at the top of the Eiffel Tower has never been more than 12 cm. The height of the tower can vary 1.25 times as much as the sway, depending on air temperature. How much can the height of the Eiffel Tower vary?

Look back at **37–40**. If you substitute your answer in the equation you wrote, can you be sure your answer is correct? Why or why not?

SUMMING UP

How would you solve $n + 5 = 11$? How would you solve $3n = 9$?

Two-Step Equations

The American Indian Theater Group has performed around the world. Member artists perform dance and music from some of the 430 Native American tribes in the United States. Sixteen more than 23 times the number of tribes represented equals the total number of tribes in the country. Find the number of tribes that the theater group represents.

Let t = number of tribes.

$$23t + 16 = 430$$
$$23t + 16 + {}^-16 = 430 + {}^-16$$
$$\frac{1}{23} \cdot 23t = \frac{1}{23} \cdot 414$$
$$t = 18$$

Use the additive inverse first.
Simplify.

Then use the multiplicative inverse.
Solution

Check $23(18) + 16 = 430$

The theater group represents 18 Native American tribes.

More Examples

a.
$$\frac{2x}{3} - 6 = {}^-14$$
$$\frac{2}{3}x + {}^-6 = {}^-14$$
$$\frac{2}{3}x + {}^-6 + 6 = {}^-14 + 6$$
$$\frac{3}{2} \cdot \frac{2}{3}x = \frac{3}{2} \cdot {}^-8$$
$$x = {}^-12$$

b.
$$-51 = 5 - 7n$$
$$^-51 = 5 + {}^-7n$$
$$^-51 + {}^-5 = 5 + {}^-5 + {}^-7n$$
$$^-56 = {}^-7n$$
$$\frac{^-1}{7} \cdot {}^-56 = \frac{^-1}{7} \cdot {}^-7n$$
$$8 = n$$

Check $\frac{2({}^-12)}{3} - 6 = {}^-14$

Check $^-51 = 5 - 7(8)$

Look back at **b.** Explain why $5 - 7n$ can be written as $5 + {}^-7n$.

Check Your Understanding

Solve and check. Explain your work.

1. $5x - 6 = 9$

2. $\frac{1}{2}n + 3 = 4$

3. $3 = 2y + 1$

4. $0 = 4 - 4x$

5. $2x + 3 = 13$

6. $4n - 1 = 19$

7. $5 = 3x + 2$

8. $11 = 5a - 19$

9. $7 - 5x = 37$

10. $\frac{y}{3} + 9 = 12$

11. $^-\frac{3}{4}x - 3 = {}^-15$

12. $0 = {}^-6x - 18$

Share Your Ideas Look back at **12**. Do you have to rewrite -18 as $+ {}^-18$? Explain how you can use the inverse operations of addition and subtraction.

Solve and check.

13. $5n + 12 = 42$

14. $7x - 13 = 15$

15. $5y - 8 = 2$

16. $^-9 = 4m + 7$

17. $^-3z - 15 = 0$

18. $9n + 6 = ^-12$

19. $8 - 11x = ^-47$

20. $7 - 5x = ^-28$

21. $4n - 7 = 13$

22. $12 - x = 12$

23. $^-x - 9 = 10$

24. $^-n + 2 = ^-11$

25. $\frac{w}{4} + 2 = 5$

26. $\frac{n}{3} + 11 = 8$

27. $\frac{2n}{3} - 16 = 0$

28. $\frac{-3x}{5} + 12 = 72$

Write an equation for each. Then solve.

29. 5 more than 2 times a number n is 11.

30. 11 less than 5 times a number x is 14.

31. One third of a number y minus 2 is 15 more than $^-10$.

32. Twenty plus the quotient of a number n and 7 is 7.

Think and Apply

33. Sixty students who attended a performance of the American Indian Theater Group voted for their favorite dance. Six more than two times the number of votes for the hoop dance equals the number of students who attended. How many students chose the hoop dance?

34. Native Americans renewed traditional dances and songs at the forty-eighth annual powwow that was held in 1989 at White Eagle, Oklahoma. In what year was the first annual gathering held?

Try to solve $2x + 3 = 5$ by first using the multiplicative inverse. Is that way easier or harder than first using the additive inverse? Explain.

Mixed Review

1. 3.5×6.24

2. $62.78 \div 4.3$

3. $0.0043 + 0.0327$

4. $1.003 - 0.078$

5. $3\frac{1}{2} - 1\frac{7}{8}$

6. $\frac{7}{16} + \frac{11}{24}$

7. $3\frac{1}{7} \times 3\frac{1}{2}$

8. $2\frac{5}{8} \div \frac{1}{32}$

9. $1.57 \div 1,000$

10. 0.62×10^2

Solve.

11. n is 15% of 85.

12. 6 is what percent of 50?

13. 25% of n is 37.5.

14. $33\frac{1}{3}\%$ of 72 is n.

15. 50% of n is 17.

Evaluate. Let $x = 2$, $y = ^-3$, and $z = 5$.

16. $3(x - 2)$

17. $(y + 7)4$

18. $5y - 3z$

19. $x^2 + y^3$

20. $(x - y)^2$

SUMMING UP

431

What property is illustrated?
$3 \cdot 5 + 9 \cdot 5 = (3 + 9)5$

Combining Terms

When Dave travels, he sends mail to his home address to increase the number of stamps in his collection. He sent one letter and two postcards from each country. If he sent 15 pieces of mail in all, how many countries did he visit?

Let n = the number of letters.
Let $2n$ = the number of postcards.

n also represents the number of countries Dave visited. Why?

$$n + 2n = 15$$
$$(1 + 2)n = 15$$
$$3n = 15$$
$$\tfrac{1}{3} \cdot 3n = \tfrac{1}{3} \cdot 15$$
$$n = 5$$

Use the Distributive Property to combine terms.

Check $5 + 2(5) = 15$

Dave visited 5 countries.

Another Example

Write an equation and then solve it.

Fifty-six stamps from Japan are owned by Jenny and Dave. If Jenny has three times as many stamps as Dave, how many do each of them have?

Let s = number of stamps Dave owns.
Let $3s$ = number of stamps Jenny owns.

$$56 = s + 3s$$
$$56 = 4s$$
$$\tfrac{1}{4} \cdot 56 = \tfrac{1}{4} \cdot 4s$$
$$14 = s$$

Check $56 = 14 + 3(14)$

Dave has 14 stamps from Japan.
How many does Jenny have? How do you know?

Check Your Understanding

Solve and check.

1. $4x + 2x = 42$
2. $8x + x = 108$
3. $3n - 5n = 6$
4. $25 = 6x - x$
5. $11 = {}^-9x - 2x$
6. $6y - 3y = {}^-39$
7. $\tfrac{3}{4}x - \tfrac{1}{2}x = 10$
8. $0 = 3x - 4x$

Share Your Ideas Solve $8n - 8n = 0$. Explain.

Solve and check.

9. $2n + 5n = 14$

10. $8n - 7n = {}^-45$

11. $3b + 8b = 55$

12. $5x - x = 36$

13. ${}^-y + 3y = {}^-24$

14. ${}^-2x - 3x = {}^-5$

15. $4n - n = 48$

16. $6x + x = 0$

17. $6x - 11x = 65$

18. ${}^-9 = {}^-5n - 4n$

19. $18 = 2b + b$

20. $7y - 9y = {}^-6$

21. $52 = 15x - 2x$

22. ${}^-12 = 3n - 6n$

23. $50 = 2x + 23x$

24. $12x + 12x = {}^-72$

25. $3x = 18$

26. $x + 2 = {}^-13$

27. $2x + 1 = {}^-3$

28. $2n + 3 = 25$

29. $\frac{1}{2}x = 5$

30. $y - 5 = 11$

31. $5y - y = {}^-4$

32. $10 = 3n - 2$

33. $17 = 4x + 1$

34. ${}^-20 = \frac{2}{3}x$

35. $124 = 3y - y$

36. $2x + 3x + x = 12$

37. $2.5x = 12.5$

38. $4\frac{1}{3}n - 1\frac{2}{3}n = 24$

39. $3x + 4x + 91 = 0$

40. $6n + 7 - 9n = 28$

Think and Apply

Antarctic explorers were commemorated by United States stamps issued in 1988.

41. Charles Wilkes led the expedition that proved Antarctica to be a continent. The 4-year expedition began in 1838 and was completed 22 years after Antarctica had first been sighted by Nathanial Palmer. In what year was Antarctica first sighted?

42. Nathanial Palmer's sighting of Antarctica occurred 115 years before Lincoln Ellsworth crossed Antarctica by air. In what year did Ellsworth make his historic flight?

43. Richard Byrd flew to the South Pole 3 years after his flight to the North Pole. If he flew to the South Pole in 1929, in what year did he fly to the North Pole?

44. Dave is using 5¢ stamps and 25¢ stamps to mail a package. If he uses three times as many 25¢ stamps as 5¢ stamps to put $2.40 postage on the package, how many of each kind of stamp does he use?

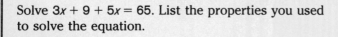

Solve $3x + 9 + 5x = 65$. List the properties you used to solve the equation.

SUMMING UP

433

Simplifying Equations

Before 1978 no woman had ever climbed to the top of an 8,000-meter mountain. Then an expedition of only women conquered the summit of Annapurna I in the Himalayas. All supplies except for 4,800 pounds were carried by 150 porters. The combined weight was as much as 250 porters could have carried. What was the average weight carried by a porter?

Let p = the average number of pounds.

$$250p = 150p + 4,800$$
$$250p + {}^-150p = 150p + {}^-150p + 4,800$$
$$100p = 4,800$$
$$\tfrac{1}{100} \cdot 100p = \tfrac{1}{100} \cdot 4,800$$
$$p = 48$$

First get the variable p on one side by adding ^-150p to both sides. Then multiply both sides by $\frac{1}{100}$.

Check $250(48) = 150(48) + 4,800$

Each porter carried an average weight of 48 pounds.

More Examples

a.
$$5x = 12x - 14$$
$$5x + {}^-12x = 12x + {}^-12x - 14$$
$$^-7x = {}^-14$$
$$x = 2$$

Check $5(2) = 12(2) - 14$

b.
$$9x - 24 = 15x$$
$$9x + {}^-9x - 24 = 15x + {}^-9x$$
$$^-24 = 6x$$
$$^-4 = x$$

Check $9({}^-4) - 24 = 15({}^-4)$

What if you solve **b** by adding ^-15x to both sides. Is the answer the same? Explain.

Check Your Understanding

Solve and check.

1. $5x + 2 = 3x$

2. $7n - 27 = {}^-2n$

3. $8p = {}^-63 + p$

4. $7 + 3y = 10y$

5. $65 - 4m = 9m$

6. $x = 2x - 5$

7. $2t - 7 = 3t$

8. $5x = 2x$

Share Your Ideas Can you solve $2x - 49 = {}^-5x$ by adding $5x$ to both sides? by adding ^-2x to both sides? Which is easier? Why?

Solve and check.

9. $6x + 12 = 7x$

10. $9n + 42 = 3n$

11. $y - 60 = 11y$

12. $3x - 72 = 11x$

13. $7a = 28 + 5a$

14. $t = 12t - 77$

15. $9 + 11y = 14y$

16. $32 + 5b = {}^-3b$

17. $x = {}^-2x + 15$

18. $5x - 12 = {}^-x$

19. $4y = 33 + y$

20. $51 - x = 2x$

21. $34 - 2n = 15n$

22. $72 - 5n = 4n$

23. $15y = {}^-65 + 2y$

24. $35y = 17 + 18y$

25. $x = {}^-2x + 9$

26. ${}^-y = {}^-7y + 48$

27. $8x - 90 = {}^-x$

28. $7n + 3 = 5n - 13$

29. $4x - 7 = 5x - 1$

Write an equation for each. Then solve and check.

30. A number n equals 18 less than 3 times the number.

31. Two times a number y is 3 times the number plus 5.

32. A number x divided by 2 equals the sum of the number and 4.

33. Six more than a number n equals 4 times the number.

34. Nine times a number x is 8 less than the number.

Think and Apply

35. Mount Everest is the highest peak on earth. It is 2,524 feet higher than Annapurna I. If Annapurna I has a height of 26,504 feet, find the height of Mount Everest.

A BASIC program with the statement $X = -B/(A - C)$ can be used to solve an equation in the form of $Ax + B = Cx$.

36. Use the BASIC program, a calculator, or paper and pencil to solve each equation.

```
10 PRINT "TO SOLVE AX + B = CX"
20 INPUT "ENTER A,B,C"; A,B,C
30 X - -B/(A - C)
40 PRINT "X = "X
```

   a. $23x + 52 = {}^-3x$
   b. $89x - 232 = 31x$
   c. $352x - 950 = 314x$
   d. $299x + 872 = 190x$
   e. $214x = 1,505 - x$

37. **Look back** at line 30 of the program in **36.** Suppose $A - C = 0$. Use $5x - 3 = 5x$ as an example. Solve it and explain.

CHINA

Annapurna

PAKISTAN

NEPAL

Mt. Everest

INDIA

If the variable is on both sides of the equation how can you decide which additive inverse to use?

SUMMING UP

Midchapter Review

Write the additive and multiplicative inverse for each.   pages 424–425

1. $\frac{2}{7}$
2. $^-5$
3. 2
4. $\frac{^-3}{8}$
5. 1
6. $^-1\frac{3}{5}$

Name the property illustrated.   pages 424–425

7. $6 \cdot {}^-5 = {}^-5 \cdot 6$
8. $15 + 0 = 15$
9. $(4 + 7) + 9 = 4 + (7 + 9)$
10. $\frac{^-2}{3} \cdot \frac{^-3}{2} = 1$
11. $^-9 + 9 = 0$
12. $4(3 + 5) = (4 \cdot 3) + (4 \cdot 5)$

Solve and check.   pages 426–429

13. $11 = {}^-3 + t$
14. $p - 23 = 0$
15. $24 + y = 13$
16. $7 = x + 37$
17. $^-3b = 15$
18. $11t = {}^-121$
19. $\frac{x}{3} = {}^-9$
20. $\frac{^-5}{2}a = \frac{^-1}{2}$

Write an equation for each sentence. Then solve.   pages 426–431

21. A number n plus 2 is 22.
22. 8 is 3 less than a number n.
23. The sum of a number n and 5 is 18.
24. The product of $^-3$ and a number n is 81.
25. $\frac{1}{2}$ of a number n is 20.
26. The quotient of a number n and 2 is $^-8$.
27. 10 less than 2 times a number n is 8.
28. 8 more than $\frac{1}{3}$ a number n is 18.

Solve and check.   pages 430–435

29. $12t + 7 = 1$
30. $10 = {}^-2y + 6$
31. $\frac{^-4}{5}x - 9 = {}^-1$
32. $3k + 11k = 56$
33. $^-42 = 4x + 2x$
34. $h + 3h + 5h = {}^-9$
35. $7x - 16 = 3x$
36. $12k = {}^-4k - 144$
37. $12c - 15 = 11c - 15$

Write the word(s) that best fits in each blank.

38. If the product of z and a is 1, then z and a are _____.

39. 0 is the _____.

40. Always _____ the solution of an equation to check that it is correct.

Words to Know
additive inverses
multiplicative inverses
multiplicative identity
substitute
additive identity

Write an equation for each. Then solve.

41. Travelers to New York City often visit the Statue of Liberty. Its full height of 305.5 ft includes a pedestal that is 154.5 ft high. How tall is the statue without the pedestal?

42. Rosa planned a school trip to Spain. There were twice as many girls as boys on the trip. How many boys were going if there were 28 people altogether, including 4 chaperones?

Exploring Problem Solving

Seeing the Sights

You are on a flight from Entebbe, Uganda, to Lagos, Nigeria. The scheduled flight time is $5\frac{1}{2}$ hours. The plane left the gate at 9:30 A.M.

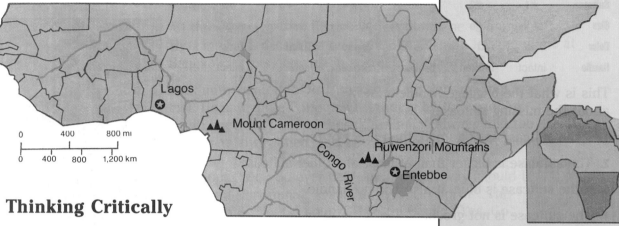

Thinking Critically

Because a movie is being shown, the pilot has requested that the window covers be closed. When should you open the window cover to see the Ruwenzori Mountains, the Congo River, and Mount Cameroon? Do not consider any changes in time zones.

Analyzing and Making Decisions

1. What should the flight path look like from Entebbe, Uganda to Lagos, Nigeria. How long is it?

2. All of the $5\frac{1}{2}$-hour flight time is not for actual flying time. Fifteen minutes are reserved at each end for take-off and landing. If the airplane speed is 420 mph, does the flight time of $5\frac{1}{2}$ hours sound reasonable? Explain.

3. About what time is the actual take-off? When should you start to look for the Ruwenzori Mountains?

4. When should you see the Congo River? Mount Cameroon?

5. **What if** you did not see the Ruwenzori Mountains until ten minutes after your estimated time? What might be the reasons for that? How would you choose your estimates for the other places?

Look Back What if you looked out and did not see the Ruwenzori Mountains? What might be the reasons for this?

Using Problem Solving

Interview: Calculators and Travelers

Mary D. Tellers is a representative for the Simon and Schuster International School Group. She lives in Wiesbaden, West Germany, and travels to Department of Defense Dependent Schools and independent schools throughout Europe. Mary often exchanges currencies (money) on her travels within Europe and when she returns to the United States.

This table shows rates of exchange with the United States dollar for six currencies. The first rate is for buying the foreign currency. The second rate is for buying United States dollars.

RATES OF EXCHANGE			
Britain	$1 = 0.625 pounds 0.675 pounds = $1	France	$1 = 6.49 francs 6.99 francs = $1
West Germany	$1 = 1.91 marks 2.07 marks = $1	Italy	$1 = 1,324.5 lire 1,526 lire = $1
Switzerland	$1 = 1.63 Sw. francs 1.79 Sw. francs = $1	Japan	$1 = 141.84 yen 153.84 yen = $1

Solve. Use a calculator.

A. The rate of exchange is the rate that a bank or exchange agent uses to exchange the currency. Mary has $50 of United States currency and she wants to exchange the money for British pounds. To find out how many pounds she would receive, she multiplies the number of dollars she has by 0.625. The result will tell how many pounds she will receive.

B. Pretend that Mary has $50 of United States currency to exchange into the currencies of the listed countries. How much of each country's currency will she receive?

C. What if Mary had 500 units of each foreign currency? How could she use the rate of exchange chart to tell how many United States dollars she would receive? Try it. How many United States dollars would she receive for each foreign currency?

Sharing Your Ideas

1. If you were going to a foreign country, why might you want to know how much of that foreign currency you could purchase with $100 of United States currency?

Practice

2. Mr. Globetrotter took short trips to many foreign countries. He liked to carry 100 United States dollars worth of the currency of the country he was visiting. On one hectic trip, the traveler visited every country on the exchange rate list on page 446. In between each foreign country, the traveler returned to the United States. Since his journey was so hectic, there was no time to spend the $100 or to replenish it. He took the $100 and exchanged it into the currency of the country he was visiting. On return to the United States, the money was changed back into U.S. currency and then converted to the nearest hundredth into the currency of the next foreign country. Make a chart that shows what happens after each exchange. How much money does the traveler have at the end of the trip?

3. Use the chart to find an exchange rate between pounds and francs. How can you do that? Make a chart to show how much of each currency you could exchange for 1 pound.

Summing Up

4. Look back at **2.** What happened to Mr. Globetrotter's $100? Why do you think this happened?

5. What if Mr. Globetrotter's bank charges a service fee of $1 for each exchange of currency? How would that change the first transaction?

EXTENSION

Polls, Statistics, and Probability

Work in a small group.

A. Choose three sports featured in the Olympics. Take a poll among members of your class, asking for TV-viewing preferences among these three sports. Record the number of students who prefer each sport and the total number of students polled.

B. Send a student from your group into several other classes in the school to gather data about their preferences. Record the data in a similar way.

C. Compute the percent of students who prefer watching each sport, using the class poll and then the school poll. How do the results compare?

Frequently statistics from one situation are used to predict the outcome in another situation. For example, if 20% of New Englanders are under 5 feet tall, a statistician might predict that in a Massachusetts town of 3,000, 20% of the people, or 600 people, will be under 5 feet tall.

D. Find out how many students are in a neighboring school. Use your statistics to predict the percent of those students who would prefer watching each sport. Do you think you should base your prediction on the class statistics or on the school statistics? Discuss. How valid do you think your results will be?

In election years, newspapers make frequent predictions about the percent of voters in favor of each candidate.

E. How do you think the newspapers reach these conclusions? How valid do you think these conclusions might be?

Maintaining Skills

Choose the correct answer. Write A, B, C, or D.

1. What is the circumference?
   Use $\pi \approx 3.14$.

   A 21.98 m   C 153.86 m

   B 43.96 m   D not given

2. What is the area of
   the shaded region?
   Use $\pi \approx 3.14$.

   A 576 m^2 C 680 m^2

   B 1,832 m^2 D not given

3. What is the volume?
   Use $\pi \approx 3.14$.

   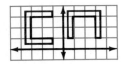

   A 254.34 m^3 C 81 m^3

   B 84.78 m^3 D not given

4. 15 L = _____ dm^3

   A 1.5   C 15

   B 0.15   D not given

5. What is P(yellow marble)?

   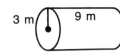

   A $\frac{1}{5}$ C 1

   B $\frac{1}{6}$ D not given

6. What is the probability of choosing 1 out
   of 2 items and 1 out of 7 items?

   A $\frac{1}{9}$ C $\frac{9}{14}$

   B $\frac{1}{14}$ D not given

7. In how many ways can 5 runners finish
   a race?

   A 120   C 5

   B 25   D not given

8. What transformation
   is illustrated?

   A reflection   C rotation

   B translation   D not given

9. What property is illustrated? $\frac{-2}{3} + \frac{2}{3} = 0$

   A Additive Inverse   C Multiplicative
                                 Inverse

   B Identity   D not given

10. Solve for x. $x + {}^-7 = 2$

    A $x = 9$ C $x = 5$

    B $x = {}^-9$ D not given

Solve.

Skip, Lenny, Bruce, and Val were standing
in a line by height. Their heights were
5 ft 2 in., 5 ft 6 in., 5 ft 3 in., and 5 ft 4 in.
Lenny is not the tallest. Bruce is taller than
Skip. Val is 2 in. taller than Bruce. Skip's
height in inches is an odd number.

11. Who is the tallest?

    A Skip   C Lenny

    B Val   D not given

12. Who is 5 ft 4 in. tall?

    A Skip   C Lenny

    B Val   D not given

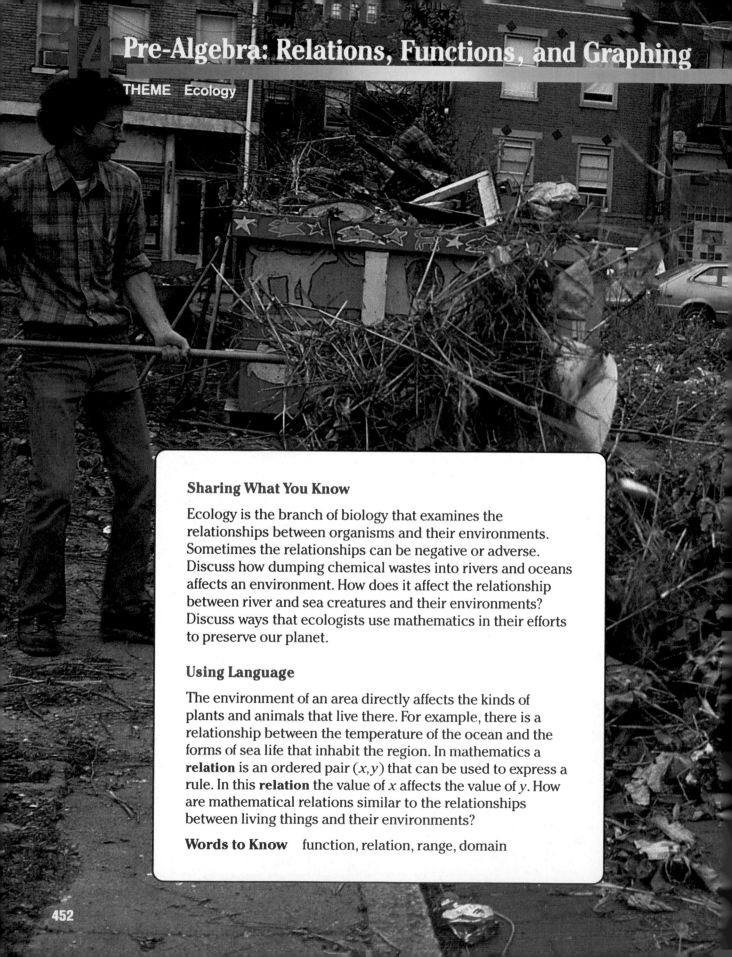

Sharing What You Know

Ecology is the branch of biology that examines the relationships between organisms and their environments. Sometimes the relationships can be negative or adverse. Discuss how dumping chemical wastes into rivers and oceans affects an environment. How does it affect the relationship between river and sea creatures and their environments? Discuss ways that ecologists use mathematics in their efforts to preserve our planet.

Using Language

The environment of an area directly affects the kinds of plants and animals that live there. For example, there is a relationship between the temperature of the ocean and the forms of sea life that inhabit the region. In mathematics a **relation** is an ordered pair (x, y) that can be used to express a rule. In this **relation** the value of x affects the value of y. How are mathematical relations similar to the relationships between living things and their environments?

Words to Know   function, relation, range, domain

Be a Problem Solver

The Sanitation Department of Beltmore can dispose of
4,000 trash cans full of waste each week for the next 3
years. If 1,430 families live in the town, how many trash
cans a week is each family allowed to put out for collection?
What if the town grew by 10%? What would you do?

Write about ways you can improve the ecosystem of your
neighborhood.

How accurately can you measure? Can you measure 1 cm? 1.4 cm? 1.41 cm?

Real Numbers

This scientist tests bacteria levels on a square lot. The square has an area of 3 m². Each side of the square is $\sqrt{3}$ m long.

$\sqrt{3} = 1.7320508 \ldots$ $\sqrt{3}$ is an irrational number.

An **irrational number** is a nonterminating and nonrepeating decimal.
π, $\sqrt{2}$, and 1.7070070007 . . . are irrational numbers.

One approximation for $\sqrt{3}$ is 1.73. 1.73 is a rational number.

A **rational number** is a terminating or a repeating decimal.
$\frac{5}{8}$ (0.625), $^-2$, and $\frac{1}{3}$ (0.$\overline{3}$) are rational numbers.

The rational numbers and irrational numbers together form the **real numbers.** Every number on the number line is a real number, either rational or irrational.

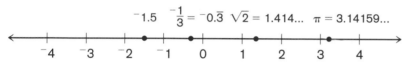

$^-1.5 \quad \frac{^-1}{3} = ^-0.\overline{3} \quad \sqrt{2} = 1.414\ldots \quad \pi = 3.14159\ldots$

Between any two real numbers, there is always another real number. This is the **Property of Density.**

Some real numbers between 3.1 and 3.2 are 3.14159 . . . , 3.15, and 3.19. Name some other real numbers between 3.1 and 3.2.

Pairs of real numbers can be located as points on a real-number plane.

Graph $A(^-3, \sqrt{2})$. From the origin, move 3 units left and $\sqrt{2}$, about 1.4, units up. Label the point A.

Check Your Understanding

Classify. Write *integer, rational, irrational,* and *real.*

1. $^-13$ **2.** $\frac{3}{4}$ **3.** $0.\overline{7}$ **4.** $\sqrt{3}$ **5.** 3.171171117 . . .

Make a real-number plane. Graph and label each point.

6. $V(5, ^-\sqrt{2})$ **7.** $W(2\frac{1}{2}, ^-4)$ **8.** $X(\sqrt{3}, ^-1)$ **9.** $Y(^-\sqrt{2}, ^-\sqrt{3})$ **10.** $Z(\frac{^-2}{3}, 0)$

Share Your Ideas   How many irrational numbers do you think there are? Explain.

Practice

Classify. Write *integer, rational, irrational,* and *real.*

11. $1.\overline{3}$

12. 3^5

13. $\sqrt{3}$

14. $^-31$

15. 3π

16. $1.374129\ldots$

Graph and label each point on a real-number plane.

17. $A(\sqrt{2}, \, ^-1)$

18. $B(0, \, ^-2)$

19. $C(^-2, \, ^-\sqrt{2})$

20. $D(^-\sqrt{3}, 2)$

21. $E(3, \sqrt{3})$

22. $F(^-\sqrt{3}, 0)$

Write *true* or *false* for each.

23. All integers are rational numbers.

24. Every decimal is a real number.

25. All irrational numbers are real numbers.

26. No terminating decimals are rational numbers.

27. The square root of a rational number is always a rational number.

28. The square of any integer is a real number.

Use a calculator to find *x*.

29. $\sqrt{x} = 2.236068\ldots$

30. $\sqrt{7} = x$

31. $x^2 = 13$

Find a real number between each pair of numbers.

32. $^-1.708$ and $^-1.8$

33. $0.\overline{3}$ and $0.\overline{45}$

34. $\sqrt{2}$ and $\sqrt{3}$

Think and Apply

35. Draw 3 circles having the same center. Use *real, rational,* and *integer* to label the diagram for the number systems. Explain your reasoning.

36. Arrange in order from least to greatest.
$0.33, 0.3, 0.\overline{3}, 0.\overline{329}, 0.35, 0.3\overline{5}$

37. Write a decimal that neither terminates nor repeats. Classify the decimal as rational or irrational.

Visual Thinking

Draw a separate graph for each. Graph the points. Find the coordinates of the missing point.

38. $(2, 3) \, (1, 0) \, (3, 1)$
Make a square.

39. $(2, 2) \, (4, 2) \, (^-2, \, ^-1)$
Make a parallelogram.

40. $(^-2, 2) \, (4, 2) \, (^-2, \, ^-1)$
Make a rectangle.

41. $(^-5, \, ^-2) \, (^-1, \, ^-2)$
Make a right triangle.

A rational approximation is needed to graph an irrational number. Why is it necessary to use a rational number approximation?

SUMMING UP

What does the word *related* mean? What does it mean for two quantities to be related?

Relations

Ethanol fuel is nonpolluting. If it costs $2.00 per gallon, how much will a tankful cost? The cost is related to the size of the tank.

The size of the tank and its corresponding cost form a relation.

▶ A **relation** is a group of ordered pairs. A relation can be shown in a table or a graph.

Number of gallons (x)	5	6	7	8	9	10
Cost in dollars (y)	$10	$12	$14	$16	$18	$20

What does each value of *x* represent?

What does each value of *y* represent?

The **domain** of a relation is the set of all the values of *x*. The **range** of a relation is the set of all the values of *y*.

Make a graph for each relation. Identify the domain and range for each graph.

1. (3, 1), (5, ⁻2), (2, 2), (⁻1, 1)

2. (4, 3), (⁻1, 2), (2, ⁻1), (3, 2), (⁻1, ⁻3), (4, 0)

3.
x	y
⁻4	⁻1
⁻2	0
0	1
2	2

4.
x	y
⁻2	4
⁻1	1
0	1
2	4

5. Each *x*-coordinate is an integer. The *y*-coordinate is 2 less than the *x*-coordinate.

6. Each *x*-coordinate is an integer. The *y*-coordinate is ⁻3 times the value of the *x*-coordinate.

Share Your Ideas   Some relations are not numeric. What ordered pairs are suggested by the relation "brother of"? Name other relations that are not numeric.

Graph each relation.

7. (3, ⁻1), (⁻1, 2), (4, 0),
(2, 2), (0, 5), (3, 5)

8. (1, 2), (⁻2, ⁻1), (⁻1, 0),
(2, 3), (3, 4), (0, 1)

9.

x	⁻2	⁻1	0	1	2
y	3	4	5	6	7

10.

x	⁻3	⁻2	0	2	3
y	⁻6	⁻4	0	4	6

11. Each x-coordinate is an integer. Each y-coordinate is 4 more than its corresponding x-coordinate.

12. Each x-coordinate is an integer. Each y-coordinate is 0.5 of its corresponding x-coordinate.

Complete each sentence to express a relation.

13. The price of an automobile is related to ____.

14. The population of a city is related to ____.

15. The distance traveled on a bicycle is related to ____.

16. The amount of heat lost through a window is related to ____.

Think and Apply

Make a table for each relation.

17. A car gets 26 miles to a gallon of fuel. Show the relationship of the number of miles driven to the number of gallons of fuel used.

18. A motorcyclist averaged 45 miles per hour. Show the relationship of the number of miles driven to the number of hours.

19. **What if** you bought a used car for $4,500? Each year its value may be reduced by $500. Show the relationship of the value of the car to the number of years you own it.

20. DATA Choose a make of car. Find newspaper ads for used models. Write ordered pairs, using the year a car was made as the first member and the price as the second member. Make a table and graph each pair. What does the graph show about the relation between the cost of a car and the year it was made? Compare your data with your classmates'. Which make of car holds its value best?

What is a relation? How can it be shown? If you know one quantity in a relation, do you know the value of the other quantity?

Mixed Review

1. $83.72 \times 1,000$

2. $1,873.4 \div 1,000$

3. $3,871.5 + 1,000$

4. $7,386.6 - 1,000$

5. $3^3 \times 1,000$

6. $5 + 7 \times 6$

7. $18 - 8 \times 3$

8. $6 - 2^3$

9. $10^2 \times 10^3$

10. $\sqrt{4 \times 9}$

Solve.

11. $x - 10 = 21$

12. $y + 12 = 30$

13. $32 = 5a$

14. $^-7b = 49$

15. $\frac{c}{4} = {^-8}$

16. $\frac{d}{10} = 5.1$

Write each number in standard form.

17. 6.2×10^3

18. 1.77×10^4

19. 5.4×10^{-2}

20. 8.31×10^{-3}

SUMMING UP

Activity

Exploring Functions

There are special relations called **functions.** What is a function? Try this experiment to find out.

Working together

Materials: grid paper

A. Each table represents a function. Make a graph for each.

x	y
⁻2	0
⁻1	1
0	2
1	3
2	4

x	y
⁻2	4
⁻1	1
0	0
1	1
2	4

x	y
⁻5	3
⁻4	3
⁻3	3
⁻2	3
⁻1	3

B. Each table does not represent a function. Make a graph for each.

x	y
⁻2	0
⁻1	1
0	2
1	3
⁻2	4

x	y
⁻2	2
⁻2	⁻2
0	0
1	2
1	⁻2

x	y
2	⁻2
2	⁻1
2	0
2	1
2	2

C. Compare the tables in **A** with those in **B.** Look at the x-coordinates in each table. How do the x-coordinates of the functions differ from those that are not functions?

D. Compare the graphs of the functions with those graphs that are not functions. Draw vertical lines on all the graphs. What do you notice? On which graphs do the vertical lines touch more than one point?

Sharing Your Results

1. With your class, develop a definition of function.

2. You can tell if a graph is a function by using vertical lines. Explain how this method works.

3. Create a list of ordered pairs that represent a function. Exchange lists with a friend to check.

Extending the Activity

Work on your own.

A **function** is a relation in which each value of x is paired only once with a value of y. That is, each value of x occurs only once.

Make a table for each relation. Which relations are functions? List the domain and range of each relation.

4.
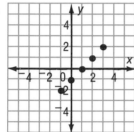

5.
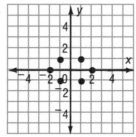

6.
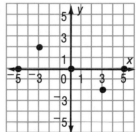

Write *function* or *not a function*. Explain your choice.

7.
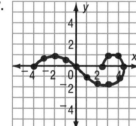

8.
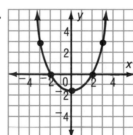

9.
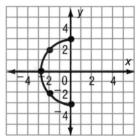

10. (0, 1), ($^-$1, 2), (3, 0), (4, $^-$2), ($^-$1, 3)

11. (1, 2), ($^-$1, 3), (0, 2), (2, 3), (3, 3)

12. the relationship between a dog's age and its weight

13. the relationship between each student in your class and the sport most enjoyed

Summing Up

14. Is every function a relation? Explain your reasoning.

15. Is every relation a function? Give one example to prove your answer.

16. How can you tell from a table of values whether the set of pairs is a function?

17. How is a function different from a relation? How is a function the same as a relation? Explain.

459

Midchapter Review

Classify. Write *integer, rational number, irrational number,* and *real number.* pages 452–453

1. $\sqrt{3}$ **2.** $\frac{16}{3}$ **3.** $^-5$ **4.** $\sqrt{4}$ **5.** $^-1.37$ **6.** π

Make a real-number plane. Graph and label each point.

7. $A(1, ^-\sqrt{3})$ **8.** $B(0, ^-5)$ **9.** $C(\sqrt{2}, 0)$ **10.** $D(^-3, ^-4)$ **11.** $E(1.5, \sqrt{2})$ **12.** $F(^-2.1, 1)$

Make a table for each relation. pages 454–455

13. 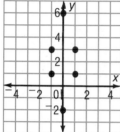   **14.** 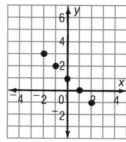   **15.**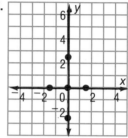

Write *function* or *not a function.* pages 456–457

16. 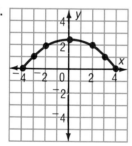   **17.** 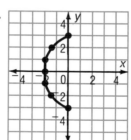   **18.**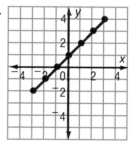

19.

x	$^-2$	$^-1$	0	1	2
y	6	7	8	9	10

20.

x	1	2	3	$^-2$	$^-1$
y	0	3	1	5	2

21.

x	$^-4$	$^-3$	$^-2$	$^-1$	0
y	8	6	4	2	0

22. the relationship of the age of a tree to its height

23. the relationship of a positive integer to its square root

Copy and complete. Use the words *function, relation, range,* and *domain.*

24. The group of ordered pairs (0, 3) (1, 4), ($^-1$, 5), and (1, 6) is a ___ but not a ___.

25. The group of ordered pairs (1, $^-1$), (2, $^-2$), and (3, $^-3$) has a ___ of $^-1$, $^-2$, and $^-3$. The ___ is 1, 2, and 3.

Exploring Problem Solving

THINK
EXPLORE
SOLVE
LOOK BACK

What Are the Chances?

You are trying to spot Great Horned Owls. They sleep during the day and are difficult to spot while they are sleeping. An experienced bird watcher has made a probability table for spotting the owl. The table is based on the time spent searching in a single section of the forest and on the resulting probability of finding an owl in that amount of time.

Thinking Critically

Suppose you have 2 hours to search for an owl, and there are 12 possible searching sections. How should you do it? The questions below will help you look at several possible ways to solve this problem.

Analyzing and Making Decisions

1. Make a line graph of the probability that results from the different times spent searching. Does the graph help you decide how to spend your time? Explain.

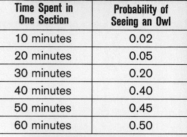

Time Spent in One Section	Probability of Seeing an Owl
10 minutes	0.02
20 minutes	0.05
30 minutes	0.20
40 minutes	0.40
50 minutes	0.45
60 minutes	0.50
(Probability does not increase after 60 minutes.)	

2. What is the probability of seeing the owl if you search in a section for 10 minutes? If you search in a section for 20 minutes you could say you had a 0.025 chance of seeing the owl for each 10 minutes of the twenty minutes. Break each search time down into 10-minute periods. How will that help you decide which is the best way to search?

3. What is the chance of not seeing an owl in a 30-minute search? What is the chance of not seeing an owl in two 30-minute searches? three 30-minute searches? four 30-minute searches? What is the chance of seeing an owl in four 30-minute searches? How can you use this idea to help you find the best use of your time? Try this with some other times.

4. How would you spend your time searching to have the greatest probability of seeing an owl. Explain.

Look Back Which method helped you the most in solving this problem? This graph has a line drawn from the origin to each point. How could this help you solve the problem?

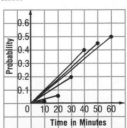

Problem Solving Strategies

Alternate Solutions

Angela and Nicholas volunteered to help plant trees in the park. On Monday, they were taught how to plant the trees and they started planting. On Tuesday, they improved and planted twice as many as on Monday. On Wednesday, their last day, they planted 5 more trees than they had on Tuesday. They planted a total of 105 trees in the 3 days. How many were planted on each day?

Many problems can be solved in more than one way. Being able to solve problems in more than one way will help you become a better problem solver.

Solving the Problem

Think   What is the problem? What are the facts?

Explore   Can you use guess and test to help you solve this problem? Explain. What if you let x stand for the number of trees planted on Monday? How many times as many trees were planted on Tuesday? How could you write that using x (the number of trees planted on Monday)? How many more trees were planted on Wednesday? How could you write that using x? What expression identifies the total for the three days?

Solve   How many trees were planted each day?

Look Back   How can you tell if your answer is reasonable?

Share Your Ideas

1. Which method of solving the problem did you prefer?

Practice

 Solve. Use a calculator where appropriate.

2. It takes two people about half an hour to clean up an empty lot. If 5 people are working, about how long should it take them?

3. Three people were cleaning geese. They divided the birds equally into 3 cages. After they had each cleaned and released 6 geese, the total number of geese left was the same number of geese that had been in one cage. With how many geese did they start?

4. A city was having trees planted along Main Street. For every three oaks planted, two maple trees were planted. A total of 175 trees were planted. How many trees of each kind were planted?

5. Several students built 3 large birdfeeders, 2 medium feeders, and 2 small feeders. A large feeder holds 3 times as much food as a small feeder. A medium feeder holds twice as much food as a small feeder. If 30 lb of food will fill all the feeders, how much food does each feeder hold?

Mixed Strategy Review

6. Susan, Miriam, Nick, and Paul each sighted a different bird. If Susan did not see the owl or the finch, Miriam saw the owl. If Nick did not see the owl, then Paul saw the woodpecker. Susan saw the crane. Who saw which bird?

A veterinarian made up bags of food for ducks and geese. Four bags of duck food and 3 bags of goose food weighed 35 ounces, while 3 bags of duck food and 4 bags of goose food weighed 42 ounces.

7. How much does a bag of duck food weigh?

8. How much does a bag of goose food weigh?

Create Your Own

Write a problem that can be solved in more than one way.

Estimate the values at points A, B, and C on this part of a number line.

2.5   3.1

A   B   C

Graphing Equations

Rain forests provide oxygen and chemicals for new medicines. Yet, every hour, 9.4 square miles are being cut down.

This equation describes the relation between time and square miles of forest being cut down.

$y = 9.4 \, x$

x represents hours
y represents square miles of forest

You can make a table of values to show the relation.

x	0	0.5	1	2	3
y	0	4.7	9.4	18.8	28.2

Is the relation a function? Explain.

To graph the relation, graph the ordered pairs (x, y) from the table. Draw a line connecting the points. The line is the graph of the equation $y = 9.4 \, x$.

All points on the line are solutions to $y = 9.4 \, x$. Name some solutions other than those in the table.

Another Example

Graph $x + y = 6$.

x	⁻2	⁻1	0	1	2
y	8	7	6	5	4

What is the y-coordinate if the x-coordinate is 0.5? 2.365?

Check Your Understanding

Make a table for each equation, using ⁻2, ⁻1, 0, 1, and 2 as the x-coordinates. Then graph each on a real-number plane.

1. $y = 3x$ **2.** $x + y = 4$ **3.** $y = x - 2$ **4.** $y = {}^-x - 1$

Estimate the y-coordinate if x = 1.76.

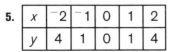

5.

x	⁻2	⁻1	0	1	2
y	4	1	0	1	4

6.

x	⁻1	0	1	2
y	4	5	6	7

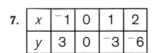

7.

x	⁻1	0	1	2
y	3	0	⁻3	⁻6

Share Your Ideas Given the function $y = x^2 + 1$, explain three ways to estimate the y-coordinate if x = 3.259.

464

Copy and complete each table. Then graph each equation.

8. $y = 5 - x$

x	y
⁻1	
0	
1	
2	

9. $y = x + 2$

x	y
⁻4	
⁻1	
0	
2	

10. $y = {}^-3x - 1$

x	y
⁻2	
⁻1	
0	
1	

11. $x + y = {}^-2$

x	y
⁻2	
⁻1	
0	
1	

Estimate the y-coordinate for each x-coordinate. Use the graphs.

12. $x = 0.5$

13. $x = 1$

14. $x = {}^-1.5$

15. $x = 4.2$

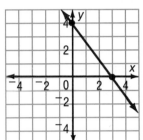

16. $x = {}^-1.5$

17. $x = 0.5$

18. $x = 1.5$

19. $x = 2.5$

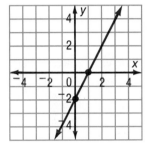

Which ordered pair is *not* a solution of the equation?

20. $y = x - 4$
   a. (5, 1)
   b. (1, 5)
   c. (3, ⁻1)

21. $y = {}^-2x + 1$
   a. (0, 1)
   b. (1, 1)
   c. (2, ⁻3)

22. $y = 4 - x$
   a. (0, 4)
   b. (3, 1)
   c. (0, ⁻4)

23. $y = \frac{2}{3}x$
   a. $\left({}^-1, \frac{2}{3}\right)$
   b. (3, 2)
   c. (0, 0)

Solve.

24. What is the least number of points needed to graph a line? Explain your answer.

25. The equation $y = 3$ can have any x-coordinate as long as each y-coordinate is 3. Graph and describe this equation.

26. The equation $x = {}^-1$ can have any y-coordinate as long as each x-coordinate is ⁻1. Graph and describe this equation.

27. How many solutions does the equation $y = 3$ have? Explain your answer.

28. **What if** the rainfall on May 1 is 3 cm and then increases 2 cm each day? Express this as an equation. Graph the equation.

29. Use your graph in **28** to find the number of days needed for the rainfall to be 21 cm.

What information about a relation is easier to see when a set of ordered pairs is graphed?

SUMMING UP

When is it hardest to ride your bicycle? When is it easiest? Describe the road conditions for each.

Slope

Erosion has worn away this mountain. The steepness, or slope, of the mountain has changed.

▶ The steepness of a line is its **slope.** Slope is expressed as a ratio, using any two points on the line.

$$\text{slope} = \frac{\text{change in } y\text{-value}}{\text{change in } x\text{-value}}$$

Use the points (4, 1) and ($^-$4, $^-$3) to find the slope of the line below representing the mountain.

$$\text{slope} = \frac{1 - (^-3)}{4 - (^-4)} = \frac{4}{8} = \frac{1}{2}$$

For every change of 2 units along the *x*-axis, there is a change of 1 unit along the *y*-axis.

The slope of the mountain is $\frac{1}{2}$.

▶ The **y-intercept** of a line is the *y*-value of the point where the line crosses the *y*-axis.

The *y*-intercept of this line is $^-$1.

The equation of any line can be written as $y = mx + b$. *m* equals the slope and *b* equals the *y*-intercept.

For the line representing the mountain, $m = \frac{1}{2}$ and $b = ^-1$. So the equation of this line is $y = \frac{1}{2}x - 1$.

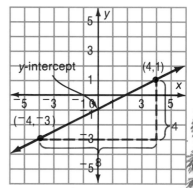

Check Your Understanding

1. What is the slope of each line shown on the graph?

Find the slope of the line containing each pair of points.

2. (3, 5), ($^-$3, $^-$1)   **3.** ($^-$2, 3), (2, 1)

Give the slope and *y*-intercept of each line.

4. $y = x + 2$ **5.** $y = \frac{1}{2}x + ^-1$ **6.** $y = 2x - 2$

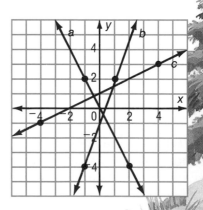

Share Your Ideas   Look back at **1.** How would the graph of line *b* change if $m = ^-3$? What do you think the line would look like if $m = 0$?

Find the slope of the line containing each pair of points.

7. $(2, 7), (^-5, 1)$

8. $(5, 2), (0, ^-3)$

9. $(^-2, 3), (^-3, 2)$

10. $(5, 8), (0, ^-2)$

Give the slope and *y*-intercept of each line.

11. $y = ^-x - 6$

12. $y = 2x + 5$

13. $y = 5$
(Hint: $y = 0x + 5$)

14. $4x + 2y = 6$

Write the equation of the line.

15. slope = 5
y-intercept = 0

16. slope = 0
y-intercept = $^-3$

17. slope = $\frac{2}{3}$
y-intercept = 4

18. $m = ^-3, b = 7$

Find the slope and *y*-intercept of each line. Then write the equation for each.

19. $\overleftrightarrow{AB}$

20. $\overleftrightarrow{CD}$

21. $\overleftrightarrow{EF}$

22. $\overleftrightarrow{GH}$

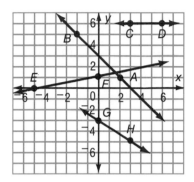

Think and Apply

Solve.

23. The Grand Canyon, in Arizona, was formed by erosion. Find the slope of this descent into the canyon.

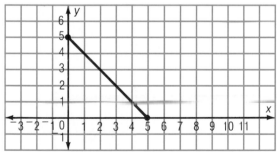

24. Graph $A(1, ^-2)$ and $B(^-3, 4)$. Connect the points to form a line. Predict three other points on the line, using your knowledge of slope. Explain how you found the points.

Logical Thinking

Slopes can be positive, negative, or 0. But, how many slopes can a line have? To find out, follow these steps.

• Draw a line through 3 points. Label the points *A*, *B*, and *C*.
• Find the slope between *A* and *B*, *B* and *C*, and *A* and *C*.
• Repeat the activity three times.

25. Draw a conclusion based on your findings. How many slopes can a line have?

Describe the difference between the slope of a line and its *y*-intercept.

SUMMING UP

The product of two numbers is 36. Their sum is 20. Can 13 and 7 be the numbers? 4 and 9? What are the numbers? Explain.

Systems of Equations

When 10 million gallons of oil spilled into the waters of Prince William Sound, teams of volunteers went to work to save animals endangered by the oil. One team of 12 student volunteers had twice as many girls as boys. How many boys and girls were there?

Write equations for the information given.

Let g = the number of girls.

Let b = the number of boys.

$\left.\begin{array}{l} b + g = 12 \\ \quad 2b = g \end{array}\right\}$ Two equations form a **system of equations.**

A graph can be used to solve a system of equations. Make a table of values for each equation. Then graph each.

$b + g = 12$

b	g
6	6
5	7
4	8

$2b = g$

b	g
1	2
2	4
3	6

Find the point where the lines intersect. Since (4,8) is a point on both lines, it is the solution of the system of equations.

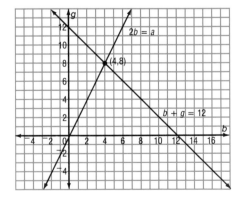

Check: Substitute (4,8) in each equation.

$b + g = 12$ $2b = g$
$8 + 4 = 12$ $2 \cdot 4 = 8$

There are 4 boys and 8 girls.

Check Your Understanding

Solve each system of equations by graphing. Check the solution.

1. $y = 2x$
   $y = x + 1$

2. $y = 3x - 2$
   $y = x + 4$

3. $y = 2x$
   $x + y = 6$

4. $y = \frac{1}{2}x$
   $y = \frac{-1}{2}x + 2$

Share Your Ideas The point at which the lines intersect is the solution of both equations. Explain why this is so.

Solve each system of equations by graphing. Check.

5. $y = x - 2$
$y = 3x$

6. $y = x - 1$
$y = 2$

7. $y = x + 5$
$y = {}^-x - 7$

8. $y = x - 3$
$y = 3x + 1$

9. $y = {}^-3$
$x = 5$

10. $y = 3x - 1$
$y = x + 1$

11. $y = x - 3$
$2x - 6 = 2y$

12. $y = {}^-x + 1$
$x + y = 3$

Which ordered pair is a solution of the system of equations?

13. $2y = 3x - 1$
$y = x + 1$

a. $(3,4)$ **b.** $(1,1)$

14. $y = x$
$y = {}^-x$

a. $(4,4)$ **b.** $(0,0)$

15. $y = 2x + 3$
$y = 3$

a. $(5,3)$ **b.** $(0,3)$

Use the graph at the right to find the solution for each system of equations.

16. $y = {}^-x + 1$
$y = {}^-\frac{1}{2}x$

17. $y = {}^-\frac{1}{2}x$
$y = x + 3$

18. $y = {}^-x + 1$
$y = x + 3$

19. $y = x + 3$
$y = 0$

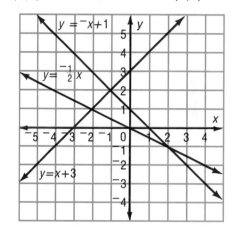

Write a system of equations. Solve by graphing.

20. Two teams cleaned 5 beaches. Team Y cleaned one beach more than team X. How many beaches did each team clean?

21. Twenty snow leopards were tracked by biologists. There were 4 more males than females. How many male snow leopards were tracked?

22. The sum of the heights of 2 bald eagles is 50 cm. The difference is 10 cm. How tall is each bald eagle?

23. The state financed 12 refuges. There are 3 times as many bird refuges as animal refuges. How many bird refuges does the state finance?

Common Error

When you write an equation, be careful not to confuse statements such as "There are 3 times as many boys as girls." The sentence is often incorrectly translated as $3b = g$. If there are 3 times as many boys, the number of boys is greater. Multiply the number of girls by 3 to get the number of boys. $3g = b$

Write an equation for each.

24. There are twice as many dogs as cats.

25. Maria's age is 4 times Ted's age.

26. The tens digit is $\frac{1}{2}$ the ones digit.

Describe a system of equations that has no solution and a system that has one point as its solution.

SUMMING UP

Graphing Inequalities

Each month the recycling center collected aluminum and newspaper. The number of tons of newspaper collected was always more than 2 times the number of tons of aluminum.

Let y = number of tons of newspaper
x = number of tons of aluminum
Then $y > 2x$ is the inequality that represents the problem.

To graph the inequality, follow these steps.

- Graph $y = 2x$. Use a dashed line to show that $y = 2x$ is not part of the inequality $y > 2x$.

- Choose a point above and a point below the line. Decide which of the points satisfies the inequality.
  (1,7) satisfies $y > 2x$. Why? (5,2) does not satisfy $y > 2x$. Why?

- Shade the region containing the point that satisfies the inequality. Would all the points in this region satisfy the inequality? Why?

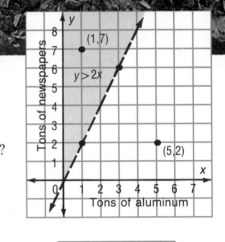

More Examples

a. Graph $y \geq x - 1$.
Why is a solid line used?

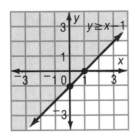

b. Graph $y < x + 2$.
Why is a dashed line used?

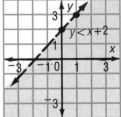

Check Your Understanding

Graph each inequality.

1. $y > 3x - 2$ 2. $y \leq {}^-x$ 3. $y \geq {}^-x - 2$ 4. $y < \frac{1}{2}x$

Write an inequality for each.

5. the region below $y = 3x + 7$
6. the line $y = {}^-2x + 4$ and the region above it

Share Your Ideas   For which inequalities would you use a solid line? Explain your choices.
a. $y > 7x$ **b.** $x + y > 5$ **c.** $y \leq {}^-3x + 1$

Graph each inequality.

7. $y < \frac{1}{3}x - 1$

8. $y \geq 2x + 3$

9. $y < {}^-3x$

10. $y \geq \frac{-1}{2}x + 1$

11. $y \leq x + 3$

12. $y > 4x - 1$

13. $y < \frac{2}{3}x - 3$

14. $y > 5x$

15. $x \leq {}^-4$

16. $y \leq 4$

17. $2x - y > 5$

18. $x + 2y < {}^-6$

Write an inequality for each graph.

19.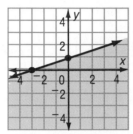

20.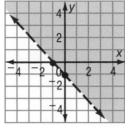

Is $(3, {}^-1)$ a solution for each inequality? Write *yes* or *no*. Explain your choice.

21. $y > x + 2$

22. $y \geq {}^-2x + 1$

23. $x + y \leq 2$

Think and Apply

Write an inequality for each. Then graph.

24. Plastic is now collected at the recycling center. The number of pounds of plastic is always less than the number of pounds of aluminum collected.

25. Each week the recycling center collects over 10 tons of newspaper and aluminum.

Graph each system of inequalities. (Hint: Find the region common to both graphs.)

26. $y > 2x$
$y \leq 3x + 1$

27. $y \leq x - 1$
$y > {}^-x + 1$

How do graphs of equations differ from graphs of inequalities?

1. 13.2×6.7

2. $25.888 \div 0.04$

3. $0.034 + 0.56$

4. $1.031 - 0.959$

5. $4\frac{2}{3} - 1\frac{5}{6}$

6. $3\frac{5}{8} + 7\frac{9}{16}$

7. $3\frac{3}{4} \times \frac{2}{3}$

8. $3\frac{1}{9} \div \frac{4}{15}$

Solve.

9. n is 35% of 127.

10. 186 is what perce of 62?

11. 52% of n is 39.

12. 42% of n is 8.82.

Find each area.

13. Square: $s = 3.5$ m

14. Rectangle: $b = 12$ cm, $h = 6.4$ cm

15. Triangle: $b = 34.2$ m, $h = 16.5$ m

16. Circle: $r = 152$ cm

Find each perimeter or circumference.

17. Equilateral triangle: $s = 85$ cm

18. Square: $s = 3\frac{3}{8}$ m

19. Rectangle: $b = 47.3$ m, $h = 16.9$ m

20. Circle: $r = 18.4$ cm

SUMMING UP

Using Problem Solving

Using Functions

The Nature Club wanted to rent a hall for their annual banquet. The club will need to pay $100 to rent the hall plus $8 per person for food.

A. Which expense will not change no matter how many people come to the banquet? Which expense will vary depending on how many people attend the banquet?

B. Write an equation to help the club determine the total cost of the banquet.

C. **What if** the club knows that at least 55 people but not more than 83 people will come to the banquet? What is the greatest and least amount of money that the club will have to pay for the banquet?

Sharing Your Ideas

1. Look at your equation. Which quantity is variable? How did you represent this?

2. **What if** you charged each person who attended the banquet $8 plus an equal share of the $100 rental fee? Write an equation that shows how to determine the cost for each person.

Practice

3. The alumni club is paying for the trip to the ball game. The bus will cost $200. They will also need to pay the $5 admission charge for each person. Write an equation that shows how to find out how much the trip will cost.

4. Terry is buying fence posts. Each post is $5. He has a coupon that will give him $3 off his bill. Write an equation that shows how to find out how much his total bill will be.

5. The money collected in the Charity Fund Drive will be divided equally among 5 charities. An anonymous donor has agreed to donate an additional $50 to each charity. Write an equation which shows how to find out how much money each charity will make. Graph the equation.

6. Sixty dollars will be divided equally among club members who complete an obstacle course. There is a $2 entrance fee to the contest. Write an equation that shows how to find out how much money a member who completes the course will gain or lose. Graph the equation.

7. Ms. Bryant pays $.50 for each pint of berries that is picked. She sells the berries for $1 per pint. Write an equation which shows how much money Ms. Bryant will make if she sells all the berries that are picked.

8. Write a problem that can be expressed as an equation. Exchange it with a partner. Write the equation and graph it.

Summing Up

9. Why are graphs helpful in working with problems like the ones in this lesson?

10. How could writing these equations be helpful to the people described in these problems?

Chapter Review

Classify. Write *integer, rational, irrational,* and *real.* pages 454–455

1. $^-1\frac{2}{3}$ 2. 5   3. $\sqrt{3}$ 4. 3.06   5. 0

Graph each relation on a real-number plane. pages 456–457

6. (3, $^-$1), (0.5, 0), ($\sqrt{2}$, 1)

7. (2, $^-$3), ($^-$1, 0), (0, 2), (4, $^-$2)

8.
x	y
1	5
0	4
$^-$1	3
$^-$2	2

9.
x	y
$^-$3	9
0	0
3	9

Write *function* or *not a function*. Explain your choice. pages 458–459

10. (3, 2), ($^-$1, 0), (0, $^-$1)

11. ($^-$3, $^-$3), ($^-$1, $^-$1), (0, 0)

12. (2, $^-$1), (3, 2), (2, $^-$2), (4, 0)

13.
x	y
$^-$2	5
$^-$1	4
0	3
1	2
2	1

14.
x	y
$^-$2	$^-$2
$^-$1	$^-$1
0	0
$^-$1	$^-$4
$^-$2	$^-$3

Graph each equation. pages 464–465

15. $y = 3x - 1$ 16. $y = ^-x + 3$ 17. $x + y = 5$ 18. $y = \frac{^-1}{2}x$

Find the slope of the line containing each pair of points. pages 466–467

19. (2, 2.5), (1, 0.5)   20. (3, $^-$1), (0, $^-$1)   21. (2, $^-$1), ($^-$3, 4)   22. ($^-$1, $^-$2), ($^-$2, $^-$1)

Give the slope and *y*-intercept of each line. pages 466–467

23. $y = 2x - 1$ 24. $y = 3x$ 25. $y = ^-x + 7$ 26. $x + y = 7$

Solve each system of equations by graphing. pages 468–469

27. $y = 2x + 3$
   $y = \frac{^-1}{2}x - 2$

28. $y = 1$
   $y = x - 1$

29. $y = 2x + 1$
   $y = 3x + 2$

30. $x = ^-3$
   $y = 2x + 3$

Graph each inequality. pages 470–471

31. $y \geq 2x - 1$ 32. $y \leq \frac{1}{2}x + 2$ 33. $y > x - 4$ 34. $y < ^-x + 2$

Solve. pages 462–463

35. A sample of fish from a lake contained 5 times as many catfish as bass. There were 42 fish in the sample. How many of each kind of fish were in the sample?

Chapter Test

Give an example of each.

1. a rational number that is not an integer

2. an irrational number

3. a negative integer

4. a rational number in decimal form

Graph each relation on a real-number plane.

5. $(6, {}^-1), (2, {}^-2), (\sqrt{2}, 1), ({}^-1.5, 0)$

6.

x	$^-2$	$^-1$	0	1	2
y	$^-4$	$^-5$	$^-6$	$^-7$	$^-8$

Graph each equation.

7. $y = {}^-2x + 5$

8. $y = 3x$

9. $y = {}^-3$

10. $x = 2$

Find the slope, y-intercept, and equation of each line.

11.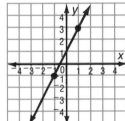

12.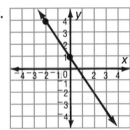

Solve each system of equations by graphing.

13. $y = x + 3$
    $y = {}^-2x$

14. $y = 3x + 2$
    $y = {}^-x$

15. $x + y = 6$
    $y = 4$

Graph each inequality.

16. $y \geq {}^-2x + 1$

17. $y < 3x$

18. $y \leq {}^-x + 4$

Solve.

19. A sample of birds' eggs showed twice as many damaged eggs as undamaged ones. There were 18 eggs in the sample. How many eggs were damaged?

20. A team of 15 ecologists arrived at the site. There were 3 more men than women. How many men were on the team?

THINK   Solve for x, y, and z.
$y = x + 2$
$3x - y = 2$
$x + y = z$

AT THE COMPUTER

Functions

The rule for the function $y = 2x + 3$ is to multiply each number by two and then add three. What is the output for $x = {}^-5$?

Materials: Logo

A. Define the procedure F that finds the output for the function $y = 2x + 3$. Enter `PRINT F 10`. What is the output for $x = 10$?

```
TO F :X
OP 2 * :X + 3
END
```

B. Use the procedure F to find the output for each input.

- 5
- ⁻3
- 0
- 40

C. Complete each procedure so that it finds the output for the function in each corresponding chart. Define and check each procedure. Then complete each chart.

```
TO G :X
OP _____
END
```

X	Y
4	7
3	4
2	1
1	⁻2
0	⁻5
⁻1	
⁻2	⁻11

```
TO H :X
OP _____
END
```

X	Y
4	⁻1
3	1
2	
1	5
0	7
⁻1	
⁻2	

```
TO J :X
OP _____
END
```

X	Y
4	12
3	11.5
2	11
1	
0	10
⁻1	9.5
⁻2	

```
TO K :X
OP _____
END
```

X	Y
	20
3	12
2	
1	2
0	0
⁻1	0
⁻2	2

D. Take turns with a partner to guess the rule. Write a procedure for any rule you choose. Challenge your partner to find the rule by calling the procedure for different values of X.

Sharing Your Results

1. Explain how you found the rule in **D**.

2. What values of X did you use to guess the rule in the fewest tries?

Extending the Activity

The graph of the function $y = 2x + 5$ is shown at the right. Is the point ($^-5$, $^-5$) on the graph? How do you know?

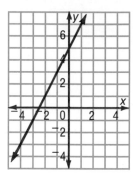

3. Define the PTONLINE procedure that inputs coordinates for x and y and prints TRUE if the point is on the line $y = 2x + 5$ or FALSE if it is not. Enter PTONLINE 3 5. Is (3, 5) on the graph?

```
TO PTONLINE :X :Y
PR :Y = 2 * :X + 5        This is equivalent to an "If then else" statement.
END                       If y = 2x + 5 then print TRUE, else print FALSE.
```

4. Use the PTONLINE procedure to find out whether each point is on the line $y = 2x + 5$. Write *yes* or *no*.

   a. (5, 15)   **b.** (0, 5)   **c.** ($^-10$, $^-15$)   **d.** ($^-1$, 7)

5. What part(s) of PTONLINE would you change for an equation of a different line? Edit the procedure and then use it to find out if each point is on the given line. Record *yes* or *no*.

   a. $y = 10x + 5$ (2, 25), ($^-5$, 0), (0, 5)

   b. $y = ^-12x + 15$ (3, 20), (0, 0), (1, 27)

   c. $y = ^-5x$ (1, $^-5$), (0, 0), (2, 10)

   d. $y = x - 20$ (10, $^-10$), (0, $^-20$), ($^-10$, $^-30$)

   e. $y = 0.5x + 10$ (20, 20), (0, 10), ($^-10$, $^-15$)

Summing Up

6. Describe a method to find out if a given point is on a given line.

7. **What if** you know the x coordinate of a point on the line $y = 5x - 2$. Explain how you can find the y coordinate of the point.

Parallel and Perpendicular Lines

These three lines are parallel. How are these equations similar?

$y = 2x + 3$
$y = 2x$
$y = 2x - 4$

▶ Parallel lines have equal slopes.

Choose the line that is parallel to the given line.

1. $y = 2x + 3$

a. $y = 3x + 2$ **b.** $y = x + 3$ **c.** $y = 2x - 1$

2. $y = 3x$

a. $y = {}^-3x$ **b.** $y = 3x - 1$ **c.** $y = x + 3$

3. $y = {}^-2x - 1$

a. $y = {}^-2x + 5$ **b.** $y = 2x$ **c.** $y = {}^-x - 2$

4. $y = \frac{1}{3}x + 5$

a. $y = 3x + 5$ **b.** $y = \frac{1}{3}x$ **c.** $y = 5x + \frac{1}{3}$

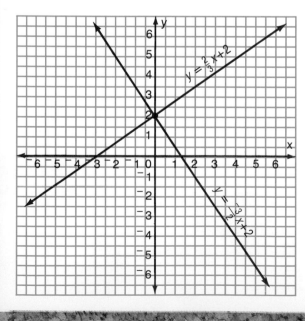

The two lines at the left are perpendicular. Look at each equation.

$$y = \frac{2}{3}x + 2$$

$$y = \frac{{}^-3}{2}x + 2$$

What is the slope of each line?

▶ The product of the slopes of two perpendicular lines is $^-1$.

Write the slope of a line perpendicular to each line.

5. $y = \frac{2}{3}x + 5$ **6.** $y = 4x - 1$

7. $y = {}^-5x + 1$ **8.** $y = \frac{{}^-1}{4}x - 2$

9. $y = \frac{{}^-3}{5}x$ **10.** $y = x$

The last four chapters of this book covered topics in probability, geometry, and algebra. Permutations and combinations are studied in probability.

What's for Dinner?

Arranging objects in a particular order is called a **permutation.** Three utensils can be arranged six different ways by being placed side by side.

In how many ways can four people sit at a table with four chairs? Try this with your family. If there are not four people available, have an imaginary guest or guests for dinner. Use one side of the table as the head chair each time you make a different seating arrangement.

Make a list of the different arrangements. Did you find 24?

In a **combination,** order is not important. Choosing two items out of three to serve for dinner is an example of a combination. Fish and rice represent the same dinner as rice and fish.

salad   peas   fish   rice   chicken legs

How many different ways can you prepare dinner, using any three of these foods? Make a list of all the different dinner combinations you can make. One combination is rice, peas, and salad.

After dinner, work together to give one example of a permutation or a combination involving the family.

Final Review

Choose the correct answer. Write A, B, C, or D.

1. Compare. 10^6 ⬤ 1,000,000

   A $<$ **C** $=$

   B $>$ **D** not given

2. 774×8.5

   A 65,790   **C** 1,006.2

   B 6,579   **D** not given

3. What is the LCM of 25 and 20?

   A 80   **C** 100

   B 5   **D** not given

4. $4\frac{3}{4} - 1\frac{7}{8}$

   A $3\frac{1}{8}$ **C** $3\frac{7}{8}$

   B $2\frac{7}{8}$ **D** not given

5. Evaluate $2a + 4b$ for $a = 2$ and $b = 6$.

   A 28   **C** 20

   B 68   **D** not given

6. Solve for m. $104 = m - 32$

   A $m = 136$ **C** $m = 62$

   B $m = 72$ **D** not given

7. How many sides does an octagon have?

   A 6   **C** 8

   B 5   **D** not given

8. What type of figure is *ABCD*?

   A square   **C** triangle

   B rectangle   **D** not given

9. $14 \cdot {}^-6$

   A 84   **C** $^-84$

   B 8   **D** not given

10. Solve for n. $6n + {}^-3 = 21$

   A $n = {}^-4$ **C** $n = {}^-6$

   B $n = 4$ **D** not given

11. What is 24,000 written in scientific notation?

   A 2.4×10^4 **B** 24×10^3

   B 2.4×10^{-4} **D** not given

12. What is $\sqrt{169}$?

   A 169   **C** 13

   B 13^2 **D** not given

13. Solve the proportion. $\frac{3}{n} = \frac{1.5}{0.45}$

   A $n = 0.4$ **C** $n = 1.728$

   B $n = 0.9$ **D** not given

14. Find t.   80 km in 1 h
              100 km in t h

   A 1.25 h   **C** 1.5 h

   B 48 min   **D** not given

15. What is $\frac{7}{8}$ as a percent?

   A 12.5%   **C** 87%

   B 78%   **D** not given

16. 72 is what percent of 120?

   A 40%   **C** $166\frac{2}{3}$%

   B 60%   **D** not given

Choose the correct answer. Write A, B, C, or D.

17. What is the area?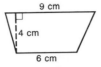

   A 108 cm^2 **C** 60 cm^2

   B 30 cm^2 **D** not given

18. What is the volume?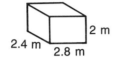

   A 14.4 m^3 **C** 13.44 m^3

   B 1,344 m^3 **D** not given

19. A card is chosen at random. What is P(vowel or f)?

   | a | b | c | d | e | f | g |

   A $\frac{2}{7}$ **C** $\frac{4}{7}$

   B $\frac{3}{7}$ **D** not given

20. What property is illustrated?

   $$\frac{^-4}{7} \cdot \frac{7}{^-4} = 1$$

   A Additive Inverse   **C** Multiplicative Inverse

   B Commutative   **D** not given

21. Solve for y. $y + 7 < 2$

   A $y < {}^-5$ **C** $y < 9$

   B $y > {}^-5$ **D** not given

22. Which classification describes $\sqrt{3}$?

   A rational   **C** integer

   B irrational   **D** not given

23. What is the slope of $y = 2x + 4$?

   A $\frac{1}{2}$ **C** 2

   B 4   **D** not given

Solve.

24. Bert bought 2 cassettes at $6.99 each, 1 compact disc at $14.99, and 3 records at $3.99 each. He had a discount coupon for 10% off. How much did he pay?

   A $40.94   **C** $36.85

   B $23.37   **D** not given

Solve.

25. 18 people rode in 6 cars on the sky ride at the theme park. The first 2 cars had 2 people in each. No other car had fewer than 3 in it. What is the greatest number of people in any of the cars?

   A 5   **C** 4

   B 6   **D** not given

Make a list to solve 26.

26. The perimeter of a rectangular garden is 76 ft. What is the greatest possible area it could have?

   A 1,444 ft^2 **C** 361 ft^2

   B 357 ft^2 **D** not given

Solve.

27. Four boys were finishing a race. Lenny finished between Pete and Owen. Sam came in before Lenny but behind Pete. In what order did they finish the race?

   A O, S, L, P   **C** P, S, L, O

   B L, S, O, P   **D** not given

Extra Practice

────────────────── **Set A** ──────────────────

Find the next 3 terms for each sequence. pages 2–5

1. 0, 6, 12, 18, _____ , _____ , _____   **2.** 7, 21, 63, 189, _____ , _____ , _____

3. 1, 1, 2, 4, 7, _____ , _____ , _____   **4.** 3, 8, 18, 38, _____ , _____ , _____

────────────────── **Set B** ──────────────────

Write each using exponents. pages 6–11

1. $8 \times 8 \times 8$ **2.** 4.3×4.3 **3.** 25   **4.** nine squared

Write each as a product of factors. Then write the number in standard form.

5. 6^4 **6.** 15^2 **7.** 2^8 **8.** 0.7^3 **9.** 10^5 **10.** three cubed

Write each number in standard form.

11. seventeen and twenty-five thousandths   **12.** 10^7

13. $\frac{9}{100}$ **14.** $4\frac{1}{2}$ million   **15.** $6 \times \frac{1}{100}$ **16.** five to the fourth power

Find each product or quotient mentally.

17. 626×100 **18.** $5{,}603 \div 1{,}000$ **19.** $59 \div 1{,}000$ **20.** 340×10^4

21. $32.5 \times 1{,}000$ **22.** $64.548 \div 10^2$ **23.** $188 \div 10^0$ **24.** 100×0.76

────────────────── **Set C** ──────────────────

Estimate. pages 22–23, 26–29

1. $\begin{array}{r} 76{,}438 \\ +\ 3{,}251 \end{array}$ **2.** $\begin{array}{r} 492{,}254 \\ -\ 56{,}381 \end{array}$ **3.** $\begin{array}{r} 8{,}712{,}594 \\ +\ 541{,}937 \end{array}$ **4.** 57×32 **5.** $63.9 \div 5.4$

6. 71.6×3.9 **7.** $751.2 \div 83.6$

────────────────── **Set D** ──────────────────

Add, subtract, multiply, or divide. pages 20–21, 24–25, 30–31

1. $\begin{array}{r} 40.78 \\ +\ 1.94 \end{array}$ **2.** $\begin{array}{r} 249.36 \\ +\ 504.27 \end{array}$ **3.** $\begin{array}{r} 1.6832 \\ -\ 0.5039 \end{array}$ **4.** $\begin{array}{r} \$25.00 \\ -\ 14.86 \end{array}$ **5.** $\begin{array}{r} 50.002 \\ -\ 1.76349 \end{array}$

6. $43.88 + 54.512 + 7.9$ **7.** $5.64 - 0.706$ **8.** $19 - 3.602$

9. $\$11.87 + \$3.70 + \$128.75$ **10.** $320.7 + 0.46 + 73.04$

11. 8.75×0.05 **12.** 2.192×60 **13.** $0.46 \overline{)13.34}$ **14.** $85.05 \div 6.3$

15. 3.4×91.28 **16.** $\$.78 \times 54$ **17.** $3.354 \div 8.6$ **18.** $0.9 \overline{)20.4678}$

19. 0.993×45.4 **20.** 5.68×78 **21.** $0.26 \overline{)226.2}$ **22.** $28.88 \div 3.8$

Set A

Write the prime factorization of each. Use exponents. pages 40–45

1. 42 **2.** 120 **3.** 169 **4.** 40 **5.** 74 **6.** 117

Find the GCF and LCM of each.

7. 40, 50 **8.** 12, 42 **9.** 45, 60 **10.** 18, 72

11. 21, 26 **12.** 15, 35 **13.** 17, 32 **14.** 6, 15, 24

Set B

Express each decimal as a fraction. pages 48–53

1. 0.6 **2.** 0.45 **3.** 0.875 **4.** 0.63

5. 1.2 **6.** 3.24 **7.** 2.41 **8.** 5.004

Express each fraction as a decimal.

9. $\dfrac{4}{5}$ **10.** $\dfrac{7}{10}$ **11.** $\dfrac{5}{8}$ **12.** $\dfrac{13}{20}$

13. $2\dfrac{3}{4}$ **14.** $3\dfrac{2}{5}$ **15.** $1\dfrac{3}{8}$ **16.** $5\dfrac{7}{20}$

Set C

Estimate first. Then add, subtract, multiply, or divide. Write each answer in lowest terms. pages 58–71

1. $\dfrac{3}{8}$ $+ \dfrac{5}{6}$ **2.** $\dfrac{1}{4}$ $+ \dfrac{5}{8}$ **3.** $5\dfrac{1}{4}$ $+ 2\dfrac{3}{5}$ **4.** $12\dfrac{5}{6}$ $- 4\dfrac{9}{10}$ **5.** $21\dfrac{3}{4}$ $- 9\dfrac{1}{2}$

6. $16\dfrac{7}{8}$ $+ 4\dfrac{1}{2}$ **7.** $3\dfrac{1}{4}$ $+ 26\dfrac{2}{3}$ **8.** $7\dfrac{1}{2}$ $- 3\dfrac{2}{3}$ **9.** $9\dfrac{14}{15}$ $- 4\dfrac{29}{30}$ **10.** $12\dfrac{1}{2}$ $+ 9$

11. $3\dfrac{4}{9} + 2\dfrac{1}{6} + 4\dfrac{5}{12}$ **12.** $4\dfrac{5}{8} + 6\dfrac{7}{8} + \dfrac{15}{16}$ **13.** $9 - 3\dfrac{4}{9}$

14. $\dfrac{3}{4} \times \dfrac{3}{5}$ **15.** $1\dfrac{4}{5} \times \dfrac{11}{12}$ **16.** $4\dfrac{2}{7} \times 6\dfrac{2}{9}$ **17.** $\dfrac{3}{10} \times \dfrac{5}{6}$

18. $2\dfrac{1}{5} \times \dfrac{5}{11}$ **19.** $2\dfrac{2}{3} \times 3\dfrac{4}{5}$ **20.** $4\dfrac{1}{2} \times 5$ **21.** $\dfrac{3}{5} \times \dfrac{1}{4} \times \dfrac{5}{8}$

22. $\dfrac{2}{3} \div \dfrac{1}{3}$ **23.** $\dfrac{1}{4} \div \dfrac{2}{3}$ **24.** $3\dfrac{1}{2} \div 4\dfrac{3}{4}$ **25.** $1\dfrac{5}{8} \div 2\dfrac{1}{4}$

26. $5\dfrac{1}{4} \div \dfrac{1}{6}$ **27.** $2.5 \div \dfrac{1}{4}$ **28.** $\dfrac{5}{12} \div 3\dfrac{1}{4}$ **29.** $6\dfrac{1}{2} \div 3$

Extra Practice

Write an expression for each. pages 82–87

1. 12 more than 9

2. a number c less than 8

3. the product of a number d and 10

4. the quotient of 15 and a number m

5. 4 more than twice a number x

6. 24 decreased by a number y

7. 75 increased by a number a squared

8. the sum of a number z and 14

Evaluate each expression.

9. $7 - 4 + 5$

10. $6 \div 3 + 15$

11. $\frac{6 + 2}{4} \times (10 + 3)$

12. $35 \cdot (2 + 5) \div 5$

13. $(12 + 5 - 3) \div 7$

14. $(9^2 + 6) \div 3$

Evaluate each expression. Let $a = 12$, $b = 3$, $c = 5$, and $d = 4$.

15. $12 - 2c$

16. $3c - d$

17. $b^2 - 9$

18. $2a + b$

19. $(b + c + d) \div a$

20. $d^2 + 16$

21. $3a \div bd$

22. $b^4 \div b^2$

Write an equation for each. pages 88–91

1. The sum of a number a and 6 is 15.

2. Ten less than a number b is 8.

3. A number x divided by 9 is 10.

4. Four less than the product of 3 and a number y is 11.

5. A number z divided by 12 is 3.5

6. 17 decreased by a number n is 4.

Use the number facts to solve mentally. Check by substitution.

7. $a - 5 = 18$

8. $b + 12 = 15$

9. $9 = c - 4$

10. $21 = 6 + d$

11. $4n = 32$

12. $180 = 6m$

13. $1.4 = \frac{84}{q}$

14. $450 = 1.5r$

Set A

Solve each equation and check. pages 96–105

1. $t + 64 = 91$ **2.** $r - 36 = 48$ **3.** $24.35 = s + 17$ **4.** $w - 42.6 = 29$

5. $108 = x + 59$ **6.** $16 = y - 35.7$ **7.** $g - 4.8 = 9.3$ **8.** $128 = g + 16.4$

9. $16c = 480$ **10.** $\frac{f}{4} = 32$ **11.** $285 = 15g$ **12.** $14 = \frac{d}{7}$

13. $a \div 8 = 18$ **14.** $7.5c = 45$ **15.** $5 = \frac{b}{3.4}$ **16.** $3e = 7.2$

17. $4x - 5 = 43$ **18.** $60 = 3n + 6$ **19.** $\frac{k}{5} + 3 = 16$ **20.** $12 = \frac{y}{4} - 8$

21. $6r + 1 = 55$ **22.** $0 = 8m - 40$ **23.** $42 = 5t + 7$ **24.** $\frac{r}{3} - 12 = 9$

Set B

Use figure 1. $\overleftrightarrow{AB}$ and $\overleftrightarrow{CD}$ intersect to form right angles. pages 116–119

1. Name two pairs of vertical angles.

2. Name a pair of adjacent angles.

3. Name a pair of adjacent angles that are not also supplementary.

4. Name a pair of complementary angles.

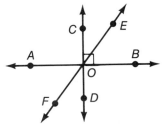

Figure 1

Find the missing measures.

5.

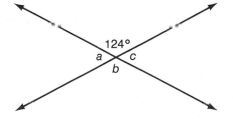

6.

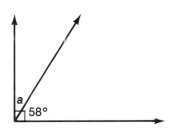

7.

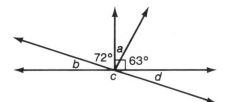

8.

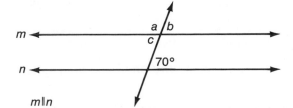

$m \| n$

Extra Practice

Find the missing angle measure in each polygon. pages 120–125, 130–133

1.

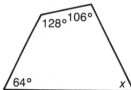

128° 106°
64° x

2.

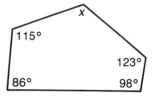

x
115°
123°
86° 98°

3.

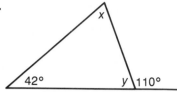

x
42° y 110°

For each triangle, find the missing measures.

4.

45°
y
x
9

5.

x
18   y
46°   46°
27

6.

12   12
x
12

The polygons in each exercise are congruent. Find the missing measures.

7.

A   c   B
70°
15   15
d
C

Z
y 40° x
X a b Y
9

8.

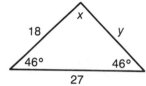

8
Q   R
10
70° 110°
P   S

L a M
c
K 110° J
b

9.

b
Q   125° R
a
T   55°   S

D   A
8
x B
y 6
C

Find the missing measures.

10.

A
x   B
O

m $\widehat{AB}$ = 80°

11.

A
x
O   B

m∠AOB = 38°

12.

A
O   C
x
B

m $\widehat{AC}$ = 148°

13.

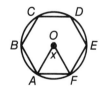

C   D
B   O   E
x
A   F

ABCDEF is a
regular hexagon

Complete. pages 134–139

1. A hexagonal prism has _____ faces, _____ vertices, and _____ edges.

2. A pentagonal pyramid has _____ faces, _____ vertices, and _____ edges.

3. A cylinder has two _____ and _____ bases.

4. A _____ has only one base and its lateral surfaces meet at one point.

5. A _____ has no flat surfaces.

Set A

Write the value of each. pages 150–151

1. |32| **2.** |⁻46| **3.** |⁻65| **4.** |53| **5.** |178|

Compare. Write <, >, or = for each ●.

6. ⁻7 ● 0   **7.** ⁻9 ● ⁻3   **8.** ⁻2 ● 8   **9.** ⁻37 ● ⁻54

10. 6 ● ⁻3   **11.** 25 ● ⁻25   **12.** 15 ● ⁻14   **13.** |12| ● |⁻13|

Order each from least to greatest.

14. ⁻2, ⁻5, 5, 2   **15.** ⁻4, 0, ⁻7, 3   **16.** ⁻3, 4, ⁻5, 2

Set B

Add, subtract, multiply, or divide. pages 152–159, 164–165

1. 9 − ⁻3   **2.** 18 + ⁻15   **3.** 8 − 17   **4.** ⁻16 − 9

5. ⁻43 − 32   **6.** ⁻56 + 19   **7.** ⁻31 − ⁻14   **8.** ⁻41 − 6

9. 27 − ⁻13   **10.** 9 − 33   **11.** ⁻12 − ⁻28   **12.** ⁻35 + 52

13. ⁻4 · ⁻19   **14.** 8 · ⁻15   **15.** ⁻45 ÷ 15   **16.** 72 ÷ ⁻12

17. ⁻64 ÷ ⁻4   **18.** ⁻98 ÷ 7   **19.** ⁻26 · 3   **20.** ⁻3 · ⁻15 · 2

21. ⁻6 · 5 · ⁻2   **22.** 8 · ⁻1 · 6   **23.** ⁻4 · 9 · ⁻3   **24.** 6 · ⁻8 · 5

Set C

Evaluate each expression. Let $a = ⁻2$, $b = ⁻3$, $c = 9$. pages 166–169

1. $5a + b$ **2.** $\frac{2c}{ab}$ **3.** $1 - ab$ **4.** $9 - c ÷ b$

Solve each and check.

5. $x - 12 = ⁻8$ **6.** $⁻4y = 56$ **7.** $a + ⁻15 = 4$ **8.** $⁻8c = ⁻96$

9. $6c + 5 = ⁻31$ **10.** $⁻7m + 19 = ⁻2$ **11.** $8w - 16 = 8$ **12.** $6 = 3t - ⁻24$

13. $18 + ⁻5n = ⁻17$ **14.** $4(5 + ⁻2) = 3x + ⁻9$ **15.** $5 - 8c = 9(⁻3)$ **16.** $27 = 4y + 43$

Set D

Using graph paper, draw the x-axis and the y-axis. Then graph each point. pages 170–171

1. $A(⁻2, 5)$ **2.** $B(4, 7)$ **3.** $C(6, ⁻3)$ **4.** $D(0, ⁻4)$ **5.** $E(⁻5, ⁻5)$

Extra Practice

Set A

Write each as the quotient of two integers in lowest terms. pages 180–183

1. $4\frac{1}{3}$ **2.** $^-3$ **3.** 0.045 **4.** $^-0.18$ **5.** $\frac{4}{72}$

Compare. Use <, >, or = for each ●.

6. $\frac{^-3}{10}$ ● $\frac{^-1}{5}$ **7.** $\frac{5}{12}$ ● $\frac{1}{3}$ **8.** $^-0.6$ ● $^-0.9$ **9.** $^-0.42$ ● $^-0.4$

Write in order from least to greatest.

10. $^-1.25, \frac{7}{8}, ^-2\frac{2}{3}$ **11.** $\frac{5}{9}, \frac{^-3}{10}, \frac{3}{5}$ **12.** $\frac{^-5}{8}, \frac{^-1}{3}, \frac{^-5}{12}$

Set B

Add, subtract, multiply, or divide. pages 184–187

1. $\frac{^-1}{3} + \frac{^-5}{6}$ **2.** $3.49 - 6.72$ **3.** $\frac{^-5}{8} + \frac{5}{12}$ **4.** $^-2\frac{4}{9} - \,^-1\frac{7}{12}$

5. $\frac{^-4}{7} \cdot \frac{^-2}{3}$ **6.** $^-2.83 \cdot 1.8$ **7.** $\frac{^-1}{4} \div 0.6$ **8.** $^-15 \div 2\frac{1}{7}$

Solve and check.

9. $2.1x - 5.3 = 2.26$ **10.** $2.8 + \,^-3.4x = \,^-12.84$ **11.** $\frac{x}{4} + 3.2 = 16.6$

12. $^-7 + 6x = 35$ **13.** $^-12x - \,^-28 = 340$ **14.** $\frac{x}{8} - \frac{3}{4} = \frac{7}{8}$

Set C

Change each to scientific notation. pages 190–195

1. $4{,}830$ **2.** $5{,}034{,}000{,}000$ **3.** 0.00074 **4.** 0.000000578

Write each in standard form. pages 200–203

5. 3.67×10^5 **6.** 3.405×10^{10} **7.** $6.07 \times 10^{^-9}$ **8.** $2.34609 \times 10^{^-3}$

Set D

Name or estimate each square root. pages 200–207

1. $\sqrt{36}$ **2.** $\sqrt{64}$ **3.** $\sqrt{144}$ **4.** $\sqrt{35}$ **5.** $\sqrt{62}$

Tell whether each is a right triangle.

6. $a = 60$ m, $b = 80$ m, $c = 90$ m   **7.** $a = 14$ m, $b = 48$ m, $c = 50$ m
8. $a = 8$ m, $b = 15$ m, $c = 17$ m

For each right triangle, find the missing measure, to the nearest unit.

9. $a = 9$ **10.** $a = $ _____   **11.** $a = 10$ **12.** $a = $ _____   **13.** $a = 200$
  $b = $ _____ $b = 13$ $b = 17$ $b = 64$ $b = $ _____
  $c = 18$ $c = 42$ $c = $ _____ $c = 102$ $c = 500$

Set A

Make a line plot and find the mode, median, mean, and range for each. pages 218–221, 226–227

1. 170, 190, 320, 240, 210, 200

2. 54, 61, 58, 55, 54, 56, 60, 57, 59

3. 403, 387, 415, 391, 387, 403, 389

4. 13, 17, 14, 18, 12, 18, 12, 12, 18, 13

5. 46, 57, 59, 51, 55, 54, 46, 48, 43, 61, 57, 47, 57, 46, 49, 39, 47, 46

6. 32, 35, 29, 28, 21, 42, 9, 32, 42, 47, 35, 38, 28, 46, 9, 9, 15, 38

Set B

Make a stem and leaf plot for each set of data. Find the mode, median, and range for each. pages 222–225

1. 51, 49, 45, 28, 32, 36, 34, 48, 60, 45, 44, 39, 52, 55, 55, 51, 53, 52, 61, 47

2. 76, 85, 64, 68, 36, 33, 38, 42, 40, 32, 33, 38, 81, 76, 74, 56, 65, 56, 53, 43

3. 34, 46, 52, 28, 29, 56, 37, 21, 53, 25, 13, 17, 31, 10, 45, 36, 18, 38, 41, 33

Make a box and whisker plot for each.

4. 52, 64, 58, 55, 52, 53, 61, 56, 54, 52, 53, 55, 62, 52, 54, 58, 54, 55, 52, 53, 53, 56, 52, 53

5. 200, 208, 225, 214, 210, 238, 212, 226, 227, 241, 208, 241, 211, 227, 212, 241, 214, 210, 241, 227, 225

Set C

Use the graph to estimate the population each year. pages 232–237

1. 1925

2. 1955

3. 1975

Use the table to estimate the population each year.

4. 1990

5. 2000

6. 2010

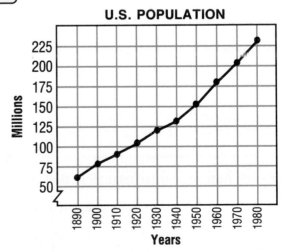

U.S. POPULATION

U.S. POPULATION (MILLIONS)			
1890	63	1940	132
1900	76	1950	151
1910	92	1960	179
1920	106	1970	203
1930	123	1980	227

Extra Practice

Set A

Use the data in the table to answer 1–5. pages 238–241

1. Make a frequency table and a histogram.

2. Use the frequency table to compute the range.

3. Use the frequency table to find the mode.

4. How many students read more than 40 books a year?

5. How many students read less than 40 books a year?

NUMBER OF BOOKS STUDENTS READ PER YEAR							
35	36	42	41	39	34	40	38
42	42	41	36	42	35	35	39
37	34	38	40	34	41	41	39
39	39	35	35	34	42	41	38
40	37	40	42	42	41	36	41
38	35	42	39	34	39	39	40

Set B

Write a ratio in fraction form for each. pages 250–257

1. 8 socks out of 12

2. 7 months out of 12

3. 4 km to 30 cm

4. 24 : 32

Find each missing term.

5. $\dfrac{\$9}{x} = \dfrac{\$1.20}{\$2.00}$

6. $\dfrac{y}{\frac{1}{4}} = \dfrac{16}{1}$

7. $\dfrac{4}{9} = \dfrac{n}{6}$

8. $\dfrac{9}{14} = \dfrac{36}{p}$

9. $\dfrac{m}{1.74} = \dfrac{2.4}{7.2}$

10. $\dfrac{8}{3} = \dfrac{x}{1.8}$

11. $\dfrac{35}{p} = \dfrac{5}{1.3}$

12. $\dfrac{8}{1.6} = \dfrac{68}{y}$

Set C

Use the scale 1 cm: 8 m. Find each missing measure. pages 256–261

1. scaled: 0.45 cm
   actual: _____

2. scaled: _____
   actual: 420 m

3. scaled: _____
   actual: 6 km

4. scaled: 25 mm
   actual: _____

Complete.

5. 116 cm in 12 s
   _____ cm in 3.6 s

6. 1.4 m in 3 s
   14 m in _____ s

7. 1,600 m in 10 min
   2,000 m in _____ min

8. 850 km in $\frac{3}{4}$ h
   204 km in _____ h

Set D

For each pair of similar triangles, find the unknown measures. pages 266–269

1.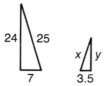

2.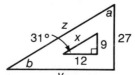

3.

Set A

Complete the chart below. pages 270–271

	Measurement	Precision	GPE	Actual measurement is between
1.	27.46 cm			
2.	19 m			

Set B

Find each missing angle to the nearest degree and each missing side to the nearest unit. pages 272–275

1.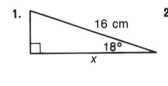
16 cm
18°
x

2.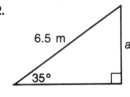
6.5 m
35°
a

3.
8 cm
b
52°

4.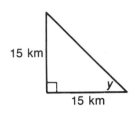
15 km
15 km
y

Set C

Write each as a percent. pages 286–293

1. $\frac{4}{5}$ **2.** 0.49   **3.** 0.7   **4.** $\frac{7}{9}$ **5.** $\frac{21}{50}$ **6.** 0.05

7. 0.324   **8.** 2   **9.** $\frac{5}{16}$ **10.** $3\frac{1}{2}$ **11.** 0.008   **12.** $\frac{3}{200}$

Write each percent as a decimal and as a ratio in lowest terms.

13. 75%   **14.** 4%   **15.** 53%   **16.** 80%   **17.** 4.8%   **18.** 14%

19. 92%   **20.** 45%   **21.** 62.5%   **22.** $\frac{1}{4}$%   **23.** $3\frac{1}{2}$%   **24.** 175%

Set D

Solve using any method. pages 298–305

1. n is $83\frac{1}{3}$% of 48.   **2.** 48 is 25% of n.   **3.** $\frac{1}{2}$% of 10 is n.

4. What percent of 112 is 14?   **5.** 24 is 60% of n.   **6.** 68 is 40% of n.

7. 69 is what percent of 23?   **8.** 192 is 40% of n.   **9.** 35 is 35% of n.

10. 160% of n is 4.   **11.** 4% of n is 20.   **12.** n is 17% of 13.

13. 16 is what percent of 24?   **14.** 500% of 18 is n.   **15.** 60% of 40 is n.

16. n is $9\frac{1}{11}$% of 220.   **17.** 6 is $1\frac{1}{2}$% of n.   **18.** $62\frac{1}{2}$% of n is 25.

19. 30% of n is 4.2.   **20.** 5% of 238.4 is n.   **21.** $92\frac{1}{2}$% of 1,000 is n.

Extra Practice

Set A

Estimate each. pages 306–307

1. 32% of 98.1

2. 21% of 38

3. 0.86% of 456

4. What percent of 317 is 82?

5. $34\frac{1}{2}$% of 87

6. 32% of 97

7. What percent of 152 is 8?

8. 17% of 58

9. 0.48% of 138

10. What percent of 14.5 is 6?

11. 241% of 60

12. 4% of 1,149

Set B

Use the data from the circle graph to answer 1 and 2. pages 308–317

1. If 50 students were surveyed, find the number of students that have each job.

2. Without measuring, find the number of degrees in the central angle for each job.

AFTER SCHOOL JOBS

Estimate the interest for each.

3. $p = \$620$
$r = 7\%$
$t = 3$ yr

4. $p = \$9,500$
$r = 6\frac{1}{2}\%$
$t = 1.5$ yr

5. $p = \$2,000$
$r = 12.6\%$
$t = 9$ mo

Find the discount and the sale price to the nearest cent.

6. regular price = $1,870
discount rate = 25%

7. regular price = $105
discount rate = $33\frac{1}{3}\%$

8. regular price = $82.38
20% off

9. regular price = $39.95
discount rate = 36%

10. regular price = $42.50
40% off

Find the selling price of each. Round to the nearest cent.

11. cost = $450
markup rate = 50%

12. cost = $2,540
markup rate = 45%

13. cost = $218
markup rate = 110%

14. cost = $564.50
markup = $169.35

Find the percent of increase or decrease.

15. from 60 to 81

16. from 24 to 21

17. from 150 to 252

18. from 120 to 40

Extra Practice

Set A

Find the area of each figure. pages 326–333

1.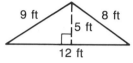
9 ft, 8 ft, 5 ft, 12 ft

2.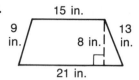
15 in., 9 in., 13 in., 8 in., 21 in.

3.
16 in., 30 in., 34 in.

4.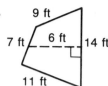
9 ft, 7 ft, 6 ft, 14 ft, 11 ft

Find the area of each shaded region. Use 3.14 for π. Round to the nearest one.

5.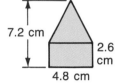
7.2 cm, 2.6 cm, 4.8 cm

6.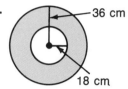
36 cm, 18 cm

7.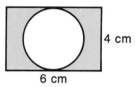
4 cm, 6 cm

8.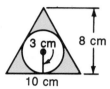
3 cm, 8 cm, 10 cm

Set B

Find the surface area of each prism. pages 338–345

1.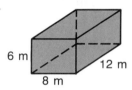
6 m, 12 m, 8 m

2.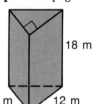
18 m, 9 m, 12 m

3.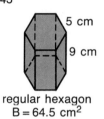
5 cm, 9 cm, regular hexagon B = 64.5 cm²

4.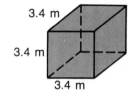
3.4 m, 3.4 m, 3.4 m

Find the volume of each solid. Use 3.14 for π. Round to the nearest one.

5.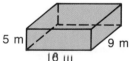
5 m, 9 m, 18 m

6.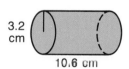
3.2 cm, 10.6 cm

7.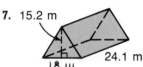
15.2 m, 24.1 m, 18 m

8.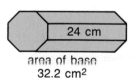
24 cm, area of base 32.2 cm²

9.
9 m, 6 m, 6 m

10.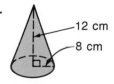
12 cm, 8 cm

Set C

Complete. pages 346–347

1. 23 L = _____ dm³

2. 2.56 mL = _____ cm³

3. _____ dm³ = 4.5 L

4. _____ mL = 6.53 cm³

5. 7.2 dm³ = _____ L

6. _____ mL = 8.9 cm³

7. 5 L of water weighs _____ kg

8. 9 cm³ of water weighs _____ g

Extra Practice

Set A

Write the probability of each event. pages 358–361

Toss a number cube with faces numbered 1 through 6.

1. P(factor of 4)   **2.** P(multiple of 10)   **3.** P(whole number less than 8)

Pick a card at random. ⁵ 5 ⁶ 6 ⁴ 4 ⁸ 8 ² 2 ⁹ 9

4. P(even number)   **5.** P(white)   **6.** P(prime number)

Set B

Six cards lettered A, B, C, D, E, F are in a box. pages 364–365

1. What are the chances of drawing two vowels if the first card is not replaced?

2. What are the chances of drawing two vowels if the first card is replaced?

Set C

A number cube is tossed. Find the number of favorable outcomes for each event. Then find the probability of A or B. pages 362–365

1. A:1   **2.** A:odd   **3.** A:5   **4.** A:factor of 4
   B:3   B:2   B:10   B:6

Set D

Find the relative frequency. pages 362–365, 372–377

1. A coin is tossed 50 times. Heads came up 32 times.

2. A number cube is tossed 30 times. Five came up 8 times.

Find the number of permutations for each.

3. In how many ways can you elect a president, vice-president, treasurer, and secretary from 18 club members?

4. How many possible arrangements are there to hang 4 pictures on a wall?

Find the number of combinations for each.

5. 2 letters from NUMBER   **6.** 3 players from 12 students

Compute.

7. $_{12}P_4$ **8.** $_{15}C_{12}$ **9.** $_{50}P_3$ **10.** $_6C_3$ **11.** $_{200}P_2$ **12.** $_{20}P_5$

Set A

Write reflection, translation, or rotation. pages 388–395

1.

2.

3.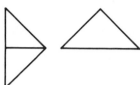

Copy figure 1 on graph paper.

4. Reflect figure 1 across the *y*-axis. Label the reflection figure 2.

5. Translate figure 1 by subtracting 8 from each *y*-coordinate. Label the translation figure 3.

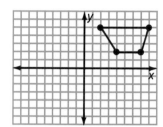

Figure 1

Copy the figure on graph paper.

6. Draw the result of $\frac{1}{4}$ turn CCW.

Set B

Which pair of triangles is congruent? Tell which rule applies. pages 402–403

1.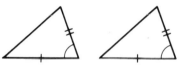

2.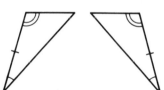

3.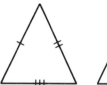

4.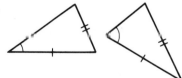

5.

6.

Set C

Trace each figure. Construct a figure congruent to each and then construct the bisector. pages 404–413

1.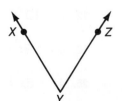

2.

3.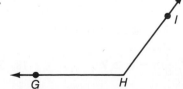

───────────────────────── **Set A** ─────────────────────────

Write the additive and multiplicative inverse for each. pages 424–435

1. $^-4$ **2.** $\frac{1}{3}$ **3.** $\frac{5}{9}$ **4.** 28   **5.** $^-1\frac{3}{4}$ **6.** $^-2.3$

Name the property illustrated.

7. $\frac{5}{6} + 0 = \frac{5}{6}$ **8.** $^-\frac{1}{4} + \frac{1}{4} = 0$ **9.** $\frac{3}{5} + \frac{1}{5} = \frac{1}{5} + \frac{3}{5}$ **10.** $4 \times \frac{1}{3} = \frac{1}{3} \times 4$

Solve and check.

11. $y + 7 = 13$ **12.** $n - 19 = 6$ **13.** $x + 3 = {}^-15$ **14.** $y - 8 = {}^-5$

15. $x + 9 = 0$ **16.** $12 = n + 3$ **17.** $^-16 + y = {}^-4$ **18.** $x + 27 = {}^-18$

19. $4x = 24$ **20.** $^-9y = 9$ **21.** $^-3n = {}^-45$ **22.** $\frac{1}{4}x = 7$

23. $16y = {}^-80$ **24.** $\frac{3n}{4} = 36$ **25.** $36 = \frac{1}{9}y$ **26.** $\frac{x}{15} = 15$

27. $3n + 14 = 35$ **28.** $6x - 12 = 18$ **29.** $^-8 = 5y + 17$ **30.** $^-4m - 20 = 0$

31. $5 - 3x = {}^-22$ **32.** $^-n - 6 = 15$ **33.** $\frac{y}{3} + 4 = 6$ **34.** $\frac{m}{5} + 12 = 9$

35. $3n + 4n = 35$ **36.** $9n - 6n = {}^-18$ **37.** $6x - x = 40$ **38.** $^-m + 4m = {}^-24$

39. $4x - 7x = {}^-9$ **40.** $3n + n + 4n = 32$ **41.** $3.2y = 12.8$ **42.** $5\frac{1}{4}n - 2\frac{3}{4}n = 10$

43. $6x + 32 = 4x$ **44.** $5n - 28 = {}^-2n$ **45.** $48 + 4y = 12y$ **46.** $m = 4m - 36$

───────────────────────── **Set B** ─────────────────────────

Solve and graph. Then check each solution. pages 440–445

1. $y + 5 > 12$ **2.** $n - 7 < 4$ **3.** $8x \geq 48$ **4.** $^-3y < 12$

5. $\frac{n}{4} \geq 2$ **6.** $8 - y > 3$ **7.** $\frac{1}{3}x < 4$ **8.** $y + 6 > {}^-13$

9. $9 < y - 8$ **10.** $28 \leq 4x$ **11.** $^-\frac{1}{2}n > 6$ **12.** $y - 10 \geq {}^-10$

13. $3x - 4 \leq {}^-25$ **14.** $4b - 5 \leq 19$ **15.** $5y + 4 < 39$ **16.** $54 < 3t + 6t$

17. $\frac{1}{3}m - 5 \geq 7$ **18.** $2 + 3y > {}^-13$ **19.** $n - 9n \leq 40$ **20.** $4x - 5x < 9$

$\boxed{\textbf{Set A}}$

Classify. Write integer, rational, irrational, or real. pages 454–455

1. 2.6   **2.** 4^3 **3.** $\sqrt{5}$ **4.** $^-19$ **5.** 2π **6.** 3.27814 . . .

Graph and label each point on a real number plane.

7. $A(\sqrt{3}, \,^-2)$ **8.** $B(^-1, \,^-\sqrt{3})$ **9.** $C(^-\sqrt{2}, 1)$ **10.** $D(2, \sqrt{2})$

$\boxed{\textbf{Set B}}$

Make a table for each relation. Which relations are functions? pages 456–459

1. 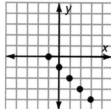   **2.** 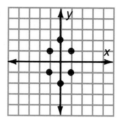   **3.**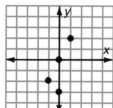

$\boxed{\textbf{Set C}}$

Copy and complete each table. Then graph each equation. pages 464–469

1. $y = 4 - x$ **2.** $y = x + 3$ **3.** $y = \,^-2x - 3$ **4.** $x + y = \,^-4$

x	y
$^-1$	
0	
1	
2	

x	y
$^-3$	
$^-1$	
0	
1	

x	y
$^-2$	
$^-1$	
0	
1	

x	y
$^-3$	
$^-2$	
0	
1	

Solve each system of equations by graphing. Check.

5. $y = x - 3$ **6.** $y = x + 4$ **7.** $y = x + 5$ **8.** $y = 2x - 1$
    $y = 2x$ $y = \,^-x - 6$ $y = \,^-3x - 3$ $y = x + 3$

$\boxed{\textbf{Set D}}$

Find the slope of the line containing each pair of points. pages 466–467

1. $(3, 5) \, (^-6, 2)$ **2.** $(4, 2) \, (0, \,^-3)$ **3.** $(^-3, 4) \, (^-4, 3)$ **4.** $(4, 7) \, (0, \,^-3)$

$\boxed{\textbf{Set E}}$

Graph each inequality.

1. $y > 3x + 2$ **2.** $y < -2x$ **3.** $y \geq 2x - 3$ **4.** $y \leq \frac{1}{2}x - 1$

Extra Practice

pages 17–19, 32–33

Set A

Solve. Use a calculator where appropriate. pages 17–19, 32–33

1. You have $8.00 to spend on school supplies. Make a list of what you would buy.

SCHOOL SUPPLIES	
3-ring binder	$3.79
200 sheets filler paper	1.29
10-pack pencils	.99
4-pack pens	.89
ruler	.29
protractor	.49
index dividers with tabs	.79
zipper pouch	1.59
eraser	.29
assignment book	.59

2. Your teachers want you to have a 3-ring binder so that you can keep lesson outlines. What other supplies will help you be more organized? How much will they cost?

3. If you have a coupon, you can buy one package of filler paper for $.79 with a purchase of $5 or more. What supplies would you buy to meet the $5.00 requirement?

4. This week you can buy 150 sheets of filler paper for $.98. How can you determine if this is a better value than the 200-sheet package?

5. Pens can be bought for $.29 each. How much is saved by buying a 4-pack instead of 4 separate pens? If you were buying 12 pens, how much would you save?

Set B

Solve. Use a calculator where appropriate. pages 55–57, 72–73

1. Betty worked 5 hours in the museum restaurant on Saturday. She made $61 including tips. What was her hourly rate of pay?

2. Kelly worked from 10:00 A.M. to 8:00 P.M. in the museum gift shop, with 30 minutes off for lunch and the same amount for dinner. How long did she work?

3. Arturo bought twenty $.25-stamps and ten $.15-post cards. How much did he pay for the stamps?

4. A weekly bus pass costs $21. The one-way fare is $2.50. Should Mr. Ky buy the pass or pay the fare each time he rides the bus to or from work?

5. One side of the Great Pyramid in Egypt is about 750 ft long. **What if** you want to make a model with a side 15 inches long? What scale would you use?

6. The Great Pyramid reaches about 450 ft above the ground. How high will your model be if you use the scale that you found in **5**?

Set A

Solve. Use a calculator where appropriate. pages 93–95, 106–107

1. From her house, Raquel rides her bike 3 blocks north, 5 blocks east, 7 blocks south, 9 blocks west, and 4 blocks north. How far is she from her house?

2. Adrian, Ben, Chin, Dean, and Emilio are the only players in a table tennis tournament. Each person must play all other persons once. How many games will be played?

Use numbers 1–5 for input. Make and graph patterns using the following rules:

3. Multiply the input by 3.

4. Multiply the input by 1, then add 2.

5. Multiply the input by $\frac{1}{2}$.

6. Multiply the input by 1, then add 4.

7. Copy the grid. Write the numbers 1, 2, 3, and 4 in the squares so that each row, column, and diagonal contains each number only once.

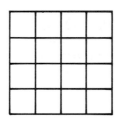

8. **What if** you had a 3 by 3 grid? Could you arrange 1, 2, and 3 in it by following the same rules? Explain.

Set B

Solve. Use a calculator where appropriate. pages 127–129, 140–141

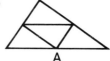

1. Each side of a triangle is divided into two equal parts, and the three bisection points are joined in all possible ways as shown in **A**. How many small triangles are formed?

2. Each side of a triangle is divided into three equal parts, and the six trisection points are joined as shown in **B**. How many small triangles are formed?

3. How many small triangles are formed when each side of the original triangle **A** is divided into 4 equal parts and the segments drawn?

4. Complete each pattern.

a.   ___ ___

b. 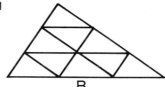 ___ ___

5. On Pep Day, everyone in Miss Jackson's homeroom wore blue—the school color. Ten students wore blue shirts, 15 wore blue pants, and 3 others wore blue shirts and blue pants. Make a Venn diagram with two circles to show these facts.

6. Use the Venn diagram you made for **5** to determine the number of students in Miss Jackson's homeroom.

Extra Practice

Set A

Solve. Use a calculator where appropriate. pages 161–163, 172–173

1. Verna bought one souvenir for $5.39 and a second one for $2.08. She received $.61 in change for the first purchase and $.02 in change for the second one. After the purchases, she had $7.03. How much did Verna start with?

2. The school day at Northside School ends at 2:45 p.m. There are six 45-minute periods, one 55-minute period, and a 30-minute lunch period. There are 5 minutes between periods and before and after lunch. At what time does school start?

3. Mr. Okada bought bait to go fishing. He gave $\frac{1}{3}$ of it to Mr. Palmer. He gave $\frac{1}{4}$ of what was left to Mr. Perez. Then he gave $\frac{1}{3}$ of the rest to Mr. Meola. Finally, Mr. Okada had 16 pieces of bait for himself. How many pieces did he buy?

4. Hector earns $4.70 per hour at a bakery. He also works part-time at a fast-food restaurant for $5.60 per hour. Last week he worked 10 hours at the bakery. His total earnings were $80.60. How many hours did he work at the fast-food restaurant?

5. A jewelry store multiplies the cost of an item by 3.2 to get the selling price. What if the store buys a watch for $15.25? What will be the selling price?

6. Look at **5**. This week, the watch is on sale for half price. A customer still pays more than what the store paid for it. How much more does the customer pay?

Set B

Solve. Use a calculator where appropriate. pages 197–199, 208—209

1. Peter has 80 coins—nickels, dimes, and quarters. He has four times as many dimes as quarters, and $\frac{1}{3}$ as many quarters as nickels. How many coins of each kind does he have?

2. Sally has a collection of 155 postcards. The number of foreign cards is $\frac{2}{3}$ the number of United States cards. How many cards of each kind does she have?

3. Mr. Stephens cashed a check for $175. He asked the teller to give him only five- and ten-dollar bills. She gave him 24 bills in all. How many bills of each kind did Mr. Stephens receive?

4. The office building parking lot has 180 parking spaces. There are four times as many spaces for full-size cars as there are for compact cars. How many spaces are there for full-size cars?

5. A 12-foot ladder just reaches the bottom of a second-floor window. The base of the ladder is $3\frac{1}{2}$ feet from the house. How far above the ground is the bottom of the window?

6. On a baseball field, it is 90 feet from one base to the next. When a catcher throws from home plate to second base, how far must the ball travel?

Set A

Solve. Use a calculator where appropriate. pages 229–231, 242–243

1. Sarah bought 2 albums and 3 cassettes. She paid $2.07 in sales tax. How much did she have to pay for her purchases?

2. Jon bought 4 compact discs and 2 cassettes. The sales tax was $3.76. He used a $25 gift certificate he had. How much additional money did he have to pay?

SALE	
Albums	6.29
Cassettes	6.98
Compact Discs	11.97

3. Which costs more—3 compact discs or 5 cassettes? How much more do they cost?

4. Laura bought 4 cassettes. Two of them were marked, "Buy one at regular price—get second one at half price." The sales tax was $1.32. How much did Laura have to pay?

5. An album weighs 8 oz; a cassette, 3 oz; and a compact disc, 4 oz. The record store orders 40 albums, 72 cassettes, and 80 compact discs from a supplier. How much will the shipment weigh?

6. The supplier wants to ship the order in **5** in two cartons. What is the best way to divide the order for shipping? Why?

Set B

Solve. Use a calculator where appropriate. pages 263–265, 276–277

1. On his pig farm Mr. Martin maintains 5 feeding stations. He starts at C and visits each location only once. How many different ways can he visit all 5 stations?

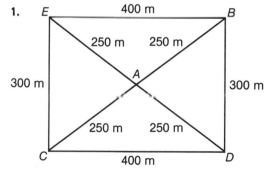

2. What is the shortest distance that he can travel and visit all 5 stations?

3. A certain polygon has 14 diagonals. How many sides does it have?

4. Another polygon has 20 diagonals. How many sides does it have?

5. The Mortons averaged 50 miles per hour on a 3-hour trip. Because of bad weather, the return trip took 2 hours longer. What was their average speed on the return trip?

6. Look back at **5.** What was the Mortons' average speed for the whole trip? Compare it with the average speed for each part of the trip.

Extra Practice

Solve. Use a calculator where appropriate. pages 295–297, 318–319

1. Four softball teams are in a double-elimination tournament. A team is not eliminated until it loses two games. What are the fewest number of games needed to determine a champion?

2. Mrs. Castillo is arranging 12 square tables. She will form a rectangle with no open space. Only one person can be seated at each open side of a table. What is the greatest number of people Mrs. Castillo can seat?

3. Amy puts 25 coins, heads up, in a row. Kay turns over the first coin and every second one after the first. Tom turns over the first coin and every third one after the first. Sara turns over the first coin and every fourth coin after the first. How many coins now show heads?

4. Baseball practice has been changed to an hour earlier. The coach calls 3 players. Each of them calls 2 other players who also call 2 other players. How many players have been told about the change?

5. To find a baseball player's fielding average, the sum of putouts and assists is divided by total chances (putouts + assists + errors). Compute the fielding averages for the players in the table.

Name	Put-Outs	Assists	Errors
Chan	6	5	1
Davis	8	2	1
Lyons	4	15	2
Perez	17	3	2

Solve. Use a calculator where appropriate. pages 334–335, 337–339

1. You have a balance with one 2-g, one 3-g, and one 5-g weights available. What different amounts could you weigh? Hint: a 4-g object can be weighed by putting it and the 3-g weight on the left side and the 2-g and 5-g weights on the right side.

2. A coin is tossed until 2 heads have appeared or 5 tosses have been made. Make a table of the possible results. (Example, HTH is one result.)

3. Two clocks both show the current time of 1:00 P.M. One runs accurately, and the other runs backwards. At what times within the next 24 hours will they both show the correct time?

4. A cube with each edge 2 in. long has a volume of 8 in.^{3} and a surface area of 24 in.^{2}. What is the volume and surface area of a cube with 3 in. edges?

5. Look back at **4.** Make a table to show the volume and surface area for cubes with edges 4, 5, and 6 inches. For what size cube will the number of units in volume equal the number of units in surface area?

Set A

Solve. Use a calculator where appropriate. pages 367–369, 376–377

1. The toll for the bridge over the Delaware River is $.50. The exact-change booth will not accept pennies. In how many ways can the exact change be paid?

2. At the refreshment stand at the football game, hot dogs are $1.00 and soft drinks $.75. Mrs. Singleton bought 5 items and paid $4.00. What did she buy?

3. A mathematics test has 30 multiple-choice questions. A student earns 5 points for each correct answer, 0 points for each incorrect answer, and 2 points for each unanswered question. Teresa had 2 incorrect answers and a score of 86. How many questions did she answer correctly?

4. Tony's grandfather gave him $10 each month. The grandfather gave Sophia $1 the first month, $2 the second month, $4 the third month, and so on, doubling the amount each month. In how many months will Sophia have received more money in total than Tony?

5. The Pizza House has tables that can seat 4 people and others that can seat 6. One night, 54 people are seated at 10 tables. How many of each kind of table are in use?

6. Draw a circle with a radius of 1 in. Then draw a square with each side 2 in. around the circle. It will just fit. Use the Monte Carlo method to find the area of the circle.

Set B

Solve. Use a calculator where appropriate. pages 395–397, 412–413

1. Manuel, Chen, and Lilia each play a different musical instrument—piano, guitar, or drums. Lilia and Chen do not use a stick. Manuel and Lilia do not pick a string. Which instrument does each person play?

2. Carter, Colby, Cathy, and Carl have red, blue, green, or orange as their favorite colors. Colby likes either orange or green. Carter does not like blue. Carl's favorite color is green. What color does each person like best?

3. The race had 5 cars and a close finish. The winning car had an even number on it and won by only one length. Car 3 beat car 5 by three lengths. Car 1 trailed car 4 by one length. Car 3 finished in third place, two lengths ahead of car 2. What was the order of finish?

4. The names of my mother, my father, my brother, my sister, and myself are Reuben, Jacob, Noah, Anna, and Barbara. I am older than Noah. Barbara is younger than I. Reuben is older than Jacob. Who am I?

5. Copy the figure. Connect the pairs of circles with the same numbers. No connectors should intersect, nor may they intersect any line segments.

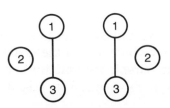

Extra Practice

Solve. Use a calculator where appropriate. pages 435–437, 444–445

For 1–4 tell whether the conclusion is correct or incorrect.

1. All Martians speak Latin. Mr. Arnold speaks Latin. Therefore, Mr. Arnold is a Martian.

2. All Martians speak Latin. Mrs. Horner is a Martian. Therefore, Mrs. Horner speaks Latin.

3. Calgary is in Canada. Peter does not live in Canada. Therefore, Peter does not live in Calgary.

4. Ankara is in Turkey. Seylan does not live in Ankara. Therefore, Seylan does not live in Turkey.

Write valid conclusions for 5–6.

5. Lake Superior is a natural lake with an area of 31,820 square miles. The Caspian Sea is the largest natural lake in the world.

6. Europe is north of the equator. Brazil is south of the equator.

7. Mary has $85. If a French franc is worth $.171, can she buy a bracelet that costs 550 francs?

8. If you were to travel to Canada, how could you find out the exchange rate between U.S. and Canadian dollars?

Solve. Use a calculator where appropriate. pages 459–461, 470–471

1. Mr. Kwan is depositing 40 five- and ten-dollar bills. The total value is $260. How many of each kind of bill are there?

2. A rectangular garden plot has an area of 90 ft^2 and requires 39 feet of fencing to enclose it. What are the dimensions of the garden?

3. A survey determines that for every 7 families in town who recycle aluminum cans, 2 other families do not. If there are 4,500 families in town, how many recycle aluminum cans?

4. The maintenance crew painted numbers from 1 to 173 on the parking spaces at the Park and Ride parking lot. How many digits did they paint?

5. For posters, a printer charges a $10 set-up fee and $.50 per poster. Write a function which shows the cost of printing posters. Graph the function.

6. Look at 5. If 20 posters are ordered, what will be the cost per poster? For 40 posters, what will be the cost per poster? Why are your answers different?

Selected Answers

1 Working with Whole Numbers and Decimals

Page 7
9. 5^2 **13.** $8 \times 8 \times 8$; 512
17. $3 \times 3 \times 3$; 27   **21.** 0.8×0.8; 0.64
27. 8   **31.** 256   **37.** 1   **41.** 10
45. 3

Page 9
9. fifty-two and eight hundredths
15. 30.05   **19.** $<$ **23.** $<$

Page 11
9. 1,600; 16,000   **13.** 42.09
15. 83.2   **17.** 0.0053   **21.** 8.438
23. 78

Page 21
9. 322   **15.** 924   **17.** 230
19. 400   **23.** $>$ **25.** $=$ **27.** $<$
29. 264   **31.** 1,470

Page 23   Estimates may vary.
7. $115   **9.** $1,000   **15.** 1,450,000
21. 19 h   **23.** $<$ **27.** exact

Page 25
5. 48.81   **7.** 60.87   **9.** $77.05
13. 73.822   **19.** 14.163
23. $0.946 - 0.754$

Page 27   Estimates may vary.
7. 56   **9.** 24,000   **11.** 568   **13.** 2,400
15. 12,500   **17.** 200   **23.** $>$ **27.** $<$

Page 29   Estimates may vary.
9. 8   **11.** 90   **17.** 3   **19.** 60
27. underestimate

Page 31
7. 2.3   **9.** 17.55   **11.** 6.3   **13.** 63
17. 12.3   **19.** $6.86   **23.** 0.065
25. 0.6419   **33.** 144.5

Pages 32–33
3. Mail packages together.

2 Number Theory and Fractions

Page 43
13. $2^3 \times 5$ **17.** $2^3 \times 11$ **19.** 3^5
21. 13^2 **23.** prime   **25.** prime
27. $3 \times 7 \times 13$ **33.** $n = 3$ **37.** 845
43. 2,303

Page 45
9. 15   **11.** 21   **13.** 216   **15.** 10, 120
17. 4, 48   **21.** 12, 72   **23.** 15, 450
29. 1, 912   **37.** true   **39.** true

Page 49
7. $\frac{1}{5}$ **9.** $\frac{5}{8}$ **11.** $\frac{29}{100}$ **21.** $2\frac{1}{125}$
27. 3.5   **33.** 1.375   **37.** c

Page 51
7. $0.\overline{27}$ **9.** $0.0\overline{9}$ **15.** 0.8   **21.** $>$
27. $<$ **31.** $\frac{5}{6}$, 0.875, $0.\overline{8}$

Page 53
11. $n = 16$ **17.** $n = 6$ **19.** $>$
23. $<$ **29.** $<$

Pages 56–57
3. Not enough information. You need to know how long it takes to listen to each tape.

Page 59   Estimates may vary.
11. 0   **13.** $\frac{1}{2}$ **17.** 1   **23.** 19
27. $11\frac{1}{2}$ **33.** 22

Page 61
7. $16\frac{3}{10}$ **9.** $16\frac{3}{8}$ **11.** $21\frac{2}{3}$
15. $73\frac{3}{8}$ **17.** $53\frac{7}{20}$ **19.** $21\frac{3}{4}$
23. $<$ **25.** $<$

Page 63

7. $7\frac{5}{9}$ **9.** $11\frac{5}{8}$ **15.** $3\frac{31}{32}$

21. $n = 15$ **25.** $6\frac{1}{8}$ **27.** $6\frac{1}{8}$

29. $5\frac{2}{3}$ **31.** 11

Page 65

9. $\frac{8}{15}$ **11.** $\frac{4}{33}$ **15.** $\frac{3}{16}$ **23.** $\frac{5}{16}$

29. $\frac{1}{6}$ **31.** $\frac{3}{16}$ **35.** $\frac{3}{14}$ **37.** $\frac{5}{12}$

41. $\frac{5}{18}$

Page 67

9. $\frac{16}{17}$ **11.** 26   **19.** 130   **27.** 10

34. $4\frac{1}{2}, 4\frac{5}{8}, 4\frac{3}{4}$

Page 69

5. 30   **7.** 90   **11.** 45   **15.** 20

19. $2\frac{1}{2} \times 50$

Page 71

7. 3   **9.** 7   **13.** $7\frac{1}{9}$ **17.** 52

19. $\frac{2}{9}$ **23.** 4   **29.** 16   **31.** $10\frac{1}{4}, 8\frac{1}{2}$

3 Pre-Algebra Expressions and Equations

Page 83   Expressions for **25, 27** may vary.

9. $7 + 4$ **13.** $50 + a$ **17.** $\frac{x}{4}$

25. a number n plus 1   **27.** 5 minus twice a number x **35.** $8n$

Page 85

7. 66   **9.** 14   **13.** 50   **19.** $5 + 7 - (4 \div 2) = 10$ **25.** $2 \times \$6 + 4 \times \$3 = 24$

Page 87

9. 22   **11.** 7   **13.** 4   **17.** 75

19. 300   **21.** 14

Page 89   Statement for **25** may vary.

9. $27n = 270$ **11.** $3.5 + b = 19.2$

25. A number x decreased by 17 is 34.

Page 91

5. no   **9.** no   **13.** 9   **15.** 3

21. 3   **25.** $2y = 24$; **c**

Pages 94–95

3. 8 minutes   **7.** not enough information

Page 97

11. multiply by 5   **17.** half 8   **23.** $\div$ 14

25. $- 16$ **27.** $\div 3$ **31.** $+$

Page 99

9. $d = 81$ **11.** $b = 108$ **15.** $n = 177$

17. $p = 65$ **19.** $r = 67$ **21.** $t = 98$

25. $w - 18 = 135$; $w = 153$

Page 101

9. $w = 20$ **11.** $y = 9$ **13.** $n = \frac{1}{2}$

21. $y = 0$ **23.** $t = 10.5$

29. $x = 45$ **33.** $23x = 161$; $x = 7$

41. $10r = \frac{1}{2}$; $r = \frac{1}{20}$

Page 103

5. subtract 12, divide by 3; $n = 20$

11. add 7, multiply by 2; $m = 38$

23. $2x + 4 = 24$; $x = 10$

Page 105

5. 18; 26; 34   **9.** 22, 27, 4.6

11. $P = 12$ cm   **15.** $V = 544$ cm^3

17. $x = 4t$ **21.** $s = \$4.25\ h$

4 Geometry

Page 117

11. $35°$ **13.** $x = 147°$, $y = 33°$, $z = 147°$

17. complement $62°$; supplement $152°$

21. false; two right angles are supplements

Page 119

3. alternate interior ∠ corresponding ∠

11. true

Page 121

3. Yes. Third angle $29°$ **9.** $x = 280°$

13. $1{,}440°$; $144°$

Selected Answers

Page 123
3. right isosceles   11. $a = 74°$; $x = 20$

Page 125
5. $A \cong D$; $B \cong E$; $C \cong F$; $c \cong f$; $d = 90°$; $e = 30°$

Pages 128–129
5. 36 blocks   9. 10 degrees

Page 133
11. inscribed: $\overarc{AD}$ 13. 42°   15. 21°
17. 72°   19. 67°

5 Pre-Algebra: Integers

Page 151
9. 500   15. $^-37$ 17. $^-3$ 19. 22
25. 107   27. 40   29. $<$ 35. $>$
43. $^-1$, 0, 10, 16

Page 155
9. $3 + {}^-1$ 11. $7 + {}^-4$
15. $8 + 0$ 21. $^-19$ 23. 41
33. 23   37. $^-57$ 39. 57   43. $^-1$

Page 157
9. $^-54$ 11. 85   15. $^-39$
21. $^-54$ 23. 96   29. 53
33. $^-27$ 35. 625

Page 159
9. $^-12$ 11. $^-12$ 15. $^-27$
17. $^-3$ 19. $^-36$ 21. $^-10$ 27. 4
33. $=$ 35. $>$

Pages 162–163
3. 37 fish   7. 1:45 P.M.

Page 165
7. Associative Property of Multiplication
15. Distributive Property of Multiplication over Addition; 6

Page 167
9. $^-28$ 11. $^-8$ 13. $^-2$ 15. $^-10$

19. $^-5$ 21. ^-32t; $t = 10$;
$^-32(10) = {}^-320$ ft per s
27. $^-54 \div (9 \div {}^-3) \div 2 = 9$

Page 169
9. $y = 9$ 11. $t = 17$ 13. $n = {}^-7$
17. $x = {}^-2$ 19. $x = {}^-5$ 21. $x = {}^-10$
31. $w = 1$ 37. $3m + 17 = 2$; $m = {}^-5$
41. $^-10$ 45. $^-4$

Pages 172–173
3. Child's Portion Menu
Swordfish $6   Halibut $5
Shark $5.25   Salmon $5.40
Tuna $4.50

6 Rational Numbers

Page 181
13. $\frac{13}{4}$ 15. $\frac{12}{1}$ 29. $\frac{7}{10}$ 33. 0.4
45. $^-20$

Page 183
9. $<$ 13. $>$ 20. 0.5; $\frac{1}{2}$
23. $^-3.25$; $\frac{^-13}{4}$ 27. $\frac{^-7}{12}$, $\frac{^-1}{2}$, $\frac{^-5}{16}$

Page 185
5. $\frac{5}{7}$ 11. $\frac{5}{36}$ 15. $\frac{^-19}{24}$ 19. $^-1\frac{5}{12}$
23. $^-1.2$ 29. $^-1\frac{1}{3}$ 35. $^-0.52$

Page 187
13. 8   15. 216   23. $^-4$
27. $2\frac{79}{100}$ 33. $^-3$

Page 189
7. $x = 4.1$ 9. $y = 6.4$ 15. $x = 12$
21. $m = {}^-17$ 25. $6t - 7 = 49$;
$t = 9\frac{1}{3}$

Page 191
17. 0.001   25. 10^3 33. 10^{-2}
35. 10^8 39. 10^{-14}

Page 193
11. 5   13. 4.321752
17. 7.89×10^6 25. 7,920,000,000
35. 1.39×10^6

Page 195
9. 2   13. $^-4$ 17. 4.0
21. 9.3×10^4 31. 0.0000000792

Pages 198–199
3. 10 whale bones and 5 walrus bones
7. $^-8$ degrees Fahrenheit

Page 205
11. no   15. yes

Page 207
11. 40 cm   15. 275 cm

7 Statistics

Page 221
5. none; 325; 175
9. 601; 610; 601; 21

Page 223
3. mode: 64; median: 64; range: 33
7. mode: 4.4; median: 5.0; range: 5.4
mode: 8.1; median: 8.1; range: 6.7

Page 227
5. mode: 64; median: 67; mean: $68\frac{11}{18}$;
range: 24

Pages 230–231
5. Oakleaf Company, 20 cuts at $15/cut =
$300   9. not enough information

Page 233
9. 10,240   13. about 3:40. 8 s

Page 235
11. about 92 persons per square mi

Page 237
5. Graph C

Page 239
7. up left to right is positive correlation

Page 241
5. 30 drivers   9. 7 cars

8 Ratio and Proportion

Page 251
7. $\frac{6}{10}$, or $\frac{3}{5}$ 11. $\frac{5}{24}$ 15. $\frac{12}{1}$
25. 6 white triangles to 9 small triangles
29. =   31. =

Page 253
7. $\frac{4}{10}, \frac{2}{5}, \frac{1}{2.5}$ 13. 120 miles per hour
19. 8 boards per wall section

Page 255
5. $\neq$ 13. =   17. $\frac{12}{34} = \frac{48}{x}$; 136
21. $\frac{25}{100} = \frac{75}{x}$; 300   29. 10

Page 257
5. $x = 10$ 9. $x = 5.6$ 17. $\frac{4}{7} = \frac{38}{x}$;
66.5 min

Page 261
5. $\frac{4.5}{13} = \frac{9}{26}$ 11. 20   15. 15.4
17. 19.2   23. c

Pages 264–265
3. 24 ways   9. 25 ft × 15 ft

Page 269
5. $x = 4$; $y = 8.5$

Page 271
9. 1 cm; 0.5 cm; 27.5 cm and 28.5 cm
17. 105 m   21. 33.6 cm

Page 273
11. 0.6947   17. 0.9994   19. 52°

Selected Answers

Page 275
5. $w = 6.1$ m; $y = 7.3$ m

9 Percent

Page 287
11. 22%   13. 28%   17. 50%

25. 40%   27. 90%   30. $\frac{1}{10}$

Page 289
19. 75%   21. 30%   27. $13\frac{1}{3}$%

31. 0.5, $\frac{1}{2}$ 35. 0.6; $\frac{3}{5}$ 43. $\frac{3}{100}$

47. 2%   53. b

Page 291
13. 10%   19. 46%   21. $\frac{1}{3}$ 27. $\frac{49}{50}$

29. 8%   33. 37.5%   41. <

Page 293
13. 150%   25. 0.5%   31. 0.001;

$\frac{1}{1000}$ 39. 2.75; $2\frac{3}{4}$ 45. $3\frac{1}{10}$; 3.1

51. $\frac{5}{8}$; 62.5%

Pages 296–297
3. $\frac{3}{4}$ of an hour   9. $.10 each; 97 balls

Page 299
9. 37   11. 10%   21. 40%   27. 70
33. 0.05   35. 100

Page 301
11. 300   17. 75%   21. 18   23. 0.994
29. 0.25; 0.5; 1.0; 2.0; double each answer

Page 303
13. $n = 1,100$ 15. $n = 100$
21. $n = 120$ 23. $n = 13$
27. $n = \frac{1}{2}$%   33. $n = 0.45$

Page 305
13. $n = 128$ 15. $n = 200$

21. $n = 35$ 23. $n = 12.46$
27. $n = 10,000$ 29. A

Page 307 Estimates may vary.
9. 7   11. 20   13. 400
25. c

Page 311   Estimates may vary.
5. $120   11. $1,400; $10,786.72

Page 313
5. $5; $10   11. $36.54; $62.21

Page 315
7. $450   17. $80; 18.75%

Page 317
11. increase, 10%   19. football

10 Geometric Measurement

Page 329
9. 850 ft^2 11. 500 ft^2 15. $8\frac{1}{3}$ ft

Page 333
5. 6,367.92 cm^2 ≈ 6,368 cm^2

Pages 336–337
3. 7:30 A.M.   7. 4 pages

Page 339
5. 124 cm^2 7. 181.5 m^2

Page 343
5. 1,056 m^3 11. C   15. 8

Page 347
7. 13   13. 4   19. 1,628 mL; 1,628 g

11 Probability

Page 359
7. 0, 1, 2, 3, 4, 5, 6, 7, 8, 9; 4   11. 2
15. 1   21. $\frac{1}{2}$

Page 363
5. 48   **11.** 24

Page 367
7. $4; \frac{2}{3}$ **13.** $\frac{5}{8}$

Pages 370–371
5. during the third year   **7.** 80 points

Page 373
9. $\frac{9!}{4!}$ **11.** $\frac{32!}{30!}$ **19.** 362,880
23. 2   **29.** 1,716   **39.** 50,616

Page 375
7. 90   **11.** 2,184   **20.** $\frac{16!}{7!}$

Page 377
9. combinations; 91   **17.** 165   **25.** 21

12 Transformations and Constructions
Page 393
5. $A_2(^-1,2)$ $B_2(^-4,5)$ $C_2(^-6,3)$ $D_2(^-4,1)$

Page 395
7. $\frac{1}{4}$ turn CW or $\frac{3}{4}$ turn CCW

Pages 398–399
5. Maria and Bernie; Elaine and Charles; Fran and Al

Page 403
9. yes; ASA

13 Pre-Algebra: Equations and Inequalities
Page 425
11. 2, $^-\frac{1}{2}$ **17.** Identity Property

Page 427
9. $n = 6$ **11.** $y = ^-13$ **13.** $x = ^-11$

37. $n + 5 = 12; n = 7$

Page 429
13. $x = 9$ **15.** $x = ^-3$ **17.** $n = 15$

Page 431
13. $n = 6$ **17.** $z = ^-5$ **23.** $x = ^-19$
29. $2n + 5 = 11; n = 3$

Page 433
9. $n = 2$ **11.** $b = 5$ **17.** $y = ^-12$
29. $x = 10$

Page 435
9. $x = 12$ **15.** $y = 3$ **21.** $n = 2$

Pages 438–439
3. correct   **7.** Louise, London; Marie, Rome; Ralph, Tokyo; John, Paris; Betty, Vienna

Page 443
9. $x > 6$ **13.** $x \le 2$ **25.** $x \le 10$
33. $=$

Page 445
7. $x \le ^-6$ **11.** $x \le 4$ **19.** $x \ge ^-3$
21. $n > 2$ **29.** $x = 3$

14 Pre-Algebra: Relations, Functions, and Graphing
Page 455
11. rational, real   **23.** true   **29.** 5

Pages 462–463
3. 9   **7.** 2 ounces

Page 465   Estimates may vary.
9. $^-2, 1, 2, 4$ **13.** y is about 2.7 ($2\frac{2}{3}$)

Page 467
7. $\frac{6}{7}$ **9.** 1   **11.** $m = ^-1; b = ^-6$
15. $y = 5x$ **19.** $m = ^-1; b = 3$;
$y = ^-x + 3$

Skill Hints

$3^4 = 3 \times 3 \times 3 \times 3 = 81$

For any number n except 0, $n^0 = 1$. $8.7^0 = 1$
When multiplying by a power of ten, move the decimal point to the right a number of places equal to the exponent.

$27.3 \times 10^3 = 27.3 \times 1,000 = 27,300$

Write each, using exponents.

1. $6 \times 6 \times 6 \times 6$

2. $8.2 \times 8.2 \times 8.2$

3. 0.5×0.5

Write each as a number in standard form.

4. 4^5

5. 2^7

6. 3.5^2

7. 9^3

8. 12^2

9. 5^0

Find n.

10. $8^n = 512$

11. $n^3 = 1,000$

12. $7^n = 1$

13. $2.6^n = 6.76$

14. $n = 3^3$

15. $n^4 = 256$

16. $10^n \times 7.3 = 7,300$

17. $892 \div 10^n = 8.92$

18. $5 \times 10^n = 5$

19. $3.6 \div 10^3 = n$

20. $n \div 10^4 = 50$

21. $10^3 n = 1.6$

Write each product or quotient.

22. 347×10^4

23. 6.2×10^3

24. 78.3×10^0

25. $27,000 \div 10^5$

26. $1,800 \div 10^2$

27. $7,000,000 \div 10^5$

H
I
N
T   In a repeating decimal, a bar is placed over the digit or digits
      that repeat.

$0.\overline{7} = 0.77777...$

$0.\overline{12} = 0.12121212...$

One way to change a fraction to a decimal is to divide the
numerator by the denominator

$\frac{1}{6}$ $\longrightarrow$ $6\overline{)1.0000}^{.1666...}$ $\longrightarrow$ $0.1\overline{6}$

Write each as a decimal.

1. $\frac{8}{9}$ 2. $\frac{3}{11}$ 3. $\frac{7}{8}$ 4. $\frac{4}{15}$ 5. $\frac{2}{3}$

6. $\frac{5}{22}$ 7. $\frac{7}{10}$ 8. $\frac{18}{25}$ 9. $\frac{4}{3}$ 10. $\frac{11}{9}$

Write each decimal without the bar.

11. $0.\overline{4}$ 12. $0.\overline{29}$ 13. $0.\overline{605}$ 14. $0.1\overline{75}$ 15. $0.15\overline{7}$

List in order from least to greatest.

16. $0.4, \frac{4}{9}, \frac{17}{50}$ 17. $\frac{5}{6}, \frac{4}{5}, 0.82$ 18. $1.7, \frac{16}{9}, 1\frac{1}{2}$

19. $\frac{1}{3}, 0.3, 0.2\overline{9}$ 20. $\frac{5}{8}, 0.6, \frac{2}{3}$ 21. $\frac{1}{6}, 0.1666, 0.1\overline{6}$

Compare. Use >, <, or = for each ⬤.

22. $\frac{1}{7}$ ⬤ 0.14 23. 0.5 ⬤ $\frac{5}{9}$ 24. $\frac{7}{8}$ ⬤ $0.\overline{8}$

25. $\frac{5}{11}$ ⬤ $0.\overline{45}$ 26. 0.3 ⬤ $\frac{1}{3}$ 27. $\frac{1}{6}$ ⬤ 0.2

28. 0.7 ⬤ $\frac{2}{3}$ 29. $\frac{3}{11}$ ⬤ 0.3 30. $0.\overline{5}$ ⬤ $\frac{5}{9}$

$\begin{smallmatrix}H\\I\\N\\T\end{smallmatrix}$ To solve an equation, use inverse operations. Use the same operations on *both* sides of the equation.

Solve. $\quad 2n+3=31$

THINK: The inverse of addition is subtraction.
Subtract 3 from both sides.
The inverse of multiplication is division.
Divide both sides by 2.

$$2n+3=31$$
$$2n+3-3=31-3$$
$$2n=28$$
$$\frac{2n}{2}=\frac{28}{2}$$
$$n=14$$

Solve and check.

1. $4n=24$

2. $12=5+y$

3. $150=10x$

4. $n-11=30$

5. $a\div 3=12$

6. $x-5=21$

7. $e+8=17$

8. $c\div 5=8$

9. $2n+1=7$

10. $4x-2=14$

11. $11=3d-19$

12. $\frac{m}{2}-5=5$

13. $6w+1=31$

14. $9=2t+9$

15. $\frac{x}{3}+5=9$

16. $3t-4=11$

Write an equation for each. Then solve.

17. 3 more than a number y is 20.

18. 7 less than a number x is 12

19. 6 more than half a number x is 16.

20. 68 is twice a number n.

21. Half a number x is 6 plus 10.

22. 2 plus 12 is a number y plus 6.

Substitute the given value in each formula. Then evaluate.

23. $3h+4=r$ (h $=9$)

24. $2a^2+3=t$ ($a=5$)

25. $3t-1.5=p$ (t $=10.5$)

26. $\frac{30}{x}-3=s$ ($x=10$)

> ^{H I N T} Three lengths will form a triangle if the sum of any two lengths is greater than the third.

Lengths: 6 in., 3 in., 7 in.
6+3>7   6+7>3   3+7>6
Yes, the lengths form a triangle.

Lengths: 1 ft, 3 ft, 1 ft
1+3>1   3+1>1   1+1<3
No, the lengths do not form a triangle

Do the lengths form a triangle?

1. 5 ft, 6 ft, 3 ft

2. 3 yd, 3 yd, 5 yd

3. 3 mi, 3 mi, 6 mi

4. 3 in., 5 in., 1 in.

5. 7 ft, 7 ft, 7 ft,

6. 30 yd, 70 yd, 45 yd

7. 13 ft, 13 ft, 13 ft

8. 16 in., 20 in., 8 in.

9. 100 mi, 40 mi, 50 mi

Write *possible* or *impossible* for each triangle.

10. right scalene

11. right isosceles

12. right equilateral

13. obtuse scalene

14. obtuse isosceles

15. obtuse equilateral

16. acute scalene

17. acute isosceles

18. acute equilateral

Find the missing angle for each triangle.

19. 60°, 92°

20. 115°, 38°

21. 12°, 48°

22. 108°, 70°

23. 63°, 65°

24. 76°, 92°

$\triangle ABC \cong \triangle DEF$. Complete.

25. $m\angle A = m\angle$ ___

26. $m\angle B = m\angle$ ___

27. $m\angle C = m\angle$ ___

28. $\overline{AB} \cong$ ___

29. $\overline{BC} \cong$ ___

30. $\overline{AC} \cong$ ___

Skill Hints

HINT To evaluate an expression, substitute the given value for each variable. Then use the order of operations.

Evaluate $a^2 - b$ for $a = 2$ and $b = {}^-1$.

Substitute 2 for a.	$2^2 - b$
Substitute ${}^-1$ for b.	$2^2 - {}^-1$
Use the order of operations.	$4 + 1 = 5$

Evaluate each. Let $a = {}^-3$, $b = {}^-2$, and $c = 5$.

1. $ab + c$

2. abc

3. $a^2 + b^2$

4. $b^2 + c$

5. $(a + b + c)^2$

6. $\dfrac{a + b}{c}$

7. $20 \div bc$

8. $3ab$

9. $2a + 3b$

10. $^-5c^2$

11. $10 - 2c$

12. $a(b + c)$

13. $b^2 - 4c$

14. ^-4bc

15. $c^2 - a^2$

16. $\dfrac{c^2}{a + b}$

Use parentheses to make each sentence true.

17. $^-3 + {}^-4 \cdot {}^-5 = 35$

18. $^-20 - 5 \div {}^-5 = 5$

19. $^-2 + {}^-3 \cdot 4 + {}^-2 = {}^-22$

20. $^-3 + 10 \cdot 2 - {}^-3 = 47$

21. $^-16 \div {}^-4 + 5 = {}^-16$

22. $^-2 \cdot {}^-3 + {}^-4 - {}^-1 = 15$

Solve and check.

23. $^-3y = {}^-540$

24. $^-2x + 4 = 12$

25. $^-35 = 5n - 50$

26. $3n = {}^-36 + {}^-24$

27. $9a - 3 = {}^-66$

28. $39 = 4w + 3$

H
I
N
T
 A number written in scientific notation has 2 factors, a number between 1 and 10 and a power of 10. A number less than 1 is written with a negative exponent. A number greater than 10 is written with a positive exponent.

$$3,200,000 = 3.2 \times 10^6$$

$$0.000358 = 3.58 \times 10^{-4}$$

Write each in scientific notation.

1. 62,000

2. 5,800,000

3. 75,000,000

4. 81,000,000,000

5. 7,890,000

6. 5,001,000

7. 0.00007

8. 0.0000853

9. 0.012

10. 0.0035

11. 0.0006

12. 0.00019

Write each in standard form.

13. 3.2×10^3

14. 3.2×10^{-3}

15. 5.81×10^4

16. 5.81×10^{-4}

17. 4.75×10^6

18. 5.005×10^9

19. 6.71×10^{10}

20. 9.19×10^7

21. 2.31×10^{-5}

22. 4.52×10^{-6}

23. 7.28×10^{-4}

24. 2.98×10^{-7}

Find n.

25. $8.931 \times 10^n = 893.1$

26. $n \times 10^5 = 800,000$

27. $n = 3.3 \times 10^{-3}$

28. $5.43 \times 10^n = 0.0543$

29. $980,600 = n \times 10^5$

30. $33,000 = n \times 10^4$

H
I
N
T To subtract rational numbers, add the opposite.

$$\dfrac{^-3}{8} - \dfrac{^-1}{6} = \dfrac{^-3}{8} + \dfrac{1}{6} = \dfrac{^-9}{24} + \dfrac{4}{24} = \dfrac{^-5}{24}$$

The product of two rational numbers with like signs is positive.

$$\dfrac{^-2}{3} \cdot \dfrac{^-3}{4} = \dfrac{1}{2}$$

The product of two rational numbers with unlike signs is negative.

$$\dfrac{^-5}{8} \cdot \dfrac{3}{5} = \dfrac{^-3}{8}$$

Add or subtract.

1. $\dfrac{2}{3} + \dfrac{^-2}{5}$

2. $\dfrac{^-5}{8} + \dfrac{^-1}{4}$

3. $\dfrac{^-7}{8} + \dfrac{1}{5}$

4. $\dfrac{2}{3} + \dfrac{5}{12}$

5. $\dfrac{1}{3} - \dfrac{5}{9}$

6. $\dfrac{^-1}{6} - \dfrac{^-1}{3}$

7. $\dfrac{1}{9} - \dfrac{5}{9}$

8. $\dfrac{^-5}{6} - \dfrac{1}{3}$

9. $\left(3\dfrac{1}{2} + \dfrac{1}{4}\right) - 2\dfrac{1}{4}$

10. $\left(\dfrac{^-1}{2} + \dfrac{1}{2}\right) + \dfrac{1}{2}$

11. $\dfrac{2}{5} - \dfrac{4}{5} - \dfrac{1}{5}$

12. $\dfrac{^-1}{4} + \dfrac{^-3}{4} + \dfrac{1}{5}$

Multiply or divide.

13. $\dfrac{^-1}{2} \cdot \dfrac{^-4}{5}$

14. $\dfrac{^-2}{3} \cdot 1\dfrac{1}{3}$

15. $\dfrac{3}{5} \cdot \dfrac{^-2}{9}$

16. $\dfrac{^-4}{7} \cdot \dfrac{5}{6}$

17. $\dfrac{^-1}{2} \div \dfrac{3}{4}$

18. $\dfrac{^-6}{11} \div \dfrac{3}{22}$

19. $\dfrac{^-3}{5} \div \dfrac{^-2}{5}$

20. $\dfrac{1}{3} \div -3\dfrac{1}{3}$

21. $\dfrac{2}{3} \cdot \dfrac{^-1}{3} \div \dfrac{1}{3}$

22. $1\dfrac{1}{3} \div \dfrac{^-2}{9}$

23. $-1\dfrac{3}{5} \div 1\dfrac{1}{3}$

24. $1\dfrac{2}{3} \cdot -2\dfrac{3}{5}$

Compare. Use <, >, or = for each ⬤.

25. $\dfrac{^-3}{8}$ ⬤ $\dfrac{^-1}{4}$

26. $\dfrac{3}{5}$ ⬤ $\dfrac{^-2}{3}$

27. $\dfrac{^-2}{3}$ ⬤ $\dfrac{^-1}{3}$

28. $\dfrac{3}{7}$ ⬤ $\dfrac{4}{5}$

29. $^-6.3$ ⬤ $^-6.03$

30. 0.2 ⬤ $^-1.2$

31. $^-0.6$ ⬤ $^-1.2$

32. $^-1.3$ ⬤ $^-1.23$

HINT The median value of a set of data is sometimes not a number included in the set. The mode is always included in the set of data.

Ages in Attendance: 13, 23, 14, 30, 28, 25, 18, 18, 24, 31

```
1 | 3488
2 | 3458
3 | 01
```

Mean: 22.4
Mode: 18

Median: 23.5
Range: $31 - 13 = 18$

Make a stem and leaf plot for each set of data. Find the mode, mean, median, and range.

1.
15	27
24	29
33	35
38	21
16	20
15	19

2.
150	171
168	155
175	182
155	161
162	167
193	189

3.
88	81
92	68
85	75
81	96
72	87
90	77

4. Closing Stock Prices: $43, 40, 37, 48, 32, 45, 45, 39

5. Miles Driven: 158, 210, 182, 195, 210, 156, 210, 187, 190

Make a line plot for each set of data. Find the mean, mode, median, and range.

6. Test Scores: 68, 82, 86, 90, 78, 88, 86, 91

7. Attendance: 780, 780, 860, 860, 890, 860, 760

8. Books Read: 28, 33, 45, 37, 29, 32, 41, 33, 33

9. Videos Rented: 85, 93, 106, 88, 97, 87, 93, 90

Skill Hints

HINT To find a unit rate, divide.

80 miles in 5 hours $\longrightarrow$ $\frac{80}{5,}$ or 16 miles in 1 hour

6 pens for $.98 $\longrightarrow$ $\frac{\$.98}{6,}$ or $.17 for 1 pen

To find the rate, or speed, divide the distance by the time.

Find the rate of a car
traveling 600 miles in 8 hours.

$$r = \frac{d}{t}$$

$$r = \frac{600 \text{ mi}}{8 \text{ h}} = 75 \text{ mph}$$

Find the unit rate for each.

1. 4 books for $6.40

2. $\frac{1}{3}$ box for 6 bulbs

3. 3 yd. for $16.80

4. $6.72 for a dozen

5. 280 beats in $\frac{1}{2}$ hour

6. 4 videos for $39.52

7. 30 dogs for 6 pens

8. 2.5 pounds for $3.50

9. 1,545 miles in 3 hours

Choose the better buy for each.

10. 12 oz for $3.75
18 oz for $4.59

11. 5 cans for $1.20
9 cans for $2.00

12. $\frac{1}{2}$ dozen for $8.40
2 dozen for $31.00

13. 3 yd for $7.98
5 yd for $13.50

14. 17 in. for $15.50
25 in. for $17.79

15. 3 packs for $2.80
13 packs for $13.00

Use $d = r \times t$. Find each missing measure.

16. 600 mi in 3 h
Find rate.

17. 126 ft in 3 s
Find rate.

18. 756 in. in 4 h
Find rate.

19. 35 mph for 6 h
Find distance.

20. 651 mph for 3 h
Find distance.

21. 88 mph for $\frac{1}{2}$ h
Find distance.

22. 360 mi at 30 mph
Find time.

23. 98 ft at 10 ft per s
Find time.

24. 770 mi at 55 mph
Find time.

^H
^I To find percent of increase or decrease, find the difference
^N between the amounts and divide by the original amount.
^T

Find the percent of
increase from 25 to 60.

$$\frac{60-25}{25} = \frac{35}{25} = \frac{140}{100} = 140\%$$

Find the percent of
decrease from 150 to 100.

$$\frac{150-100}{150} = \frac{50}{150} = \frac{1}{3} = 33\frac{1}{3}\%$$

Write *increase* or *decrease*.

1. from 10 to 55

2. from 32 to 27

3. from 18 to 81

4. from 139 to 119

5. from 58 to 73

6. from 385 to 151

Find the percent of increase or decrease.

7. from 80 to 100

8. from 100 to 80

9. from $60 to $90

10. from $75 to $200

11. from $200 to $75

12. from 80 to 50

13. from 125 to 170

14. from 18 to 30

15. from 30 to 18

16. from 50 to 250

17. from 250 to 50

18. from 600 to 882

Find each missing value.

19. n is 115% of 30.

20. 80 is 200% of n.

21. What percent of 80 is 15?

22. 56 is 10% of n.

23. n is 28% of 16

24. 90 is 90% of n.

25. What percent of 30 is 3?

26. What percent of 5 is 2.5?

27. n is 35% of 82.

28. 15% of n is 60.

29. n is 3% of 180.

30. What percent of 500 is 175?

$\overset{H}{\underset{T}{\overset{I}{N}}}$ To find the volume of a prism or cylinder, multiply the area of the base by the height. Be sure to use cubic units.

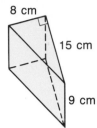

8 cm
15 cm
9 cm

$V = $ area of base $\times$ height

$= (\frac{1}{2} \times 8 \times 15) \times 9$

$= 60 \times 9$

$= 540$

$V = 540$ cm^3

Find the volume of each solid. (Use 3.14 for π.)

1. rectangular prism
   base: 17mm by 16mm
   height: 3mm

2. triangular prism
   base: 8 m by 9 m
   height of triangle: 6 m

3. cube
   side: 3.7 m

4. cylinder
   circular base: radius of 5 cm
   height: 17 cm

5. octagonal prism
   area of base: 117 cm^2
   height: 80 cm

6. rectangular prism
   base: 8.5 dm by 9.2 dm
   height: 5.7 dm

$\overset{H}{\underset{T}{\overset{I}{N}}}$ To find the volume of a pyramid or cone, find $\frac{1}{3}$ the product of the area of the base and the height.

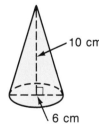

10 cm
6 cm

$V = \frac{1}{3} \times \pi r^2 \times h$

$= \frac{1}{3} \times (\pi \times 3^2) \times 10$

$= \frac{1}{3} \times 3.14 \times 9 \times 10$

$= 94.2 \quad V = 94.2$ cm^3

Find the volume of each solid. (Use 3.14 for π.)

7. cone
   radius of base: 6 mm
   height: 12 mm

8. square pyramid
   side of square: 8 cm
   height: 9 cm

9. rectangular pyramid
   length: 7 m width: 9 m
   height: 20 m

10. square pyramid
    side of square: 6 dm
    height: 18 dm

11. cone
    radius of base: 10 cm
    height: 27 cm

12. triangular pyramid
    area of base: 6 m^2
    height: 10 m

HINT In a permutation, order is important.
20 books, arranged 3 at a time

In a combination, order is *not* important.
3 books from 20

How many arrangements are possible?

How many selections are possible?

$$_{20}P_3 = 20 \cdot 19 \cdot 18 = 6,840$$

$$_{20}C_3 = \frac{_{20}P_3}{_3P_3} = \frac{20 \cdot 19 \cdot 18}{3 \cdot 2 \cdot 1} = 1,140$$

Compute each number of permutations.

1. $_5P_2$

2. $_8P_5$

3. $_7P_3$

4. $_{10}P_6$

5. $_{12}P_2$

6. $_{15}P_6$

7. $_{18}P_4$

8. $_{20}P_5$

Compute each number of combinations.

9. $_{10}C_3$

10. $_9C_2$

11. $_8C_6$

12. $_{12}C_4$

13. $_9C_6$

14. $_7C_1$

15. $_8C_8$

16. $_{11}C_3$

Find the number of permutations for each.

17. In how many ways can 2 roles be filled from 17 actors?

18. In how many ways can 10 books be arranged, 6 at a time?

19. In how many ways can first- and second-place winners be selected from 9 students?

20. In how many ways can 7 out of 12 photographs be arranged on a shelf?

Find the number of combinations for each.

21. How many different committees of 3 can be formed from 15 students?

22. How many ways can 5 out of 10 toppings be chosen?

23. How many ways can 6 people be chosen from 11?

24. How many ways can 3 shirts be chosen from 30?

Skill Hints

H
I
N
T
In congruent triangles, use the order of the letters to find congruent angles and sides.

△ABC ≅ △DEF

∠A ≅ ∠D   ∠B ≅ ∠E   ∠C ≅ ∠F

$\overline{AB} \cong \overline{DE}$ $\overline{BC} \cong \overline{EF}$ $\overline{AC} \cong \overline{DF}$

Use these rules to be sure triangles are congruent.

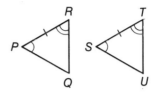

SSS   SAS   ASA
△XYZ ≅ △GHI   △JKL ≅ △MNO   △PQR ≅ △STU

Which pairs of triangles are congruent? Name the rule that applies.

1.   2.   3.

4.   5.   6.

Write the corresponding congruent parts for each.

7. △CAT ≅ △SIP   8. △RAT ≅ △ETC   9. △BAT ≅ △SPY

Which pairs of triangles are congruent?

10. triangle with sides measuring 6 in., 10 in., and 14 in.
    triangle with sides measuring 10 in., 6 in., and 14 in.

11. triangle with angles measuring 30°, 60°, and 90° and sides measuring 4 ft, 8 ft, and 6.9 ft
    triangle with angles measuring 30°, 60°, and 90° and sides measuring 8 ft, 16 ft, and 13.8 ft

H
I When multiplying by a negative number to solve an inequality,
N reverse the inequality symbol.
T

$$^-2n \geq 12$$

$$\frac{^-2n}{^-2} \geq \frac{12}{^-2}$$

$$n \leq\; ^-6$$

$$\frac{x}{^-3} <\; ^-5$$

$$\frac{x}{^-3} \cdot\, ^-3 <\; ^-5 \cdot\, ^-3$$

$$x > 15$$

Solve and check each inequality.

1. $3x > 9$

2. $x - 3 \leq\; ^-5$

3. $^-5x \geq\; ^-25$

4. $7 > x - 3$

5. $x + 5 >\; ^-1$

6. $^-6x \geq\; ^-30$

7. $\frac{x}{3} >\; ^-4$

8. $^-60 \geq 6x$

9. $4 < x + 2$

10. $\frac{x}{^-4} \leq 2$

11. $3x + 4x >\; ^-14$

12. $\frac{x}{2} - 3 > 0$

13. $3 + x <\; ^-4$

14. $5x + 2 > 12$

15. $8x - 1 \leq 41$

16. $^-7x - x <\; ^-8$

17. $5x - 2x \leq 18$

18. $x - 5 \leq\; ^-3$

19. $^-2 \leq \frac{x}{3}$

20. $5 + x > 6$

Solve and check each equation.

21. $x + 7 = 20$

22. $x - 18 =\; ^-3$

23. $x - 6 =\; ^-19$

24. $x + 0 =\; ^-5$

25. $x - 5.2 =\; ^-4$

26. $x + 3 =\; ^-13$

27. $^-3x =\; ^-27$

28. $^-4x = 36$

29. $^-15x =\; ^-75$

30. $^-33x = 99$

31. $\frac{x}{^-5} =\; ^-4$

32. $\frac{x}{^-6} = 18$

33. $5x + 3 =\; ^-12$

34. $^-2x + 1 =\; ^-0$

35. $^-x - 9 =\; ^-20$

36. $\frac{N}{3} + 7 = 4$

37. $4x - x =\; ^-39$

38. $^-5x + x =\; ^-48$

39. $10x - 12x = 7$

40. $^-2x - 4x = 30$

A relation is a *function* if each *x* value is matched with only one *y* value.

function

(3,0) (⁻1,0) (2,⁻3) (⁻2,0)

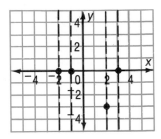

Each vertical line passes through only 1 point of the function.

not a function

(3,0), (⁻1,2) (2,⁻3) (2,4)

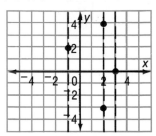

Which relations are functions?

1.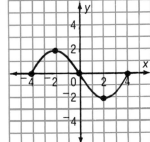

2.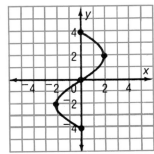

3.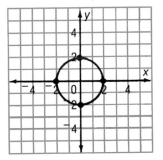

Write *function* or *not a function*.

4. (3,4), (3,5), (3,6), (3,7)

5. (4,3), (5,3), (6,3), (7,3)

6. (5,0), (6,1), (7,2), (8,3)

7. (4,⁻2), (5,⁻3), (6,⁻4), (7,⁻5)

8. the relationship between the number of gallons of gasoline and the price

9. the relationship between the age of an oak tree and its height

10.

x	⁻2	⁻1	0	1	2
y	5	6	7	8	9

11.

x	5	3	1	0	⁻1	3
y	4	3	⁻1	0	1	2

12.

x	25	16	0	16	25
y	5	4	0	⁻4	⁻5

13.

x	3	2	1	0	⁻1	⁻2
y	9	4	1	0	1	4

14. the graph of a horizontal line

15. the graph of a regular pentagon

ᴴ ᴵ ᴺ ᵀ To graph an equation, make a table of values. Then graph each point, using the *x*- and *y*-coordinates, on a real-number plane.

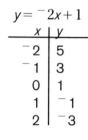

$y = {}^-2x + 1$

x	y
$^-2$	5
$^-1$	3
0	1
1	$^-1$
2	$^-3$

$y = (^-2)(^-2) + 1 = 5$
$y = (^-2)(^-1) + 1 = 3$
$y = (^-2)(0) + 1 = 1$
$y = (^-2)(1) + 1 = {}^-1$
$y = (^-2)(2) + 1 = {}^-3$

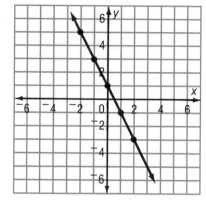

Make a table for each equation, using $^-2, {}^-1, 0, 1,$ and 2 as *x*-coordinates. Graph on a real-number plane.

1. $y = {}^-x + 2$ 2. $x + y = {}^-3$ 3. $y = 3x$

4. $y = 5 - x$ 5. $y = x - 5$ 6. $y = 10 - x$

Copy and complete each table.

7. $y = {}^-2x - 7$

x	$^-2$	$^-1$	0	1
y				

8. $y = 5x$

x	$^-3$	0	3	6
y				

9. $x + y = {}^-5$

x	$^-3$	$^-1$	0	1	3
y					

10. $y - x = 3$

x	$^-3$	$^-1$	0	1	3
y					

11. $y = {}^-x - 1$

x	$^-2$	0	2	5
y				

12. $y = {}^-2x$

x	$^-3$	$^-2$	$^-1$	0	1	2
y						

Which ordered pair is a solution of the system of equations?

13. $y = 4x$
$y = x + 3$
a. (2, 5)   **b.** (1, 4)

14. $x + y = {}^-5$
$y = {}^-2x$
a. (5, $^-10$)   **b.** (0, $^-5$)

15. $y = {}^-x - 6$
$y = x + 4$
a. (1,5)   **b.** ($^-5, {}^-1$)

16. $y = 10 - x$
$2x + y = {}^-3$
a. (0, $^-3$)   **b.** ($^-13, 23$)

17. $y = 5$
$y = x + 1$
a. (4, 5)   **b.** (5,5)

18. $y - x = {}^-3$
$y = 3x + 3$
a. ($^-3, {}^-6$)   **b.** ($^-2, {}^-3$)

Glossary

absolute value The distance a number is from 0 on the number line.   p. 150

acute angle An angle with a measure less than 90°.   p. 116

acute triangle A triangle with three acute angles.   p. 122

additive inverse property The sum of a number and its additive inverse is 0.   p. 424

additive inverses Two numbers whose sum is 0.   p. 154

angle Two rays with a common endpoint called the vertex.   p. 116

arc A part of the circumference of a circle.   p. 132

area The number of square units needed to cover a region.   p. 326

associative property of addition The way that addends are grouped does not change the sum.   p. 164
Example: $(a + b) + c = a + (b + c)$

associative property of multiplication The way that factors are grouped does not change the product.   p. 164
Example: $(a \times b) \times c = a \times (b \times c)$

base (of a polygon) p. 328

base

base (of a space figure) p. 342

base

bisect To divide into two congruent parts.   p. 406

box and whisker plot A method of displaying the quartiles and the range of the data.   p. 224

central angle An angle that has its vertex at the center of a circle.   p. 132

chord A line segment with both endpoints on the circle.   p. 132

circle A closed plane figure with all points the same distance from a point called the center.   p. 132

circumference The distance around a circle.   p. 330

combination A selection in which order is not important.   p. 376

common factor A factor of two or more numbers.   p. 44

common multiple A multiple of two or more numbers.   p. 44

commutative property of addition The order of the addends does not change the sum.   p. 20, 164
Example: $a + b = b + a$

commutative property of multiplication The order of the factors does not change the product.   p. 20, 164
Example: $a \times b = b \times a$

complementary angles Two angles the sum of whose measures is 90°.   p. 116

composite number A whole number greater than 1 that has more than two factors.   p. 40

compound event Two or more events considered together.   p. 364

cone A space figure with a circular base and one vertex.   p. 136

congruent figures Figures that have the same size and shape.   p. 124

conjecture A statement that has not been proven true or false.   p. 46

coordinate plane The plane determined by a horizontal number line, called the *x*-axis, and a vertical number line, called the *y*-axis, intersecting at a point called the origin. Each point of the plane corresponds to an ordered pair of numbers.   p. 170

counterexample An example that proves a statement to be wrong.   p. 46

counting principle If a first event has *n* outcomes and a second event has *m* outcomes, then the first event followed by the second event has $n \times m$ outcomes.   p. 362

cross products Products obtained by multiplying the numerator of one fraction by the denominator of a second fraction and the denominator of the first fraction by the numerator of the second fraction.   p. 52, 302

Example: $\frac{1}{2} = \frac{3}{6}$

$1 \times 6 = 2 \times 3$

cube A space figure with six square faces.   p. 338

cubed (in numeration) To use a number as a factor three times. The cube of 4 is $4 \times 4 \times 4 = 4^3$ p. 6

cylinder A space figure with two parallel bases that are congruent circles.   p. 136

data Information that is gathered.   p. 220

decagon A polygon with ten sides.   p. 120

decimal A number with one or more places to the right of a decimal point.   p. 8

degree (°) A unit for measuring angles.   p. 116

denominator The number below the fraction bar in a fraction.   p. 52

dependent events Two events in which the outcome of the second is affected by the outcome of the first.   p. 364

diagonal A segment joining any two nonadjacent vertices in a polygon.   p. 120

diameter A line segment that passes through the center of a circle and has both endpoints on the circle.   p. 132

discount The amount that a regular price is reduced.   p. 312

distributive property of multiplication over addition If one factor is a sum, multiplying before adding does not change the product.   p. 20, 164
Example: $a \times (b + c) = (a \times b) + (a \times c)$

divisible A number is divisible by another number if, after dividing, the remainder is 0.   p. 42

domain All possible values of x in a relation.   p. 456

edge The segment formed where two faces of a space figure meet.   p. 134

endpoint A point at the end of a segment or ray.   p. 116

equation A number sentence with an equals (=) sign.   p. 88

equilateral triangle A triangle with all sides congruent.   p. 122

equivalent fractions Fractions that name the same number.   p. 52

error of measurement The difference between the actual measure and the approximate measurement.   p. 270

estimate To give an approximate rather than an exact answer.   p. 22

event One or more outcomes of an experiment.   p. 358

experiment To carry out a plan to test a prediction.   p. 360

exponent A number that tells how many times the base is used as a factor.   p. 6

expression A mathematical phrase made up of a variable or combination of variables and/or numbers and operations.   p. 82
Examples: $5n$; $4x - 7$, $(5 \times 3) + (10 \div 2)$

extrapolation Estimating values beyond known values.   p. 232

face A flat surface of a space figure.   p. 134

factorial Written $n!$, the product of all whole numbers from n to 1.   p. 372

factors Numbers that are multiplied to obtain a product.   p. 40
Example: $3 \times 8 = 24$ 3 and 8 are factors of 24.

formula An equation that states a fact or rule.   p. 104

fraction A number in the form $\frac{a}{b}$ that names part of a region or part of a group. The number below the fraction bar is the denominator. The number above the fraction bar is the numerator.   p. 52

frequency The number of times a given item occurs in a set of data.   p. 240

frequency table A listing of data together with their frequencies.   p. 240

function A relation in which each value of x is paired only once with a value of y.   p. 458

Glossary

graph A drawing used to present data. Some types are bar graphs, line graphs, and circle graphs.   p. 232, 234, 236

greatest common factor (GCF) The greatest number that is a factor of each of two or more numbers.   p. 44

greatest possible error (GPE) In any measurement, one half the precision of the measurement.   p. 270

height (of a parallelogram) A segment that joins opposite sides and is perpendicular to the base.   p. 328

Example: height

height (of a triangle) A segment drawn perpendicular to a side of a triangle from the opposite vertex.   p. 328

heptagon A polygon with seven sides.   p. 120

hexagon A polygon with six sides.   p. 120

histogram A way of displaying large quantities of data in graph form.   p. 240

hypotenuse In a right triangle the side opposite the right angle.   p. 204

identity property of addition The sum of any number and 0 is that number.   p. 164
Example: $a + 0 = a$

identity property of multiplication The product of any number and 1 is that number.   p. 164
Example: $a \times 1 = a$

improper fraction A fraction in which the numerator is greater than or equal to the denominator.   p. 62

independent events Two events in which the outcome of the second is not affected by the outcome of the first.   p. 364

inequality A mathematical sentence that uses one of the symbols $<$, $\leq$, $>$, $\geq$, or $\neq$.   p. 440, 442, 470

inscribed angle An angle whose vertex is on a circle and whose sides contain chords of the circle.   p. 132

integer The numbers ... $^-3$, $^-2$, $^-1$, 0, $^+1$, $^+2$, $^+3$, ...   p. 150

intercepted arc The arc of a circle within an inscribed angle.   p. 132

interest The charge for borrowing money or the amount paid for the use of money.   p. 310

interpolation Estimating values between two known values.   p. 232

intersecting lines Lines that have exactly one point in common.   p. 116
Example: $\overleftrightarrow{AB}$ below intersects $\overleftrightarrow{CD}$ at point *F*.

inverse operations Two operations that are opposite in effect. Addition and subtraction are inverse operations. Multiplication and division are inverse operations.   p. 96

irrational number A nonterminating and nonrepeating decimal.   p. 454

isosceles triangle A triangle with two congruent sides.   p. 122

least common denominator (LCD) The least common multiple of the denominators of two or more fractions.   p. 60

least common multiple (LCM) The least nonzero number that is a multiple of each of two or more numbers.   p. 44

line The collection of points along a straight path. A line has no endpoints.   p. 116

line of symmetry A line that divides a figure into two congruent parts.   p. 390

line plot A method of showing each item of data on a number line.   p. 220

line segment A part of a line having two endpoints.   p. 116

locus A path of points.   p. 400

lowest terms A fraction is in lowest terms or simplest form, when the GCF of the numerator and the denominator is 1.   p. 52

markup The amount by which a regular price is increased.   p. 314

mean In a collection of data, the sum of all the data divided by the number of data.   p. 226

measure of central tendency A measure that describes a characteristic of data. Mean, median, and mode are all measures of central tendency.   p. 226

median The middle number or average of the two middle numbers in a collection of data when the data are arranged in order.   p. 220

midpoint A point that divides a segment into two congruent segments.   p. 116

mixed number A number written as a whole number and a fraction.   p. 60

mode The number or numbers that occur most often in a collection of data.   p. 220

multiple of a number The product of that whole number and any other whole number.   p. 44

multiplicative inverse The reciprocal of a given number.   p. 96

multiplicative inverse property The product of a number and its multiplicative inverse is 1.   p. 424

mutually exclusive events Events that cannot occur at the same time.   p. 366

negative integer An integer less than 0.   p. 150

nonagon A polygon with nine sides.   p. 120

numerator The number above the fraction bar in a fraction.   p. 52

obtuse angle An angle with a measure greater than 90° but less than 180°.   p. 116

obtuse triangle A triangle with one obtuse angle.   p. 122

octagon A polygon with eight sides.   p. 120

opposites Two numbers that are the same distance from 0 on the number line but in opposite directions.   p. 150
Example: 2 and 2 are opposite integers.

ordered pair A pair of numbers used to locate a point in the coordinate plane.   p. 170

origin The point of intersection of the *x*-axis and *y*-axis in a coordinate plane.   p. 170

outcome A possible result of a probability experiment.   p. 358

parallel lines Lines in the same plane that never intersect.   p. 118

parallelogram A quadrilateral with opposite sides parallel. Each pair of opposite sides and angles is congruent.   p. 130

pentagon A polygon with five sides.   p. 120

percent A ratio whose second term is 100. Percent means parts per hundred. The symbol % is used for percent.   p. 286

perimeter The distance around a polygon.   p. 326

permutation An arrangement in which order is important.   p. 374

perpendicular lines Two lines that intersect to form right angles.   p. 116

pi π The ratio of the circumference of a circle to its diameter. The ratio is the same for all circles. $\pi \approx 3.14$ or $\frac{22}{7}$.   p. 330

plane A flat surface extending endlessly in all directions.   p. 118

point A location in a plane or in space.   p. 116

polygon A closed plane figure made up of line segments.   p. 120

polyhedron A space figure whose surfaces, or faces, are all flat.   p. 134

positive integer An integer greater than 0.   p. 150

prime factorization Writing a number as the product of prime factors.   p. 42

Example: $24 = 2 \times 2 \times 2 \times 3$

prime number A whole number greater than 1 with only two factors—itself and 1.   p. 40

principal An amount of money borrowed or loaned.   p. 310

prism A polyhedron with two parallel, congruent faces called bases.   p. 134

probability The ratio of favorable outcomes to possible outcomes of an experiment.   p. 358

product The answer in multiplication.   p. 26

proper fraction A fraction in which the numerator is less than the denominator.   p. 62

property of density Between any two real numbers, there is always another real number.   p. 454

proportion A sentence that states two ratios are equal.   p. 254

Example: $\frac{3}{6} = \frac{8}{16}$

Glossary

pyramid A space figure whose base is a polygon and whose faces are triangles with a common vertex. p. 344

Pythagorean rule For every right triangle, the sum of the squares of the legs equals the square of the hypotenuse. $a^2 + b^2 = c^2$ p. 204

quadrant One of 4 regions determined by the x- and y-axes in a coordinate plane. p. 170

quadrilateral A polygon with four sides and four angles. p. 130

quotient The answer in division. p. 28

radius A line segment with one endpoint on the circle and the other endpoint at the center. p. 132

range (function) All possible values of y in a relation. p. 456

range (statistics) The difference between the greatest and the least numbers in a collection of data. p. 220

rate A ratio that compares different kinds of units. p. 252

ratio A pair of numbers that compare two quantities or describe a rate. p. 250

rational number Any number that can be expressed as the quotient of two integers where the divisor is not 0. p. 180

ray A part of a line that has one endpoint and extends endlessly in one direction. p. 116

real numbers All rational and irrational numbers. p. 454

reciprocals Two fractions whose product is 1. p. 70

Example: $\frac{3}{4} \times \frac{4}{3} = 1$

rectangle A parallelogram with four right angles. p. 130

reflection A change in position resulting from a flip. p. 390

regular polygon A polygon with all sides congruent and all angles congruent. p. 120

relation A group of ordered pairs (x, y). p. 456

relative frequency The ratio of the number of favorable outcomes to the total number of trials. p. 360

repeating decimal A decimal in which a digit or a group of digits repeats unendingly. p. 50

rhombus A parallelogram with all sides congruent. p. 130

right angle An angle that measures 90°. p. 116

right triangle A triangle with one right angle. p. 122

rotation A transformation obtained by rotating a figure through a given angle about a point. p. 394

sample space All the possible outcomes for an experiment. p. 358

scale drawing A drawing that is an enlargement or reduction of an actual object. p. 258

scalene triangle A triangle that has no congruent sides. p. 122

scattergram A graph made by plotting points on a coordinate plane. p. 238

scientific notation Writing a number as the product of two factors. The first factor is a number from 1 to 10. The second factor is a power of 10 in exponent form. p. 192

sequence A list of numbers related by a rule or a pattern. p. 4

similar figures Figures that are the same shape but not necessarily the same size. p. 266

skew lines Lines that do not intersect and are not in the same plane. p. 116

slope The steepness of a line. Slope is expressed as a ratio, using any two points on the line. p. 466

$$\text{slope} = \frac{\text{change in } y\text{-value}}{\text{change in } x\text{-value}}$$

solution The value of a variable that makes a number sentence true. p. 90

solve To find all the solutions of an equation. p. 90

space figure A geometric figure whose points are in more than one plane. p. 134

sphere A space figure with all points an equal distance from a point called the center. p. 136

square (in geometry) A rectangle with all sides congruent.   p. 130

square (in numeration) To multiply a number by itself.   p. 6
Example: The square of 7 is 7×7 $7^2 = 49$

square root The square root of a, written $\sqrt{a}$, is the number whose square is a.   p. 200
Example: The square root of 36 is 6, since $6^2 = 36$.

statistics The science of collecting, organizing, and analyzing data.   p. 220

stem and leaf plot A method of organizing data for comparison purposes.   p. 222
Example:

straight angle An angle that measures 180°.   p. 117

supplementary angles Two angles the sum of whose measures is 180°.   p. 116

surface area The sum of the areas of all the faces of a space figure.   p. 338

terminating decimal A decimal that ends or repeats only zeroes.   p. 48
Examples: 0.5 and 0.625 are terminating decimals.

tessellation A design in which congruent figures are arranged to fill the plane in such a way that no figures overlap and there are no gaps.   p. 388

transformation A change in the size, shape, or position of a figure.   p. 390

translation A change in position resulting from a slide without any turn.   p. 390

transversal A line that intersects two or more lines at different points.   p. 118

trapezoid A quadrilateral with exactly one pair of parallel sides.   p. 328

tree diagram A diagram used to show outcomes of an experiment.   p. 362

triangle A polygon with three sides.   p. 122

unit price The ratio: price per unit of measure.   p. 252

variable A letter used to stand for a number in an expression or equation.   p. 86

Venn diagram A special diagram using overlapping circles to show the relationship between groups of objects.   p. 140

vertex A point where two or more sides of a geometric figure meet.   p. 116

vertical angles A pair of opposite angles formed by intersecting lines.   p. 118

volume The number of cubic units needed to fill a space figure.   p. 342

x- and y-axes The horizontal and vertical number lines in a coordinate plane.   p. 170

y-intercept The y value of the point where a line crosses the y-axis.   p. 466

zero property of multiplication The product of any number and 0 is 0.   p. 164
Example: $a \times 0 = 0$ and $0 \times a = 0$

Glossary

Computer Terms

BACK n (BK n) Moves the turtle backward n turtle steps.

BASIC A computer language.

cell The smallest unit of a spreadsheet located by a column and a row.

CLEARSCREEN (CS) Clears the screen. In some versions, also homes the turtle.

DRAW or CG In some versions, clears the screen and homes the turtle.

FORWARD n (FD n) Moves the turtle forward n turtle steps.

HIDETURTLE (HT) Makes the turtle not visible on the screen.

HOME Positions the turtle in the middle of the screen, heading straight up

IF condition [ ] [ ] If condition is true, executes command(s) in first [ ]. If false, executes command(s) in second [ ].

IF . . . THEN . . . ELSE Equivalent to IF condition in some versions of Logo.

ITEM n [ ] Returns the nth item in a list.

LEFT n (LT n) Turns the turtle left n degrees from its current heading.

Logo A computer language.

MAKE "X n Assigns the value n to the variable named.

OUTPUT (OP) In a procedure, returns a value.

PENDOWN (PD) Allows turtle to draw again.

PENERASE (PE) Allows turtle to erase a line segment. (Use command with PENDOWN.)

PENUP (PU) Allows turtle to move without drawing.

PRINT (PR) A Logo command that shows information on the screen.

procedure Creates a new Logo command that can execute a specified set of commands. A procedure is called by entering its name.

RANDOM n Returns a whole number from 0 to n − 1.

REMAINDER n1 n2 Returns the remainder of n1 ÷ n2.

REPEAT n [ ] A Logo command that repeats commands within brackets n times. *Example:* REPEAT 4 [FD 10] moves the turtle 10 turtle steps forward four times.

RIGHT n (RT n) Turns the turtle right n degrees from its current heading.

SETPOS [n1 n2] Positions the turtle at a specified point (n1, n2). (Some versions of Logo)

SETXY n1 n2 Positions the turtle at (n1, n2). (Some versions of Logo)

SHOWTURTLE (ST) Makes the turtle visible on the screen.

spreadsheet Data consisting of rows and columns of numbers. A computer spreadsheet records data and performs calculations.

TO procedure name, . . . END Defines a procedure.

turtle step A measure of turtle movement.

N	N²	√N
1	1	1.00
2	4	1.41
3	9	1.73
4	16	2.00
5	25	2.24
6	36	2.45
7	49	2.65
8	64	2.83
9	81	3.00
10	100	3.16
11	121	3.32
12	144	3.46
13	169	3.61
14	196	3.74
15	225	3.87
16	256	4.00
17	289	4.12
18	324	4.24
19	361	4.36
20	400	4.47
21	441	4.58
22	484	4.69
23	529	4.80
24	576	4.90
25	625	5.00
26	676	5.10
27	729	5.20
28	784	5.29
29	841	5.39
30	900	5.48
31	961	5.57
32	1,024	5.66
33	1,089	5.74
34	1,156	5.83
35	1,225	5.92
36	1,296	6.00
37	1,369	6.08
38	1,444	6.16
39	1,521	6.24
40	1,600	6.32
41	1,681	6.40
42	1,764	6.48
43	1,849	6.56
44	1,936	6.63
45	2,025	6.71
46	2,116	6.78
47	2,209	6.86
48	2,304	6.93
49	2,401	7.00
50	2,500	7.07

N	N²	√N
51	2,601	7.14
52	2,704	7.21
53	2,809	7.28
54	2,916	7.35
55	3,025	7.42
56	3,136	7.48
57	3,249	7.55
58	3,364	7.62
59	3,481	7.68
60	3,600	7.75
61	3,721	7.81
62	3,844	7.87
63	3,969	7.94
64	4,096	8.00
65	4,225	8.06
66	4,356	8.12
67	4,489	8.19
68	4,624	8.25
69	4,761	8.31
70	4,900	8.37
71	5,041	8.43
72	5,184	8.49
73	5,329	8.54
74	5,476	8.60
75	5,625	8.66
76	5,776	8.72
77	5,929	8.77
78	6,084	8.83
79	6,241	8.89
80	6,400	8.94
81	6,561	9.00
82	6,724	9.06
83	6,889	9.11
84	7,056	9.17
85	7,225	9.22
86	7,396	9.27
87	7,569	9.33
88	7,744	9.38
89	7,921	9.43
90	8,100	9.49
91	8,281	9.54
92	8,464	9.59
93	8,649	9.64
94	8,836	9.70
95	9,025	9.75
96	9,216	9.80
97	9,409	9.85
98	9,604	9.90
99	9,801	9.95
100	10,000	10.00

N	N²	√N
101	10,201	10.05
102	10,404	10.10
103	10,609	10.15
104	10,816	10.20
105	11,025	10.25
106	11,236	10.30
107	11,449	10.34
108	11,664	10.39
109	11,881	10.44
110	12,100	10.49
111	12,321	10.54
112	12,544	10.58
113	12,769	10.63
114	12,996	10.68
115	13,225	10.72
116	13,456	10.77
117	13,689	10.82
118	13,924	10.86
119	14,161	10.91
120	14,400	10.95
121	14,641	11.00
122	14,884	11.05
123	15,129	11.09
124	15,376	11.14
125	15,625	11.18
126	15,876	11.22
127	16,129	11.27
128	16,384	11.31
129	16,641	11.36
130	16,900	11.40
131	17,161	11.45
132	17,424	11.49
133	17,689	11.53
134	17,956	11.58
135	18,225	11.62
136	18,496	11.66
137	18,769	11.70
138	19,044	11.75
139	19,321	11.79
140	19,600	11.83
141	19,881	11.87
142	20,164	11.92
143	20,449	11.96
144	20,736	12.00
145	21,025	12.04
146	21,316	12.08
147	21,609	12.12
148	21,904	12.17
149	22,201	12.21
150	22,500	12.25

Sines, Cosines, and Tangents

Degrees	Sin	Cos	Tan
1	0.0175	0.9998	0.0175
2	0.0349	0.9994	0.0349
3	0.0523	0.9986	0.0524
4	0.0698	0.9976	0.0699
5	0.0872	0.9962	0.0875
6	0.1045	0.9945	0.1051
7	0.1219	0.9925	0.1228
8	0.1392	0.9903	0.1405
9	0.1564	0.9877	0.1584
10	0.1736	0.9848	0.1763
11	0.1908	0.9816	0.1944
12	0.2079	0.9781	0.2126
13	0.2250	0.9744	0.2309
14	0.2419	0.9703	0.2493
15	0.2588	0.9659	0.2679
16	0.2756	0.9613	0.2867
17	0.2924	0.9563	0.3057
18	0.3090	0.9511	0.3249
19	0.3256	0.9455	0.3443
20	0.3420	0.9397	0.3640
21	0.3584	0.9336	0.3839
22	0.3746	0.9272	0.4040
23	0.3907	0.9205	0.4245
24	0.4067	0.9135	0.4452
25	0.4226	0.9063	0.4663
26	0.4384	0.8988	0.4877
27	0.4540	0.8910	0.5095
28	0.4695	0.8829	0.5317
29	0.4848	0.8746	0.5543
30	0.5000	0.8660	0.5774
31	0.5150	0.8572	0.6009
32	0.5299	0.8480	0.6249
33	0.5446	0.8387	0.6494
34	0.5592	0.8290	0.6745
35	0.5736	0.8192	0.7002
36	0.5878	0.8090	0.7265
37	0.6018	0.7986	0.7536
38	0.6157	0.7880	0.7813
39	0.6293	0.7771	0.8098
40	0.6428	0.7660	0.8391
41	0.6561	0.7547	0.8693
42	0.6691	0.7431	0.9004
43	0.6820	0.7314	0.9325
44	0.6947	0.7193	0.9657
45	0.7071	0.7071	1.0000

Degrees	Sin	Cos	Tan
46	0.7193	0.6947	1.0355
47	0.7314	0.6820	1.0724
48	0.7431	0.6691	1.1106
49	0.7547	0.6561	1.1504
50	0.7660	0.6428	1.1918
51	0.7771	0.6293	1.2349
52	0.7880	0.6157	1.2799
53	0.7986	0.6018	1.3270
54	0.8090	0.5878	1.3764
55	0.8192	0.5736	1.4281
56	0.8290	0.5592	1.4826
57	0.8387	0.5446	1.5399
58	0.8480	0.5299	1.6003
59	0.8572	0.5150	1.6643
60	0.8660	0.5000	1.7321
61	0.8746	0.4848	1.8040
62	0.8829	0.4695	1.8807
63	0.8910	0.4540	1.9626
64	0.8988	0.4384	2.0503
65	0.9063	0.4226	2.1445
66	0.9135	0.4067	2.2460
67	0.9205	0.3907	2.3559
68	0.9272	0.3746	2.4751
69	0.9336	0.3584	2.6051
70	0.9397	0.3420	2.7475
71	0.9455	0.3256	2.9042
72	0.9511	0.3090	3.0777
73	0.9563	0.2924	3.2709
74	0.9613	0.2756	3.4874
75	0.9659	0.2588	3.7321
76	0.9703	0.2419	4.0108
77	0.9744	0.2250	4.3315
78	0.9781	0.2079	4.7046
79	0.9816	0.1908	5.1446
80	0.9848	0.1736	5.6713
81	0.9877	0.1564	6.3138
82	0.9903	0.1392	7.1154
83	0.9925	0.1219	8.1443
84	0.9945	0.1045	9.5144
85	0.9962	0.0872	11.4301
86	0.9976	0.0698	14.3007
87	0.9986	0.0523	19.0811
88	0.9994	0.0349	28.6363
89	0.9998	0.0175	57.2900
90	1.0000	0.0000	——

Measures

METRIC		CUSTOMARY	
LENGTH	1 millimeter (mm) = 0.001 meter (m)	**LENGTH**	1 foot (ft) = 12 inches (in.)
	1 centimeter (cm) = 0.01 meter		1 yard (yd) = 36 inches
	1 decimeter (dm) = 0.1 meter		1 yard = 3 feet
	1 dekameter (dam) = 10 meters		1 mile (mi) = 5,280 feet
	1 hectometer (hm) = 100 meters		1 mile = 1,760 yards
	1 kilometer (km) = 1,000 meters		
MASS/WEIGHT	1 milligram (mg) = 0.001 gram (g)	**WEIGHT**	1 pound (lb) = 16 ounces (oz)
	1 centigram (cg) = 0.01 gram		1 ton (T) = 2,000 pounds
	1 decigram (dg) = 0.1 gram		
	1 dekagram (dag) = 10 grams	**CAPACITY**	1 cup (c) = 8 fluid ounces (fl oz)
	1 hectogram (hg) = 100 grams		1 pint (pt) = 2 cups
	1 kilogram (kg) = 1,000 grams		1 quart (qt) = 2 pints
	1 metric ton (t) = 1,000 kilograms		1 quart = 4 cups
			1 gallon (gal) = 4 quarts
CAPACITY	1 milliliter (mL) = 0.001 liter (L)	**AREA**	1 square foot (ft^2) = 144 square inches ($in.^2$)
	1 centiliter (cL) = 0.01 liter		1 square yard (yd^2) = 9 square feet
	1 deciliter (dL) = 0.1 liter		1 acre = 43,560 square feet
	1 dekaliter (daL) = 10 liters		1 square mile (mi^2) = 640 acres
	1 hectoliter (hL) = 100 liters		
	1 kiloliter (kL) = 1,000 liters	**TIME**	1 minute (min) = 60 seconds (s)
			1 hour (h) = 60 minutes
AREA	1 square centimeter (cm^2) = 100 square millimeters (mm^2)		1 day (d) = 24 hours
	1 square meter (m^2) = 10,000 square centimeters		1 week (wk) = 7 days
	1 hectare (ha) = 10,000 square meters		1 year (yr) = 12 months (mo)
	1 square kilometer (km^2) = 1,000,000 square meters		1 year = 52 weeks
			1 year = 365 days
			1 century (c) = 100 years

Formulas

$P = 2(l + w)$	Perimeter of a rectangle	$V = lwh$	Volume of a rectangular prism
$P = 4s$	Perimeter of a square	$V = Bh$	Volume of any prism
$P = ns$	Perimeter of a regular polygon	$V = \pi r^2 h$	Volume of a cylinder
	n = number of sides	$V = \frac{1}{3}Bh$	Volume of a pyramid
$A = lw$	Area of a rectangle	$V = \frac{1}{3}\pi r^2 h$	Volume of a cone
$A = s^2$	Area of a square	$SA = 2\pi r^2 + \pi dh$	Surface area of a cylinder
$A = bh$	Area of a parallelogram	$a^2 + b^2 = c^2$	Pythagorean Theorem
$A = \frac{1}{2}bh$	Area of a triangle	$I = prt$	Simple interest
$A = \frac{1}{2}h(b_1 + b_2)$	Area of a trapezoid	$d = rt$	Distance
$C = \pi d$, or $2\pi r$	Circumference of a circle		
$A = \pi r^2$	Area of a circle		

Symbols

$=$	is equal to	π	pi (approximately 3.14)	$\perp$	is perpendicular to
$\neq$	is not equal to	°	degree	2:5	ratio of 2 to 5
$>$	is greater than	°C	degree Celsius	10^2	ten to the second power
$<$	is less than	°F	degree Fahrenheit	$\sqrt{}$	square root
$\geq$	is greater than or equal to	$\overleftrightarrow{AB}$	line AB	$^+4$	positive 4
$\leq$	is less than or equal to	$\overline{AB}$	line segment AB	$^-4$	negative 4
$\approx$	is approximately equal to	$\overrightarrow{AB}$	ray AB	$|^-4|$	absolute value of $^-4$
$\cong$	is congruent to	$\angle ABC$	angle ABC	$(3, ^-4)$	ordered pair 3, $^-4$
$\sim$	is similar to	$m\angle ABC$	measure of angle ABC	$P(E)$	probability of event E
$\ldots$	continues without end	$\triangle ABC$	triangle ABC	sin 45°	sine of 45°
$1.\overline{3}$	repeating decimal 1.333 . . .	$\overset{\frown}{AB}$	arc AB	cos 45°	cosine of 45°
%	percent	$\parallel$	is parallel to	tan 45°	tangent of 45°

Index

Absolute value, 150-151
Activity lessons
  exploring addition and subtraction of integers, 152-153
  exploring the area of a circle, 330-331
  exploring conjectures, 46-47
  exploring cylinders, cones, and spheres, 136-137
  exploring different perspectives, 138-139
  exploring functions, 458-459
  exploring geometric patterns, 388-389
  exploring geometric relationships, 400-401
  exploring number patterns, 2-3
  exploring number sequences, 4-5
  exploring number systems, 14-15
  exploring polyhedra, 134-135
  exploring primes, 40-41
  exploring quadrilaterals, 130-131
  exploring relative frequency, 360-361
  exploring sampling, 218-219
  exploring scattergrams, 238-239
  exploring square roots, 200-201
  exploring surface area of cylinders, 340-341
  exploring volume of pyramids and cones, 344-345
  relating perimeter and area, 326-327
  understanding and estimating square roots, 202-203
  understanding place value, 12-13, 168-169
Acute angles, 122-123
Acute triangles, 122-123
Addition
  of decimals, 24-25
  equations involving, 98-99, 426-427, 430-435
  and estimating, 22-23, 58-59
  of fractions, 60-61
  of integers, 152-155
  of mixed numbers, 60-61
  properties of, 20-21, 164-165
  of rational numbers, 184-185
Additive inverses, 154-155, 164-165, 424-425
Adjacent angles, 116-117
Alternate exterior angles, 118-119
Alternate interior angles, 118-119
Alternate solutions, 18-19, 462-463
Analyzing and making decisions.
  See Problem Solving.
Angle(s)
  acute, 122-123
  adjacent, 116-117
  alternate exterior, 118-119
  alternate interior, 118-119
  bisector, 406-407
  central, 132-133
  complementary, 116-117
  congruent, 124-125, 404-405
  corresponding, 118-119
  estimating, 146
  exterior, 121
  inscribed, 132-133
  obtuse, 122-123
  right, 116-117
  straight, 116-117
  supplementary, 116-117
  vertical, 116-117
Angle-side-angle rule (ASA), 402-403
Arc, 132-133
Area
  of a circle, 330-331
  of irregular regions, 332-333, 378-379
  of a rectangle, 326-327
  of regular polygons, 330
  of a square, 332-333
  of a trapezoid, 326-327
  of a triangle, 326-327
Associative property
  of addition, 20-21, 164-165, 424-425
  of multiplication, 20-21, 164-165, 424-425
Averages, 226-227. *See also* Mean.
Axis, 170-171

Bar graphs, 234-237
Base(s)
  of figures, 134-137, 328-329, 342-345
  of a power, 6-7
Binary search, 246
Bisecting figures, 406-407
Bisector
  angle, 406-407
  perpendicular, 406-407
Box and whisker plot, 224-225

Calculator
  and addition, 2
  and logical thinking, 31
  and the museum, 276-277
  and order of operation, 85
  and probability, 364-365
  and relative frequency, 360-361
  at a restaurant, 172-173
  and scientific notation, 193
  and sports, 318-319
  and square roots, 200-203
  and travelers, 446-447
Calculator interviews, 172-173, 276-277, 318-319, 446-447
Capacity
  metric units of, 346-347
Careers, 62, 120, 180, 188, 221, 224, 226, 232, 260, 292, 306, 388, 430, 454
Centimeter (cm)
  cubic (cm³), 342-343
  square (cm²), 326-327
Central angle, 132-133
Central tendency, 220-221, 226-227
Chapter review, 34, 74, 108, 142, 174, 210, 244, 278, 320, 350, 380, 416, 448, 474
Chapter test, 35, 75, 109, 143, 175, 211, 245, 279, 321, 351, 381, 417, 449, 475
Choices, 5, 7, 23, 25, 31, 43, 49, 85, 87, 105, 157, 159, 167, 181, 185, 205, 253, 255, 257, 261, 271, 273, 275, 288-289, 301, 312-313, 315, 329, 373, 375, 377
Chord, 132-133
Circle
  arc of, 132-133
  area of, 330-331
  central angle of, 132-133
  chord of, 132-133
  circumference of, 330-331
  diameter of, 132-133
  inscribed angle of, 132-133
  and pi (π), 330-331
  radius of, 132-133
Circle graph, 234-235, 308-309
Circumference, 330-331
Combinations, 376-377
Combining terms, 432-433
Common error, 25, 63, 85, 165, 293, 469
Common factor, 44-45
Common multiple, 44-45
Communicating mathematics
  discuss, 2-5, 10, 21, 23, 26, 29, 46, 67, 69, 83, 96-97, 118-119, 134, 137, 139, 153, 206, 218, 222-223, 254, 257, 329, 332-333, 341, 346-347, 364, 389-390, 400, 425, 440-441, 466-467, 469
  explain reasoning, 6-9, 20, 22-24, 27-28, 30-31, 40, 45-47, 52, 58, 60-61, 64-65, 69-71, 82-83, 87, 90, 99, 101, 103, 118-120, 122, 131, 150, 154, 158, 164-165, 167, 180-181, 183-185, 188, 192-193, 195, 200, 204-206, 219, 222, 225,

231, 233-235, 241, 258-259, 261, 266-267, 272-274, 287, 292, 298-300, 303, 307, 309-310, 312, 315-317, 328-329, 338, 341, 343, 359, 361-362, 365-367, 374-375, 377, 388, 391, 405, 424, 427-428, 430, 432, 454-455, 458-459, 465, 467-468, 470-471

justify thinking, 28, 43-44, 47, 62, 64, 85, 117, 130, 201, 204, 218, 224, 226, 232, 236-237, 270, 286, 288-289, 291, 300-305, 308, 313, 339, 358, 403-404, 410, 426, 429-431, 434, 440, 444, 455, 468

write, 9, 11, 13, 27, 41, 88, 104, 121

Commutative property
of addition, 20-21, 164-165, 424-425
of multiplication, 20-21, 164-165, 424-425

Comparing
decimals, 8-9, 182-183
fractions, 52-53
integers, 150-151

Compass, 308-309, 400-401, 404-413

Compatible numbers, 28-29

Complementary angles, 116-117

Composite numbers, 40-41

Compound events, 362-365

Computer
basic, 435
logo, 76-77, 123, 144-145, 280-281, 382-383, 418-419, 476-477
spreadsheets, 280-281, 373
in Think and Apply, 123, 373, 435

Computer links
batting averages, 382-383
coordinates and geometric motions, 418-419
Euclidean algorithm, 76-77
Fibonacci sequence, 280-281
functions, 476-477
polygons and stars, 144-145

Concrete functions, 106-107

Cones, 136-139
volume of, 344-345

Congruent figures, 124-125, 402-405, 410-411

Conjectures, 46-47

Connections
archaeology, 62-63
architecture, 124, 266
art, 48, 388
astronomy and aerospace, 8, 188-189, 192-193, 335, 445
geography, 10-11, 157-158, 184, 223, 239, 435
history, 2-3, 9, 47, 49-51, 60, 66, 83, 220-221, 223, 232, 250-251, 254-

255, 268, 433-434
science, 134, 170, 180, 190-191, 194-195, 464
sports and recreation, 25, 59, 233, 235, 256, 292-293, 299-301, 305-307, 309, 430-431
travel, 182, 260-261, 274, 426-427, 429, 442-444, 446-447

Constructions, 404-413

Consumer math, 21-25, 27, 29-31, 69, 86-87, 91, 101, 103-105, 155, 157, 169, 185, 189, 193, 225, 234, 237, 240-241, 252-253, 310-315, 433, 457

Continued fraction, 78

Cooperative learning, 2-5, 12-15, 40-41, 46-47, 130-131, 134-135, 150-153, 200-203, 218-219, 238-239, 326-327, 330-331, 340-341, 344-345, 360-361, 364-365, 388-389, 400-401, 458-459

Coordinate plane, 170-171,
origin, 170-171
x-axis, 170-171
y-axis, 170-171

Correlation, 238-239

Corresponding angles, 118-119, 266-269, 402-403, 410-411

Corresponding parts, 124-125, 266-269, 402-403, 410-411

Cosine ratio, 272-275

Counting principle, 362-363

Create your own problem, 5, 25, 27, 88, 101, 104, 152, 155, 169, 189, 207, 251, 363, 413

Cross products, 52-53, 250-251, 254-261

Cube, 338-339, 342-343
of a number, 6-7, 203

Cubic units, 342-349

Cumulative review, 112-113, 214-215, 354-355, 480-481

Cylinders, 136-139
surface area of, 340-341
volume of, 342-343

Data
collecting and organizing, 29, 40-41, 59, 83, 130, 134, 138, 157, 189, 200, 202, 218, 235, 259, 289, 293, 308-309, 326-327, 333, 340, 343-345, 360-361, 363, 364, 382-383, 457
and computers, 382-383
graphing, 222-225, 234-241
using, 220-221, 234-237

Decimals
adding, 24-25

comparing, 8-9
dividing, 30-31
in equations, 98-105, 426-429
estimating, 22-23, 26-29
and fractions, 48-51, 182-183
multiplying, 30-31
ordering, 182-183
and percents, 288-289, 300-301
and place value, 8-9
repeating, 48-51, 180-181, 454-455
rounding, 22-23, 26-29
standard form, 8-9
subtracting, 24-25
terminating, 48-49, 180-181, 454-455

Degrees
for angle measurement, 116-123, 132-133

Density, property of, 181, 454-455

Dependent events, 364-365

Diagonals, 120-121

Diameter, 132-133

Differences, estimating, 22-23, 58-59

Discount, 312-313

Distance, rate, time, 260-261

Distributive property, 20-21, 164-165, 424-425

Divide and conquer, 230-231

Divisibility, 42-43

Division
of decimals, 30-31
equations involving, 100-101, 428-429
and estimating, 28-29
and finding averages, 226-227
of fractions, 70-71
of integers, 158-159
of mixed numbers, 70-71
by powers of ten, 10-11, 190-191
of rational numbers, 186-187

Dodecahedron, 135

Domain, 456-457

Equal ratios, 250-251

Equations
combining terms, 432-433
graphing solutions, 440-441
and formulas, 104-105
graphing, 464-465, 468-469
and integers, 168-169
and inverse operations, 98-101, 426-429
involving addition, 98-99, 426-427
involving decimals, 98-105, 426-429
involving division, 100-101, 428-429

Index

involving fractions, 98-105, 426-429

involving multiplication, 100-101, 428-429

involving percents, 304-305

involving subtraction, 98-99

of a line, 466-467

and rational numbers, 188-189

simplifying, 434-435

solution of, 90-91

systems, 468-469

two-step, 102-103, 430-431

writing, 88-89, 322, 426-431

Equilateral triangle, 122-123

Equivalent fractions, 52-53

Estimating

angles, 146

with decimals, 22-23

differences, 22-23, 58-59

with fractions, 58-59, 68-69

length, 146

percents, 306-307

products, 26-27, 68-69

quotients, 28-29

rational numbers, 184-187

square roots, 202-203

sums, 22-23, 58-59

Estimation strategies

clustering, 22-23

compatible numbers, 28-29

front-end, 22-23

rounding, 22-23, 26-27

Event(s), 358-359

compound, 362-365

dependent, 364-365

independent, 364-365

mutually exclusive, 366-367

Expansion, 420

Exponents, 6-7, 192-195

and base, 6-7

and powers of ten, 10-11, 190-191

and scientific notation, 192-195

Expressions

evaluating, 84-87, 110, 166-167

and variables, 82-83, 86-87, 166-167

writing, 82-83

Extensions

Binary Search, 246

Continued Fractions, 78

Exasperating Expression, 110

Graphing Pictures, 176

Hole in One, 146

Magic Squares, 36

Mathematical Boxes, 322

Möbius Strip, 352

Parallel and Perpendicular Lines, 478

Pascal's Triangle and Probability, 384

Polls, Statistics, and Probability, 450

Significant Digits and Accuracy, 282

Transformations: Expansion and Reduction, 420

Triangles and the Pythagorean Rule, 212

Exterior angles, 121

Extra practice, 482-498

for problem solving, 499-505

Extrapolation, 232-233

Factor(s), 6-7, 40-41

common, 44-45

common prime, 44-45

greatest common (GCF), 44-45

prime, 42-43

Factor tree, 42-43

Factorial, 372-373

Family math, 111, 213, 353, 479

Fibonacci sequence, 4-5

and computers, 280-281

Figures

bisecting, 406-407

congruent, 124-125, 402-405, 410-411

constructing, 404-413

transformations of, 388-395, 418-420

Formulas, 104-105, 135, 326-333, 338-345

Fractions

adding, 60-61

comparing, 52-53, 182-183

continued, 78

and decimals, 48-49, 182-183

dividing, 70-71

in equations, 98-105, 426-433

equivalent, 52-53

and estimating, 58-59, 68-69

improper, 62-63

least common denominator (LCD), 60-63

in lowest terms, 60-63

and mixed numbers, 58-63, 66-71

multiplying, 64-65

ordering, 52-53

and reciprocals, 70-71

as repeating or terminating, 48-51

subtracting, 62-63

Frequency tables, 240-241

Front-end estimating, 22-23

Functions, 458-459, 472-473

and computers, 476-477

Greatest common factor (GCF), 44-45

Geoboard, 130-131

Geometric patterns, 388-389

Geometry

angles, 116-119, 121-125, 132-133

circles, 132-133, 330-331

and computers, 144-145, 418-419

cones, 136-139, 344-345

congruence, 124-125, 402-405, 410-411

constructing figures, 404-413

cylinders, 136-139, 342-343

diagonals of polygons, 120-121

intersecting lines, 116-117

lines, 116-119

parallel lines, 118-119,

parallelograms, 130-131, 326-329

perpendicular lines, 118-119

polygons, 120-121, 124-125, 130-131, 266-267, 326-333, 412-413

prisms, 134-135, 138-139, 342-343

pyramids, 134-135, 138-139, 344-345

Pythagorean rule, 204-207

quadrilaterals, 130-131, 326-329

rays, 116-117

reflections, 390-393

rotations, 394-395

similar figures, 266-269

spheres, 136-139

squares, 130-131

symmetry, 390-391

transformations, 390-395

translations, 390-393

transversals, 118-119

triangles, 122-123, 204-207, 268-269, 272-275, 328-329, 402-403

Graphing

data, 234-235

equations, 440-441, 464-465

functions, 458-459

inequalities, 440-441, 470-471

on a number line, 440-442

ordered pairs, 170-171, 176, 454-455

skill hints, 512-527

slope, 466-467

systems of equations, 468-469

transformations, 392-393, 420

Graphs

bar, 234-235

box and whisker plot, 224-225

circle, 234-235, 308-309

histograms, 240-241

line, 232-235

number line plot, 220-221

scattergrams, 238-239

stem and leaf plot, 222-223
Greatest common factor (GCF), 44-45
and computers, 76-77
Greatest possible error (GPE), 270-271, 282
and precision, 270-271
Guess and test, 90-91, 198-199

Histograms, 240-241
Hypotenuse, 204-207, 272-275

Identity property
of addition, 164-165, 424-425
of multiplication, 164-165, 424-425
Improper fractions, 62-63
Independent events, 364-365
Inequalities
graphing, 440-445, 470-471
solving, 442-445
Inscribed angle, 132-133
Integers
absolute value of, 150-151
adding, 152-155
additive inverse of, 154-155
comparing, 150-151
dividing, 158-159
in equations, 168-169
as exponents, 190-191, 194-195
expressions involving, 166-167
graphing ordered pairs of, 170-171
multiplying, 156-157
ordering, 150-151
properties, 164-165
subtracting, 152-155
writing, 150-151
Intercepted arc, 132-133
Intercepts, 466-467
Interest
compound, 310-311
simple, 310-311
Interpolation, 232-233
Intersecting lines, 116-119
Inverse
additive, 154-155, 164-165, 424-425
multiplicative, 164-165, 424-425
Inverse operations, 96-97
Inverse property
of addition, 164-165, 424-425
of multiplication, 164-165, 424-425
Irrational numbers, 454-455
Isosceles triangles, 122-123

Lateral surface, 135
Least common denominator (LCD), 60-63
and computers, 76-77

Least common multiple (LCM), 44-45
Legs of triangle, 204-205, 272-275
Length
estimating, 146
metric units of, 270
Line(s)
constructing, 408-409
intersecting, 116-117
parallel, 118-119
perpendicular, 116-117
skew, 118-119
of symmetry, 390-391
transversal, 118-119
Line graph, 234-235
Line plot, 220-221
Liquid volume, 346-347
Locus, 400-401
Logic, 398-399, 438-439
Logical thinking, 31, 61, 121, 181, 313, 315, 373, 393, 445, 467
Lowest terms, 60-63

Magic square, 36
Maintaining skills, 37, 79, 112-113, 147, 177, 214-215, 247, 283, 323, 354-355, 385, 421, 451
Making and using drawings, 94-95
Making and using tables, 336-337
Manipulative activities, 2-5, 12-15, 46-47, 130-131, 134-139, 200-203, 238-239, 326-327, 340-341, 344-345, 360-361, 364-365, 400-401, 458-459
Markup, 314-315
Mass
metric units of, 346-347
Math history
multiplication symbols, 83
percent notation, 287
pi (π), 333
Mean, 226-227
Measure(s)
of central tendency, 220-221, 226-227
of data, 220-221, 226-227
Measurement
of angles, 116-117
area, 326-333
circumference, 330-331
and greatest possible error (GPE), 270-271
metric, 270-271, 346-347
perimeter, 326-327
precision of, 270-271
surface area, 338-341
volume, 342-345
Median, 220-221

using, 226-227
Mental math
percents, 290-291
powers of ten, 10-11
using common percents, 298-299
using properties and strategies, 20-21
Metric units of measure.
See Capacity, Length, Mass.
Midchapter Review, 16, 54, 92, 126, 160, 196, 228, 262, 294, 334, 368, 396, 436, 460
Mixed numbers
adding, 60-61
dividing, 70-71
and fractions, 58-63, 66-71
multiplying, 66-67
subtracting, 62-63
Mixed Review, 29, 43, 69, 87, 99, 125, 157, 167, 205, 225, 257, 269, 311, 329, 339, 367, 375, 409, 431, 441, 457, 471
Mode, 220-221
using, 226-227
Models, 138-139, 340-341, 344-345
Multiple(s)
common, 44-45
least common (LCM), 44-45
Möbius strip, 352
Modular arithmetic, 14-15
Multiplication
of decimals, 30-31
equations involving, 100-101, 428-429
and estimating, 26-27, 68-69
of fractions, 64-65
of integers, 156-157
of mixed numbers, 66-67
and multiplicative inverses, 164-165
by powers of ten, 10-11, 190-191
properties, 20-21, 164-165,
of rational numbers, 186-187
Multiplicative inverse, 424-425
Mutually exclusive events, 366-367

Negative exponents, 190-191
Negative integers, 150-151
Number(s)
composite, 40-41
decimals, 8-9
integers, 150-151
irrational, 454-455
place value of, 8-9, 12-13
prime, 40-41
rational, 180-183, 454-455
real, 454-455
standard form of, 8-9

Index

Number line, graphing on, 440-441
Number sense, 2-13, 20-23, 26-29, 39-45, 150-153, 164-165, 180-183, 192-193, 200-203, 290-291
Number theory
  divisibility, 42-43
  factors, 6-7, 40-45
  greatest common factor (GCF), 44-45
  least common multiple (LCM), 44-45
  multiples, 44-45
  prime and composite, 40-41

Obtuse angle, 122-123
Obtuse triangle, 122-123, 212
Opposites, 150-151, 180-181
Order of operations, 84-85, 157, 166-167
Ordered pairs, 170-171, 176, 454-455
Ordering
  decimals, 8-9
  fractions, 52-53
  integers, 150-151
  rational numbers, 182-183
Organized listing, 370-371
Origin, 170-171
Outcome(s)
  equally likely, 358-359
  favorable, 358-359
  possible, 358-359

Parallel lines, 118-119, 408-409, 478
Parallelograms, 130-131
  area of, 326-327
Pascal's triangle, 2-3, 384
Patterns
  geometric, 388-389
  number, 2-3
  powers of 10, 10-11, 190-191
  problem solving, 128-129
Percents
  and circle graphs, 308-309
  and compound interest, 310-311
  and decimals, 288-289, 300-301
  and discount, 312-313
  estimating, 306-307
  greater than 100, 292-293
  of increase or decrease, 316-317
  and interest, 310-311
  less than one, 292-293
  of markup and selling price, 314-315
  mental math, 290-291, 298-299
  and proportion, 302-303
  and ratios, 286-291, 300-301
  using equations, 304-305
Perfect square, 200-201

Perimeter of polygon, 326-327
Permutation, 374-375
Perpendicular bisector, 406-407
Perpendicular lines, 408-409, 478
Pi (π), 330-331
Plane
  coordinate, 170-171
  real number, 454-455
Polls, 450
Polygons
  area of, 326-329, 332-333
  and computers, 144-145
  congruent, 124-125
  constructing, 412-413
  diagonals of, 120-121
  drawing similar, 266-267
  perimeter of, 326-327
  quadrilaterals, 130-131
  regular, 120-121
  similar, 266-267
  sum of angle measures, 120-121
Polyhedrons, 134-135
Positive integers, 150-151
Powers of ten, 10-11, 190-195
  divide by, 10-11, 190-191
  multiply by, 10-11, 190-191
Precision of measurement
  and greatest possible error (GPE), 270-271, 282
Predictions, 360-361
Prime factorization, 42-45
Prime number(s), 40-41
Principal, 310-311
Prisms, 134-135, 138-139
  surface area of, 338-339
  volume of, 342-343
Probability, 358-359, 450
  of compound events, 362-365
  and counting principle, 362-363
  of dependent events, 364-365
  of equally likely events, 358-359
  of independent events, 364-365
  of mutually exclusive events, 366-367
  and outcomes, 358-359
  and Pascal's triangle, 384
  and predictions, 360-361
  range of, 358-359
  and relative frequencies, 360-361
  and sample space, 358-359
  and tree diagrams, 362-363
Problem solving,
  alternate solutions, 18-19, 462-463
  analyzing and making decisions, 17, 55, 93, 127, 161, 197, 229, 263, 295, 335, 369, 397, 437, 461
  area, 348-349, 378-379
  average speed, 263

  be a problem solver, 1, 39, 81, 115, 149, 179, 217, 249, 285, 325, 357, 387, 423, 453
  and calculators, 18-19, 57, 93-95, 129, 163, 172-173, 199, 209, 230-231, 265, 276-277, 295, 297, 318-319, 336-337, 446-447, 463
  codes, 72-73
  and computers, 76-77, 144-145, 280-281, 382-383, 418-419, 476-477
  create your own problem, 19, 57, 95, 129, 163, 199, 231, 265, 297, 337, 371, 399, 439, 463
  currency, 446-447
  design, 55, 397
  divide and conquer, 230-231
  and estimation, 127, 437
  extra practice, 488-505
  and functions, 106, 472-473
  and geometry, 208-209, 348-349
  and graphing, 106-107, 461
  guess and test, 90-91, 198-199
  logic, 398-399, 438-439
  making a list, 370-371
  making and using tables, 19, 32-33, 161, 197, 229, 242-243, 295, 318-319, 336-337
  maps, 208-209
  mixed strategy review, 19, 57, 95, 129, 163, 199, 231, 265, 297, 337, 371, 399, 439, 463
  Monte Carlo method, 378-379
  patterns, 128-129, 335
  and probability, 369, 461
  simulation, 94-95, 296-297
  solving a simpler problem, 264-265
  too much or too little information, 56-57
  topology, 414-415
  Venn diagrams, 140-141
  working backwards, 162-163
Problem solving strategies
  Alternate solutions, 18-19, 462-463
  Divide and conquer, 230-231
  Extra practice, 499-505
  Guess and test, 90-91, 198-199
  Logic, 398-399, 438-439
  Making a list, 370-371
  Making and using tables, 336-337
  Patterns, 128-129
  Simulation, 94-95, 296-297
  Solving a simpler problem, 264-265
  Too much or too little information, 56-57
  Working backwards, 162-163
Products

cross, 52-53, 250-251, 254-255, 260-261

estimating, 26-27, 68-69

Properties

additive inverse, 164-165, 424-425

associative, 20-21, 164-165, 424-425

commutative, 20-21, 164-165, 424-425

of density, 181, 454-455

distributive, 20-21, 164-165, 424-425

identity, 164-165, 424-425

mental math, 20-21

multiplicative inverse, 164-165, 424-425

zero, 164-165

Proportions

and cross products, 254-255, 260-261

for percents, 302-303

in scale drawings, 258-259

in similar polygons, 266-267

in similar triangles, 268-269

Protractor, 116-117, 130-131, 136-137, 344-345

Pyramids, 134-135, 138-139

volume of, 344-345

Pythagorean rule, 204-207, 212

Pythagorean triple, 205

Quadrants, 170-171

Quadrilaterals, 130-131

Quartile, 224-225

Quotients

estimating, 28-29

negative, 158-159

positive, 158-159

Radius, 132-133

Random sample, 218-219

Range, 220-221

of relation, 456-457

Rate, distance, time, 260-261

Rational numbers

adding, 184-185

comparing, 182-183

as decimals, 180-181

density, 181

dividing, 186-187

and equations, 188-189

as fractions, 180-181

and irrational numbers, 454-455

multiplying, 186-187

on a number line, 180, 182-183

and ordered pairs, 454-455

ordering, 182-183

and powers of ten, 190-195

and scientific notation, 192-195

and square roots, 200-203

subtracting, 184-185

Ratios

cosine (cos), 272-275

equal, 250-251

and percents, 288-289, 300-301

and rates, 252-253

and scale drawings, 258-259

sine (sin), 272-275

tangent (tan), 272-275

trigonometric, 272-275

and unit price, 252-253

Rays, 116-117

Real numbers, 454-455

Reasoning

analyzing and making decisions, 17, 55, 93, 127, 130, 161, 197, 229, 231, 263, 295, 335, 369, 397, 437, 461

explain reasoning, 6-9, 20, 22-24, 27-28, 30-31, 40, 45-47, 52, 58, 60-61, 64-65, 69-71, 82-83, 87, 90, 99, 101, 103, 118-120, 122, 131, 150, 154, 158, 164-165, 167, 180-181, 183-185, 188, 192-193, 195, 200, 204-206, 219, 222, 225, 231, 233-235, 241, 258-259, 261, 266-267, 272-274, 287, 292, 298-300, 303, 307, 309-310, 312, 315-317, 328-329, 338, 341, 343, 359, 361-362, 365-367, 374-375, 377, 388, 391, 405, 424, 427-428, 430, 432, 454-455, 458-459, 465, 467-468, 470-471

justify thinking, 28, 43-44, 47, 62, 64, 85, 117, 130, 201, 204, 218, 224, 226, 232, 236-237, 270, 286, 288-289, 291, 300-305, 308, 313, 339, 358, 403-404, 410, 426, 429-431, 434, 440, 444, 455, 468

Reciprocals, 70-71

Rectangles, 130-131

area of, 326-327

perimeter of, 326-327

Rectangular prism, 134-135

Reduction, 420

Reflections, 390-393

Regular polygons, 120-121

Relations, 456-459

Relative error, 282

Relative frequency, 360-361

Repeating decimals, 48-51, 454-455

Review. *See* Mixed Review and Chapter Review.

Rhombus, 130-131

Right angle, 116-117

Right triangle, 122-123, 204-207, 212, 272-275

Rotation(s), 394-395

Rounding

decimals, 22-23

fractions, 58-59

whole numbers, 22-23

Sample space, 358-359

Scale drawing, 258-259

Scalene triangles, 122-123

Scattergrams, 238-239

Scientific notation, 192-195

Segments, congruent, 404-405

bisecting, 406-407

constructing, 404-405

Selling price, 314-315

Semicircle, 332-333

Sequences, 4-5

Side-angle-side rule (SAS), 402-403

Side-side-side rule (SSS), 402-403

Significant digits, 282

Similar polygons, 266-267

Similar triangles, 268-269

Simulation, 94-95, 296-297

Sine ratio, 272-275

Skew lines, 118-119

Skill hints, 512-527

Slope, 466-467, 478

Solid figure. *See* Space figures.

Solving a simpler problem, 264-265

Space figures, 134-135, 138-139

Spheres, 136-139

Square, 130-131

area of, 332-333

of number, 200-201

perfect, 200-201

perimeter of, 326-327

Square pyramids, 134-135

Square root, 200-201

estimating, 202-203

Standard form, 6-9, 192-195

Statistics

and central tendency, 220-221, 226-227

and computers, 382-383

and frequency, 240-241

histograms, 240-241

and predictions, 450

Stem and leaf plot, 222-223

Straight angle, 117, 121

Subtraction

of decimals, 24-25

equations involving, 98-99, 426-427, 430-435

and estimating, 22-23, 58-59

of fractions, 62-63

of integers, 152-155

of mixed numbers, 62-63

of rational numbers, 184-185

Index

Sums, estimating, 22-23, 58-59
Supplementary angles, 116-117
Surface area
    of a cube, 338-339
    of a cylinder, 340-341
    lateral, 338-339
    of a prism, 338-339
Surface
    lateral, 340
Symmetry, 390-391
Systems of equations, 468-469

Tables
    decimal place value, 8
    of measures, 537
    of sines, cosines, and tangents, 536
    of squares and square roots, 535
Tangent (tan), 272-275
Tangent ratio, 272-275
Terminating decimals, 48-49, 454-455
Tessellations, 388-389
    and computers, 418
Test Taker, 71, 97, 251, 377
Thinking critically. *See* Problem solving: analyzing and making decisions.
Too much or too little information, 56-57
Topology, 414-415
Transformations, 390-395, 420
    and computers, 418-419
Translations, 390-393
Transversal, 118-119
Trapezoids, 130-131
    area of, 328-329
Tree diagrams, 362-363
Triangles
    acute, 122-123
    area of, 326-327
    classified by angles, 122-123
    classified by sides, 122-123
    congruent, 124-125, 402-403, 410-411
    equilateral, 122-123
    hypotenuse of, 204-205, 272-275
    isosceles, 122-123
    legs of, 204-205, 272-275
    obtuse, 122-123
    perimeter of, 326-327
    and the Pythagorean rule, 204-207, 212
    right, 122-123, 204-207, 272-275
    scalene, 122-123
    similar, 268-269
    sum of angle measures, 120-121
Triangular numbers, 4-5
Triangular prisms, 134-135

Triangular pyramids, 134-135
Trigonometric ratios, 272-275

Unit price, 252-253

Venn diagrams, 140-141
Vertex (vertices), 116-117
Vertical angles, 116-117
Visual thinking, 7, 23, 91, 133, 159, 183, 241, 261, 307, 317, 391, 403, 425, 455
Vocabulary, xii, 38, 80, 114, 148, 178, 216, 248, 284, 324, 356, 386, 422, 452
Volume
    of a cone, 344-345
    of a cube, 342-343
    of a cylinder, 342-343
    of a prism, 342-343
    of a pyramid, 344-345

Working backwards, 162-163

x-axis, 170-171
x-intercept, 466-467

y-axis, 170-171
y-intercept, 466-467

Zero, property of, 164-165

Credits